Physical Methods in Inorganic Chemistry

Reinhold Chemistry Textbook Series

Consulting Editors' Statement

Physical methods have become so much a part of modern inorganic chemical research, that it is not surprising to find that numerous authors have written books concerning the theoretical bases for such methods. There are, however, few books which within a single volume, treat the more important physical methods in a manner which makes it convenient for the student or the practicing chemist to learn how to use each method and the kind of information which can be obtained from each. Professor Drago, from his own research, is highly qualified to fill this important gap in the chemical literature. His experience as a teacher and a writer assures the reader that this volume will not only be a trustworthy guide but that its use will be both pleasant and inspiring. We are proud to add this book to the REINHOLD CHEMISTRY TEXTBOOK SERIES.

HARRY H. SISLER
CALVIN A. VANDERWERF

Physical Methods in Inorganic Chemistry

RUSSELL S. DRAGO

Department of Chemistry and Chemical Engineering
University of Illinois
Urbana, Illinois

New York
REINHOLD PUBLISHING CORPORATION
Chapman and Hall Ltd., London

TO RUTH

Illustrations by Howard Burns

Preface

THE CONTENTS of current research and modern textbooks in the area of inorganic chemistry indicate beyond a doubt that modern inorganic chemists must have a working knowledge of various physical methods. Anyone challenging this statement need only read a current issue of a good inorganic journal, a recent volume in the several series devoted to inorganic chemistry, or a modern inorganic textbook to find many examples in which inorganic problems have been solved by employing physical methods. The modern well-trained inorganic or organic chemist applies any physical method which may possibly produce the results needed to solve his problems. It is necessary to understand the basic principles and limitations of these methods in order to do good research and to read the literature critically. Considering the many incorrect interpretations of results from spectroscopic methods that have appeared in the literature, the latter consideration is most important. It is impossible to be an active, modern, inorganic or organic chemist without a knowledge of the principles, limitations, and different kinds of applications of spectroscopic methods.

This brings up an interesting point concerning current course offerings in inorganic chemistry in many universities. One finds in most inorganic textbooks and in most inorganic course offerings detailed discussions of quantum mechanical calculations (at least for H_2^+ and H_2), procedures for determining electronegativities, and means of evaluating the covalent and ionic radii of atoms. Often very little mention is made of the application and intelligent use of physical methods in inorganic chemistry. The author invites you to investigate the last six issues of *Inorganic Chemistry* and count the number of inorganic research problems solved by physical methods and compare these with the number of times inorganic problems have been solved by making quantum mechanical calculations, using ionic radii, and evaluating electronegativities. This comparison is made not to de-emphasize the importance of these latter subjects, but to emphasize the importance of giving graduate students instruction in physical methods.

At Illinois, this problem has been in part resolved by offering a course devoted to the application of physical methods in inorganic chemistry. This text has evolved from this course, and it is hoped that it will be influential in initiating instruction of this material to all inorganic chemists. The author feels that the material in this text should be presented either in the senior year or in the first year of graduate school after the student has had an introductory course in inorganic chemistry. The course on physical methods can be followed by special topics courses in transition metal ion chemistry, group theory and molecular orbital theory, nonaqueous solvents, chemistry of the familiar and less familiar elements, etc. These special topics can be treated at an advanced level and the results from studies employing physical methods integrated into these courses with meaning.

If the student has had an introductory inorganic course, the material in the first three chapters of this text is review. This material has been treated in many places, in varying degrees of thoroughness. The main reason for including it in this text is to indicate the level of proficiency needed in these areas to be able to read the ensuing chapters on physical methods. In the course described above, this material is assigned reading and only three lecture periods are spent on various aspects of the material. Special help sessions are held for those having difficulty with the material in the first three chapters.

Two references are used in the course described above to supplement the material in this text: *Chemical Applications of Group Theory* by F. A. Cotton (see Chapter 4 for the complete reference) and *Molecular Structure* by P. J. Wheatley. The former is employed as a reference for lectures on the use of symmetry considerations in ligand field and molecular orbital calculations and the latter as a reference for lectures on dipole moments, x-ray, electron, and neutron diffraction. In view of the length of this text and since the two above mentioned texts should be in the library of most inorganic chemists, this material has not been covered here. In the event that an inorganic chemist may not be concerned with molecular orbital calculations and group theory, Chapter 4 is presented as a brief treatment of symmetry and group theory. It contains the minimum amount of information on this subject necessary for an understanding of physical methods at the level presented in this text.

The level at which the fundamental principles pertaining to the physical methods are presented is introductory and the reader will be far from expert after digesting the material contained in this text. The approach will be qualitative and, where possible, simplified physical pictures will be presented to aid in understanding the essential principles underlying the application of these methods. The emphasis has been on clarity of presentation for a chemist who is not mathematically inclined. It should be recognized that this procedure often results in incompleteness and oversimplification. However, to do a thorough job would take at least a full semester on any one of these chapters.

The depth at which the topics have been treated is that which the author feels should be background information for a nonspecialist, for example, researchers in nonmetal chemistry should be expected to know at least as much about the electronic spectra of complexes as is presented here. Specialists will have to know considerably more. It is hoped that this treatment will motivate the inorganic chemist to read, and make it easier for him to understand, the more advanced treatments available for each of the spectroscopic methods. At the very least he will know which expert to call upon for help in the solution of his problem.

In addition to the treatment of the fundamental principles, each chapter on physical methods contains examples which describe the application of these methods to the solution of inorganic problems. These examples have been selected to demonstrate the different kinds of information that can be obtained by employing the various physical methods. The coverage is not encyclopedic and, where appropriate, the examples have been selected from the author's research program, for he is most familiar with these problems. Since reasoning by analogy has been used effectively by synthetic chemists for many years, it is hoped that the examples selected will suggest methods for the solution of a broad spectrum of inorganic problems.

In offering any graduate course, it is essential to update the material with recent references from the literature. For a course using this text this should involve mainly presenting new applications and covering different examples.

I would like to take this opportunity to thank several individuals for their assistance and encouragement. I am very grateful to my colleagues, Professors T. L. Brown and T. S. Piper, for several discussions pertaining to material in this text. Many contributions were made by graduate students in my research group who read the chapters and offered many important suggestions. I also consider myself very fortunate to have been associated with some very fine teachers, Professors Harry H. Sisler, John

C. Bailar, and Reynold C. Fuson. I would like to acknowledge my indebt-
edness to them for giving so freely of their time and helping me in many
ways. Finally, I would like to express thanks to my parents, wife, and
children for their encouragement and sacrifices.

RUSSELL S. DRAGO

Contents

PART I

Atomic and Molecular Structure

BECAUSE a discussion of physical methods requires a qualitative background in quantum mechanical principles, a brief review of this material is presented in Part I. The background presented in Chapters 1 and 2 will not be rigorous, but will be what the author considers a minimum for a qualitative understanding of the physical methods discussed. The mathematical equations employed in this treatment are presented without proof. The level in these chapters is intended to be about the same as that in the Cotton and Wilkinson text.

This presentation will indicate the assumptions involved and general procedure utilized in arriving at many of the qualitative quantum mechanical concepts currently being used by inorganic chemists concerned with molecular structure, syntheses, and reaction mechanisms.

1 *Atomic Structure*

WAVE PROPERTIES OF ELECTRONS

As EARLY as the 19th century, it was recognized that light has wave properties, as evidenced by diffraction from a grating. However, subsequent interpretation of the photoelectric effect* required an assignment of corpuscular behavior to light, thereby ascribing to radiation dual properties, those of matter and of waves. The following equations quantitatively describe this duality by relating both the mass and frequency, ν, of radiation to its energy, E:

$$E = \mathbf{h}\nu = mc^2 \tag{1-1}$$

where $\mathbf{h}$ is Planck's constant, $\mathbf{h}\nu$ is the energy of a photon whose mass equivalent is m, and c is the speed of light. Frequency is related to wavelength, λ, by equation (1-2):

$$\nu = c/\lambda \tag{1-2}$$

Combining (1-1) and (1-2) produces:

$$\lambda = \mathbf{h}/mc \tag{1-3}$$

In 1924, de Broglie proposed that particles, acknowledged to be matter, might also have wave properties. An equation, (1-4), similar to equation (1-3), relates the wavelength of these particles to their mass, m, and velocity, v:

$$\nu = \mathbf{h}/mv \tag{1-4}$$

*For a complete description of this experiment, see: L. Pauling, "General Chemistry," p. 167, W. H. Freeman, San Francisco, 1958; S. Glasstone, "Textbook of Physical Chemistry," pp. 13–34, Van Nostrand, New York, 1946.

By simple substitution of values for **h**, m, and v in equation (1-4), the wavelength for various particles moving at specified velocities can be calculated (Table 1-1). These calculations indicate that objects with a mass of 1 gram or greater and with normal velocities have wavelengths so small that they cannot be measured. However, it can be seen (Table 1-1) that electrons with appropriate velocities have wavelengths that correspond to internuclear distances in molecules and crystals. In 1927,

TABLE 1-1. WAVELENGTHS CALCULATED FOR VARIOUS "PARTICLES"

Particle	Mass, m (g)	Velocity, v (cm/sec)	λ (cm)
Slow electron	9×10^{-28}	100	7×10^{-2}
Fast electron[a]	9×10^{-28}	5.9×10^{8}	1×10^{-8}
α particle (Ra source)	6.6×10^{-24}	1.5×10^{9}	6×10^{-13}
Mass of 1 g	1	1	6×10^{-27}
Tennis ball	40	2500	6×10^{-32}
Baseball	140	2500	2×10^{-32}

[a]Accelerated with a 100 volt potential.

Davisson and Germer provided experimental support for the de Broglie assumption by showing that an electron beam is diffracted by a nickel crystal in the same manner that x-ray radiation is diffracted. The atoms in the crystal serve as a diffraction grating, demonstrating the wave properties of an electron.

DESCRIPTION OF THE POSITION AND MOMENTUM OF AN ELECTRON

The Heisenberg uncertainty principle states that it is impossible to determine *precisely* and *simultaneously* the *momemtum* and *position* of an electron. This statement can be illustrated by the following discussion. In any measurement of the position of an electron, the radiation used to observe the electron must undergo a change. The measured quantity is the change that occurs in the photon upon contacting the electron. Hence, it is impossible to detect accurately an object smaller than the wavelength of radiation employed to measure it. As a result, detection of a particle as small as an electron would require very low wavelength, λ, and thus very high energy radiation, $E = hc/\lambda$. However, since the electron is so small, collision with the high energy photon can change the momentum of the electron. As a result, the more accurately the position is measured (by using small wavelength, high energy photons), the less accurately can the momentum be measured simultaneously, and vice versa.

The Bohr model violates the uncertainty principle, for it describes simultaneously both the location and momentum of the electron. Instead, for a given energy a correct theory can only state the probability of finding the electron at a designated position. After the de Broglie proposal, Schrödinger intuitively selected an equation for a wave as the model to describe the behavior of an electron in an atom. This model incorporates the requirements stated in the uncertainty principle.

MATHEMATICAL DESCRIPTION OF WAVES

Let us digress for a moment from our description of atomic structure to review the mathematical description of wave motion. Consider the wave illustrated in Fig. 1-1a, which, after a time interval, progresses

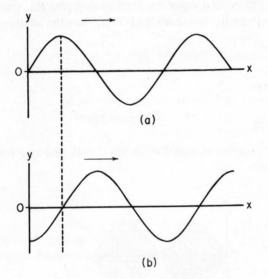

(a)

(b)

Fig. 1-1. A Moving Wave

along the x axis in the direction indicated by the arrow to the position illustrated in Fig. 1-1b. This wave motion can be described quantitatively by the differential equation:

$$\partial^2 A/\partial x^2 = (1/c^2)(\partial^2 A/\partial t^2) \tag{1-5}$$

where A is the amplitude, i.e., the height of the wave measured (along the y axis) at a particular distance x along the x axis; c is the velocity at which the wave is traveling; and t is the time. This differential equation (1-5) has a solution:

$$A = a \ \sin \ 2\pi(x/\lambda - \nu t) \tag{1-6}$$

where λ is the wavelength, ν is the frequency, and a is a constant. The amplitude A, for a time t and position x, can be calculated from (1-6).

Another type of wave motion, a standing wave, results when a string whose ends are fixed is plucked. A standing wave results in a stationary pattern (see Fig. 1-2) where the actual profile is fixed instead of traveling along the x axis as the wave illustrated in Fig. 1-1 does. Empirically, it is found that this model (extended to a three-dimensional wave as in equation 1-9) best describes the behavior of an electron attracted by a nucleus. The differential equation used to describe this one-dimensional standing wave is similar to equation (1-5) and has the solution (1-7):

$$A = 2a \ \sin \ 2\pi x/\lambda \ \cdot \ \cos \ 2\pi\nu t \tag{1-7}$$

or, more simply,

$$A = f(x) \ \cos \ 2\pi\nu t \tag{1-8}$$

where $f(x)$ is an abbreviation for $2a \sin 2\pi x/\lambda$ and is a function of the x coordinate only.

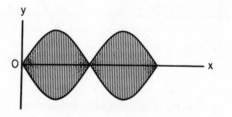

Fig. 1–2. A Standing Wave

The second derivative of equation (1-8) with respect to time can be obtained and combined with equation (1-5) to eliminate the quantity t. The resulting equation for the standing wave can be converted to equation (1-9) to describe a three-dimensional wave:

$$\partial^2\psi/\partial x^2 + \partial^2\psi/\partial y^2 + \partial^2\psi/\partial z^2 + 4\pi^2\psi/\lambda^2 = 0 \tag{1-9}$$

where ψ is the counterpart in the three-dimensional system of A in equation (1-5). Abbreviating

$$\partial^2/\partial x^2 + \partial^2/\partial y^2 + \partial^2/\partial z^2$$

as ∇^2, one obtains:

$$\nabla^2\psi + 4\pi^2\psi/\lambda^2 = 0 \qquad (1\text{-}10)$$

Equation (1-9) or (1-10) is a differential equation similar to equation (1-5) except that this equation specifically relates to a stationary, three-dimensional wave and has the variable t eliminated from it. This variable is eliminated to produce an equation whose solutions are time independent. The differential equation (1-9) can be solved more easily than those that contain t.

THE SCHRÖDINGER EQUATION

Schrödinger selected the mathematical description of a standing wave as the basis of his model for the structure of an atom. He incorporated intothe expression for a standing wave (equation 1-10) the de Broglie assumption, $\lambda = \mathbf{h}/mv$, and obtained:

$$\nabla^2\psi + (4\pi^2 m^2 v^2/\mathbf{h}^2)\psi = 0 \qquad (1\text{-}11)$$

By combining equation (1-11) and the equation relating total energy, E, potential energy, V, and kinetic energy, $\frac{1}{2}mv^2$, i.e.,

$$E = V + \tfrac{1}{2}mv^2 \quad \text{or} \quad v^2 = 2(E - V)/m \qquad (1\text{-}12)$$

one obtains a familiar form of the Schrödinger equation:

$$\nabla^2\psi + (8\pi^2 m/\mathbf{h}^2)(E - V)\psi = 0 \qquad (1\text{-}13)$$

It is well to remember that equation (1-13) is not derived from first principles but is the equation which results from: (a) empirically selecting the equation for a standing wave as the model for the behavior of an electron in an atom and (b) incorporating the de Broglie assumption. Justification for the above "derivation" is found in the fact that the solution of equation (1-13) yields values for the energy, E, which correspond closely to those obtained experimentally from atomic spectra. This will be discussed in more detail subsequently.

Further discussion of the symbol ψ in equation (1-13) is warranted. Since ψ is analogous in three dimensions to A (the amplitude of a planar wave), ψ is referred to as the amplitude function. Physical significance cannot be attributed to ψ but $\psi\psi^*$ *may be shown to be proportional to the probability of locating the electron at a given position* (here ψ^* is *the complex conjugate of* ψ). *The quantity* $\psi\psi^*d\tau$ *gives the probability of finding the electron in a volume element* $d\tau$. If ψ is a real number, $\psi\psi^*$ becomes ψ^2. In this text the possibility of a complex function will be understood even though the symbol ψ^2 will be used.

THE SOLUTION OF THE SCHRÖDINGER EQUATION

A qualitative description of the method employed to solve equation (1-13) as it applies to a hydrogen atom will now be discussed. The first step to simplify the solution is a transformation of equation (1-13) from Cartesian coordinates (x, y, and z axes) to spherical polar coordinates. Location of a point p in a spherical coordinate system is illustrated (relative to a set of Cartesian coordinates) in Fig. 1-3. The line from the origin

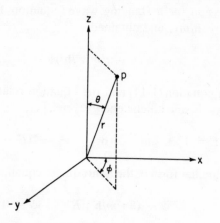

Fig. 1–3. Location of a Point p in the Spherical Coordinate System Relative to Cartesian Coordinates

to p has a length r, and θ is the angle made by this line and the z axis. The projection of this line in the x–y plane makes an angle with the x-axis indicated by ϕ. The parameters θ, ϕ and r locate the point p.

Equation (1-14) results from equation (1-13) by transforming the coordinate system:

$$\left(\frac{1}{r^2}\right)\left(\frac{\partial}{\partial r}\right)\left(r^2\frac{\partial\psi}{\partial r}\right) + \left(\frac{1}{r^2\sin\theta}\right)\left(\frac{\partial}{\partial\theta}\right)\left(\sin\theta\frac{\partial\psi}{\partial\theta}\right) + \left(\frac{1}{r^2\sin^2\theta}\right)\left(\frac{\partial^2\varphi}{\partial\phi^2}\right)$$

$$+ \frac{[8\pi^2\mu(E-V)]}{h^2}\psi = 0 \quad (1\text{-}14)$$

where μ is the reduced mass, i.e.,

$$\mu = mM/(m + M) \quad (1\text{-}15)$$

where M is mass of nucleus and m is mass of electron. Equation (1-14) is separable into simpler equations which contain the single parameters r, θ, and ϕ, and these equations are solved individually. There are an infinite number of solutions to these equations. Solutions which satisfy the requirements (*a* to *c*) listed below are the only meaningful solutions in terms of describing the behavior of an electron in an atom. Each allowed, meaningful solution is a wave function, ψ, which represents an orbital in the atom. The following limitations can be imposed upon the infinite number of solutions to obtain meaningful ones: (a) The wave function must be finite and continuous, i.e., it can never approach infinity for any value of θ, ϕ, or r (the function can have a value of zero). (b) The solution must be single valued, i.e., at a given point there can never be more than one value for the amplitude, ψ, (c) The solutions must be normalized. This requires that if a solution, ψ, is squared, multiplied by $d\tau$, and integrated over all space, the result must equal 1; i.e.,

$$\int_0^{+\infty} \psi^2 d\tau = 1 \quad (1\text{-}16)$$

Equation (1-16) indicates that ψ must approach zero as r becomes infinite. Since $\psi^2 d\tau$ is related to the probability of finding the electron in volume element, $d\tau$, the integration in equation (1-16) simply requires that there be unit probability of finding the electron somewhere in space.

There are only a limited number of solutions to the Schrödinger equation for an un-ionized atom that satisfy all of the above requirements. The allowed solutions are called eigenfunctions, and each one represents an orbital with a capacity of two electrons in the atom. The meaningful solutions for the first three shells of *a hydrogen atom* are contained in

Table 1-2. The different orbitals are distinguished by different subscripts for ψ, and each orbital is uniquely labeled by a set of quantum numbers n, l, and m, where n corresponds to the principal shell number (we shall have more to say about quantum numbers subsequently). The equations for ψ_{np}, are factored into a radial part, $\psi_{(r)}$ (i.e., a dependence on distance r), and an angular part, $\psi_{(\theta,\phi)}$, which is a function of the angles θ and ϕ. The total wave function is simply the product of these two parts; i.e., $\psi = \psi_{(\theta,\phi)}\,\psi_{(r)}$. The equations for s orbitals do not contain any angular dependence, and as a result they are spherically symmetrical.

The number of solutions indicates how many orbitals of a given energy (i.e., principal shell) will exist. There is only one solution, ψ_{1s}, for an orbital corresponding to the shell $n = 1$ (i.e., the lowest energy shell). For energy values corresponding to $n = 2$, there are two very slightly different energies,* corresponding to the wave functions ψ_{2s} and ψ_{2p}. There is one solution for ψ_{2s}, and there are three solutions for ψ_{2p} corresponding to three orbitals ψ_{2p} , ψ_{2p} and ψ_{2p} . These three $2p$ orbitals are all of equal energy. The term *"triply degenerate" is employed to describe the equivalence in energy of the three orbitals.* For energies corresponding to the shell $n = 3$, there are nine solutions corresponding to one ψ_{3s} orbital; three degenerate ψ_{3p} orbitals; and, five degenerate ψ_{3d} orbitals. There are no solutions corresponding to ψ_{1p} or ψ_{2d} orbitals, and there are no such orbitals. Thus, by selecting the model of a stationary wave, incorporating the de Broglie assumption, and selecting physically meaningful solutions of the resulting equation, the number of possible orbitals that are present in a hydrogen atom can be calculated.

QUANTUM NUMBERS

The complete description of all possible orbitals for the first three shells by quantum numbers is also contained in Table 1-2. A series of rules can be presented for determining the possible values for n, l, and m_l. The quantum number n can have any positive integral value except zero. All possible l values corresponding to this n are given by: $l = n - 1, \ldots, 0$, where , . . ., refers to all integers necessary to complete the series. The possible m_l values corresponding to a given l are: $m_l = +l, (l - 1), \ldots, 0, \ldots, (-l + 1), -l$. Each orbital can accommodate two electrons, and these are distinguished by a *spin magnetic moment quantum* number, m_s, of either $+\frac{1}{2}$ or $-\frac{1}{2}$.

---

*The treatment described above indicates ψ_{2s} and ψ_{2p} have similar energies, but a more refined calculation introducing relativity theory indicates there are slight differences. These differences are detected experimentally as fine structure in the atomic spectra.

TABLE 1-2. SOLUTIONS FOR EQUATION (1-14) CORRESPONDING TO ORBITALS IN A HYDROGEN ATOM[a]

Quantum Numbers			Radial Part, $\psi_{(r)}$	Angular Part, $\psi_{(\theta,\phi)}$[b]	Symbol
n	l	m			
1	0	0	$\psi_{1s} = 2(Z/a_0)^{3/2}e^{-\rho}$	$(2\sqrt{\pi})^{-1}$	$1s$
2	0	0	$\psi_{2s}{}^{(4)} = (Z/2a_0)^{3/2}(2-\rho)e^{-\rho/2}$	$(2\sqrt{\pi})^{-1}$	$2s$
2	1	0	$\psi_{2p} = (1/2\sqrt{6})(Z/a_0)^{3/2}\rho e^{-\rho/2}$	$\tfrac{1}{2}\sqrt{3/\pi}\,\cos\theta$	$2p_z$
2	1	1	$\psi_{2p} = \;''$	$''\quad \sin\theta\cos\phi$	$2p_x$
2	1	−1	$\psi_{2p} = \;''$	$'',,,\; \sin\theta\sin\phi$	$2p_y$
3	0	0	$\psi_{3s} = (2/81\sqrt{3})(Z/a_0)^{3/2}(27-18\rho+2\rho^2)e^{-\rho/3}$	$(2\sqrt{\pi})^{-1}$	$3s$
3	1	0	$\psi_{3p} = (4/81\sqrt{6})(Z/a_0)^{3/2}(6\rho-\rho^2)e^{-\rho/3}$	$\tfrac{1}{2}\sqrt{3/\pi}\,\cos\theta$	$3p_z$
3	1	1	$\psi_{3p} = \;''$	$''\quad \sin\theta\cos\phi$	$3p_x$
3	1	−1	$\psi_{3p} = \;''$	$''\quad \sin\theta\sin\phi$	$3p_y$
3	2	0	$\psi_{3d} = (4/81\sqrt{30})(Z/a_0)^{3/2}\rho^2 e^{-\rho/3}$	$\tfrac{1}{4}\sqrt{5/\pi}\;(3\cos^2\theta-1)$	$3d_{z^2}$
3	2	1	$\psi_{3d} = \;''$	$2^{-3/2}\sqrt{30/\pi}\,\sin\theta\cos\theta\cos\phi$	$3d_{xz}$
3	2	−1	$\psi_{3d} = \;''$	$''\quad \sin\theta\cos\theta\sin\phi$	$3d_{yz}$
3	2	2	$\psi_{3d} = \;''$	$\tfrac{1}{4}\sqrt{15/\pi}\;\sin^2\theta\cos 2\phi$	$3d_{x^2-y^2}$
3	2	−2	$\psi_{3d} = \;''$	$''\quad \sin^2\theta\sin 2\phi$	$3d_{xy}$

[a]The total equation for ψ is obtained by multiplying the radial and angular parts. The following symbols are employed: $a_0 = h^2/4\pi^2 me^2$ (h is Planck's constant, m and e are the mass and charge of the electron, respectively); Z = nuclear charge; and $\rho = Zr/a_0$.

[b]The angular part of the solutions which are obtained directly from the Schrödinger equation corresponding to ψ_{np} and ψ_{nd} (except-ing those in which $m = 0$) consist of both real and imaginary parts, the imaginary part being of the form: $e^{i\phi}$ where $i = \sqrt{-1}$. By taking linear combinations of these equations, the real functions listed in Table 1-2 are obtained. The shapes of the p and d orbitals will be discussed shortly. Since these depend on the angular part of the wave function, they result from this linear combination.

The n, m_l, and l quantum numbers and the above rules are consequences of the solution of the Schrödinger equation as discussed in the previous section. The following interpretations of these quantities will be of considerable importance in much of our discussion of physical methods. The principal quantum number, n, arises from the solution for the radial part of ψ and to the first approximation determines the energy of the orbital. The principal quantum number is also qualitatively related to the distance from the nucleus to the most probable position of finding the electron. This quantum number corresponds to the K, L, M etc. shells in the Bohr model.

The quantum numbers l and m_l arise from the solution of the angular part of ψ and refer, respectively, to the magnitude and orientation of the angular momentum (angular velocity times the moment of inertia) of an electron in a particular orbital. The angular momentum associated with the orbital is related to the l quantum number of that orbital by:

$$\text{angular momentum} = \sqrt{l(l+1)}\mathbf{h}/2\pi \qquad (1\text{-}17)$$

An orbital with $l = 0$ is spherical, has no angular momentum and is designated by the letter s. The following symbols are most commonly used: s for $l=0$, p for $l=1$; d for $l=2$, and f for $l=3$.

The angular momentum is a vector quantity. When an external magnetic field is applied to the system, the quantum number m_l can be employed to indicate the direction and magnitude for the component of the projection of the angular momentum vector relative to the applied field. The principal component of this vector can only occupy certain quantized positions relative to the field. The number of positions are given by the number of different possible values for m_l: i.e., $+l$, . . ., 0, . . ., $-l$. The orientations of the angular momentum vector for the five d orbitals relative to the external field, H, are indicated in Fig. 1-4, and the appropriate m_l quantum numbers are indicated for each orbital. The observed component of the angular momentum in the direction of the applied field depends upon the orbital and is given by:

$$\text{component of the angular momentum} = m_l\mathbf{h}/2\pi \qquad (1\text{-}18)$$

The maximum value for the d orbitals is observed for $m_l = +2$ and the minimum for -2. The lowest energy orbital in a magnetic field has the m_l value of $+2$.

The spin quantum numbers $m_s = +\frac{1}{2}$ or $-\frac{1}{2}$ do not arise from the above solution of the Schrödinger equation, but are required to label uniquely all the electrons in an atom. This quantum number is associated with the electron spin angular momentum (as a crude physical model this property can be thought to arise from the electron spinning on its axis). The spin angular momentum vector can be aligned parallel or antiparallel

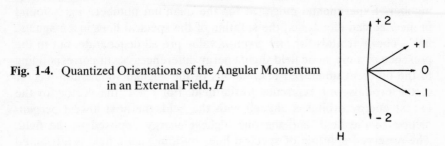

Fig. 1-4. Quantized Orientations of the Angular Momentum in an External Field, H

to the external field direction, and the corresponding values of the spin momentum are:

$$\text{spin momentum} = +\tfrac{1}{2}(\mathbf{h}/2\pi) \quad \text{and} \quad -\tfrac{1}{2}(\mathbf{h}/2\pi) \quad (1\text{-}19)$$

the former being slightly lower in energy in a magnetic field.

In describing an orbital it is common to indicate the principal quantum number n and the $s, p, d,$ or f abbreviation of the orbital quantum number l, e.g., $3p$. There are three such $3p$ orbitals corresponding to: $m_l = +1$, $0, -1$. The $3p_x$, $3p_z$, and $3p_y$ orbitals, which lie along x, z, and y axes, respectively (see Fig. 1-8), are the real orbitals related to these quantum numbers. It is a common feature of differential equations that various combinations of the solutions to differential equations are also solutions. The actual solutions for ψ_{2p} corresponding to $m = \pm 1$ consist of both real and imaginary parts. The ψ_{p_x} and ψ_{p_y} functions, in Table 1-2, are linear combinations of the actual solutions so taken as to produce real functions. The d orbital functions were obtained in the same way.

Experimental evidence for the existence of these various orbitals is obtained from atomic spectra. Electronic transitions from one orbital to another (i.e., to different energy levels) are accompanied by the absorption (if the electron is excited to a higher energy orbital) or emission (if the electron falls to a lower energy orbital) of radiation whose frequency, ν, is related to the energy difference between the orbitals by the equation: $E = \mathbf{h}\nu$. The principal lines in atomic spectra correspond to large energy differences and result from electronic transitions between energy levels with different values of n. Transitions involving the same n but different l values (i.e., s, p, d, and f) give rise to fine structure in the principal lines because of the small energy differences corresponding to different l values. This fine structure is evidence for the l quantum number. Experimental evidence for the quantum number, m_l, is found in the Zeeman effect, i.e., the splitting of the spectral lines in a magnetic field. The p orbitals for any given n value are all degenerate, but in the presence of a magnetic field slight energy differences occur corresponding to the different quantized orientations of the angular momentum vector of the orbitals with reference to the field. For $l = 1$, the vector for the lowest energy orbital is aligned with the field, the next lowest perpendicular to the field, and the one highest energy opposed to the field. The observed splitting of spectral lines by a magnetic field is attributed to transitions involving these different energy orbitals.

THE PHYSICAL PICTURE OF ATOMIC ORBITALS

An important contribution of the Schrödinger derivation to the experimental chemist is the resulting physical picture of the various orbitals described by the equations (Table 1-2) which represent meaningful solu-

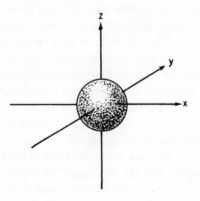

Fig. 1-5. The Angular Dependence of an s Orbital

tions of the Schrödinger equation. Recall that the Uncertainty Principle requires that our discussion of finding the electron in certain positions for the various orbitals (s, p, and d) must be in terms of probabilities, ψ^2.

Let us examine the s orbitals in detail. Equations for $1s$, $2s$, and $3s$ orbitals (in Table 1-2) and similar equations for other s orbitals indicate that the amplitude, ψ, is independent of angle, as θ and ϕ do not appear. Since $\psi^2 d\tau$ is independent of angle, the s orbitals must be spherically symmetrical about the nucleus, as illustrated by the boundary surface in Fig. 1-5. This surface describes the shape of the s orbital and is a plot of r vs. θ and ϕ in spherical coordinates (see Fig. 1-3) for a constant value of ψ_{1s}^2 (see Table 1-2 for the equation for ψ_{1s}) so selected that $\int_0^r \psi^2 d\tau$ will give an arbitrary percentage (say 90 per cent) probability of finding the electron within the resulting surface. If a value of 100 per cent probability were selected instead of a smaller one, r would be infinity as indicated by the limit of the integral of the normalization

Fig. 1-6. Probability Plot for a $1s$ Orbital

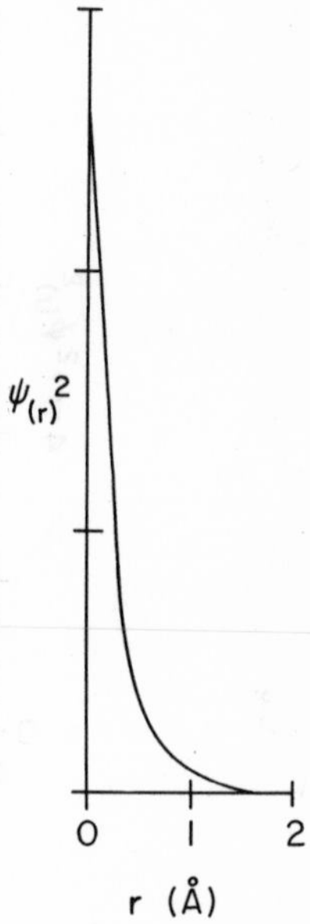

requirement: $\int_0^\infty \psi^2 d\tau = 1$. The requirement of 90 per cent allows us to construct a surface within which there is 90 per cent probability of finding

atom, it may seem awkward to speak of "electron density." It is, however, a convenient description, and the two terms electron density and
probability will be used interchangeably.

In Fig. 1-9, plots of $4\pi r^2 \psi_{(r)}^2$ vs. r are illustrated for various orbitals.

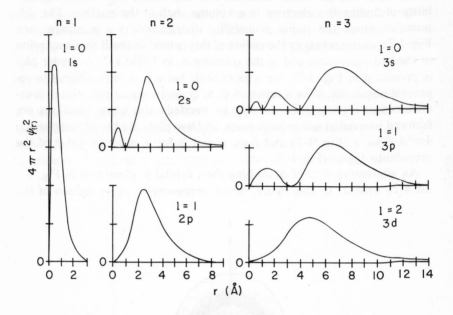

Fig. 1–9. Radial Distribution Functions Giving the Probability of Finding
Electrons at Distances, r, from the Nucleus

Fig. 1-10 illustrates the angular dependence for p and d orbitals (r vs.
angle), again arbitrarily drawn to include 90 per cent ($\psi^2 = 0.9$) of the
electron density. Since the value of ψ for a given p or d orbital is a function
of the angle θ and ϕ (see Table 1-2), these plots are not spherically
symmetrical, and ψ^2 has the value zero for certain values of the angles.

The angular dependence plots are representations of the probability
distributions for various orbitals. The actual orbital is described by the
equation for ψ. The probability plots have physical significance, but
actual orbitals are often employed mathematically. The angular depen-
dences of the 1s, 2s, and 2p orbitals (obtained for constant values of ψ)
are indicated in Fig. 1-11. There is a slight difference in the shape of the
boundary surface for ψ^2 and ψ plots, but the main qualitative difference
arises in that ψ may have a negative sign in some regions. The significance

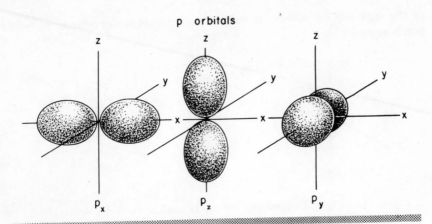

p orbitals

p_x p_z p_y

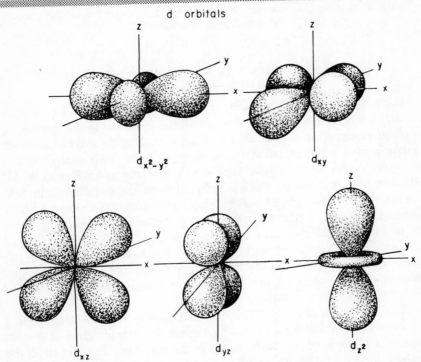

d orbitals

$d_{x^2-y^2}$ d_{xy}

d_{xz} d_{yz} d_{z^2}

Fig. 1–10. Total Angular Dependence of the p and d Orbitals. The p orbitals are three-dimensional surfaces that can be visualized by considering the surface generated when the two-dimensional representation is rotated 180° around its axis as the center. The d orbitals are also three-dimensional surfaces; $d_{x^2-y^2}$ lies along the x and y axes; d_{xy} lies between the x and y axes, d_{yz} between the y and z axes, d_{xz} between the x and z axes, and d_{z^2} along the z axis

of the sign will be discussed later when orbitals are combined to form bonds in molecules.

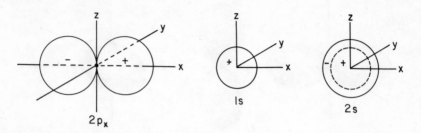

Fig. 1–11. Angular Dependence for 1s, 2s, and 2p Orbitals. Note: The 2s orbital in the figure consists of two spherical shells of different sign. The value of ψ is equal to zero at the boundary and for any s orbital there are $n-1$ such nodes were $\psi = 0$.

EXTENSION OF THE WAVE EQUATION TO ATOMS OTHER THAN HYDROGEN

The above discussion has been concerned with orbitals in a hydrogen atom. In larger atoms the influence of all the electrons in the system on a given electron introduces an additional complication making an exact solution of a wave equation exceedingly difficult. Two approximation methods for the solution have been developed: one by D. R. and W. H. Hartree and modified by Fock is referred to as the self-consistent field treatment, and the second one by Slater produces the so-named Slater orbitals. The self-consistent field treatment in effect simplifies the problem to that of a single electron moving in a spherically symmetrical field of force provided by the nucleus and the average field produced by all the other electrons. The calculations are complicated and lengthy. The final atomic orbitals obtained are given in a numerical table and are thus difficult to convert to a physical model.

The second approach by Slater is based upon a single electron moving in a central field which results from an effective nuclear charge of $(Z-S)$, where Z is the nuclear charge and S is the screening constant of all the other electrons.[1] The screening constant is a measure of how well the inner electrons shield the outer electron from the nuclear charge.

Except for the absence of radial nodes, Slater orbitals have the same general shape as the orbitals described by the equations in Table 1-2, for the effective nuclear charge changes only the radial part of the wave function. The complete details for writing down analytical functions for various orbitals are presented by Coulson.[1] The procedure will be demonstrated for the atomic $2p_x$ orbital of carbon. In Coulson's book, the equation: $\psi_{2p_x} = N_{2p} \times \exp(-cr/2)$ is found along with rules for evaluating N_{2p} and c by simply counting the number of electrons in the various orbitals of the atom. The value of x in the above equation expressed in polar coordinates is: $x = r \sin\theta \cos\phi$ (or for p_y and p_z orbitals, $y = r \sin\theta \sin\phi$ and $z = r \cos\theta$). The angular part of the wave function for ψ_{2p_x} is contained in x, which, as indicated in Table 1-2, is $\sin\theta \cos\phi$ for ψ_{2p_x}. After c and N have been evaluated, the equation for ψ_{2p_x} becomes $\psi_{2p_x} = 3.58r \sin\theta \cos\theta \exp(-3.07r)$ (taking θ as the angle to the z axis and ϕ in the x–y plane; see Fig. 1-3). For a representation of the p_x orbital in the x–y plane (θ is 90°), a constant value of ψ^2 is selected (say 0.9, i.e., $\psi = (0.9)$ and the above equation is solved for r for various values of ϕ in the x–y plane. Negative values of ψ are used for $\phi = 90$ to 270°, and a plot of r vs. ϕ produces an orbital similar in shape to that in Fig. 1-11. The equation for s, p, and d orbitals resulting from this treat-

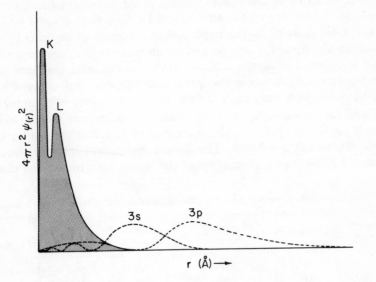

Fig. 1–12. Radial Plot for the Orbitals in a Sodium Atom

ment produce shapes for these orbitals which are similar to those obtained for hydrogen. Although Slater orbitals are simpler to work with, they are intrinsically inferior to Hartree-Fock functions.

The principal difference between the hydrogen atom and a multi-electron atom lies in the effectiveness with which the inner electrons screen the nuclear charge from the outer electron. As indicated in Fig. 1-12 for a sodium atom, the $3s$ electron, whose radial plot is indicated by a dotted line, has a considerable probability of being in close to the nucleus underneath the inner electrons. The inner electrons do not completely shield the nuclear charge from the s electron in this case. The p electron is shielded a little more effectively. As can be seen from the radial plots (Fig. 1-9), the amount of penetration decreases in the order $3s > 3p > 3d$.

RELATIVE ENERGIES OF THE ORBITALS

Since inner electrons do not always effectively screen outer electrons, the relative energies of the orbitals vary with change in nuclear charge of the atoms.[2] The following order can be employed for writing the atomic structure of most of the atoms in the periodic table: $1s < 2s < 2p < 3s < 3p < 4s < 3d < 4p < 5s < 4d < 5p < 6s < 4f < 5d < 6p < 7s$. This order pertains to the hypothetical synthesis of an atom by simultaneous addition of a proton and an electron to the preceding element and is referred to as the *Aufbau order*. As the main quantum number increases, the difference in energy between the orbitals decreases. Beyond $7s$ there are only very slight differences. In describing the atomic structure of the elements by the s, p, d, and f notation, one simply adds two electrons to the s orbitals, six to the p orbitals, ten to the d orbitals, and fourteen to the f orbitals. The lowest energy orbitals are filled first. Table 1-3 contains a description of the atomic structure of the elements

TABLE 1-3. ELECTRONIC ORBITAL CONFIGURATION OF SOME OF THE ELEMENTS

Atomic Number	Element	Electronic Configuration	Atomic Number	Element	Electronic Configuration
1	H	$1s^1$	10	Ne	$-2s^22p^6$
2	He	$1s^2$	11	Na	$[Ne]3s^1$
3	Li	$[He]2s^1$	12	Mg	$-3s^2$
4	Be	$-2s^2$	13	Al	$-3s^23p^1$
5	B	$-2s^22p^1$	14	Si	$-3s^23p^2$
6	C	$-2s^22p^2$	15	P	$-3s^23p^3$
7	N	$-2s^22p^3$	16	S	$-3s^23p^4$
8	O	$-2s^22p^4$	17	Cl	$-3s^23p^5$
9	F	$-2s^22p^5$	18	Ar	$-3s^23p^6$

TABLE 1-3. Continued

Atomic Number	Element	Electronic Configuration	Atomic Number	Element	Electronic Configuration
19	K	$[Ar]4s^1$	61	Pm	$-4f^56s^2$
20	Ca	$-4s^2$	62	Sm	$-4f^66s^2$
21	Sc	$-3d^14s^2$	63	Eu	$-4f^76s^2$
22	Ti	$-3d^24s^2$	64	Gd	$-4f^75d^16s^2$
23	V	$-3d^34s^2$	65	Tb	$-4f^85d^16s^2$
24	Cr	$-3d^54s^1$	66	Dy	$?(10)6s^2$
25	Mn	$-3d^54s^2$	67	Ho	$?(11)6s^2$
26	Fe	$-3d^64s^2$	68	Er	$?(12)6s^2$
27	Co	$-3d^74s^2$	69	Tm	$-4f^{13}6s^2$
28	Ni	$-3d^84s^2$	70	Yb	$-4f^{14}6s^2$
29	Cu	$-3d^{10}4s^1$	71	Lu	$-4f^{14}5d^16s^2$
30	Zn	$-3d^{10}4s^2$	72	Hf	$-4f^{14}5d^26s^2$
31	Ga	$-3d^{10}4s^24p^1$	73	Ta	$-4f^{14}5d^36s^2$
32	Ge	$-3d^{10}4s^24p^2$	74	W	$-4f^{14}5d^46s^2$
33	As	$-3d^{10}4s^24p^3$	75	Re	$-4f^{14}5d^56s^2$
34	Se	$-3d^{10}4s^24p^4$	76	Os	$-4f^{14}5d^66s^2$
35	Br	$-3d^{10}4s^24p^5$	77	Ir	$-4f^{14}5d^76s^2$
36	Kr	$-3d^{10}4s^24p^6$	78	Pt	$-4f^{14}5d^96s^1$
37	Rb	$[Kr]5s^1$	79	Au	$-4f^{14}5d^{10}6s^1$
38	Sr	$-5s^2$	80	Hg	$[Au^+]6s^2$
39	Y	$-4d^15s^2$	81	Tl	$-6s^26p^1$
40	Zr	$-4d^25s^2$	82	Pb	$-6s^26p^2$
41	Nb	$-4d^45s^1$	83	Bi	$-6s^26p^3$
42	Mo	$-4d^55s^1$	84	Po	$-6s^26p^4$
43	Tc	$-4d^55s^2$	85	At	$-6s^26p^5$
44	Ru	$-4d^75s^1$	86	Rn	$-6s^26p^6$
45	Rh	$-4d^85s^1$			
46	Pd	$-4d^{10}$			
47	Ag	$-4d^{10}5s^1$			
48	Cd	$-4d^{10}5s^2$			
49	In	$-4d^{10}5s^25p^1$			
50	Sn	$-4d^{10}5s^25p^2$			
51	Sb	$-4d^{10}5s^25p^3$			
52		$-4d^{10}5s^25p^4$			
53	I	$-4d^{10}5s^25p^5$			
54	Xe	$-4d^{10}5s^25p^6$			
55	Cs	$[Xe]6s$			
56	Ba	$-6s^2$			
57	La	$-5d^16s^2$			
58	Ce	$-4f^15d^16s^2$			
59	Pr	$-4f^36s^2$			
60		$-4f^46s^2$			

up to radon by this convention. There are several exceptions to this pattern (e.g., Cr, Cu, La, etc.). Stability associated with a half-filled or filled subshell accounts for these exceptions.

In the above description of atomic structure, two quantum numbers, n and l, have been employed. A more nearly complete description of the electrons in an atom can be obtained by employing all four quantum numbers: n, l, m_l, and m_s. A box diagram representation is one method employed to indicate all four quantum numbers. Usually only the valence electrons are indicated. The s orbitals are indicated by a single box □. The p orbitals are indicated by three boxes, ▢▢▢, one each for the p_x, p_z, and p_y orbitals. The d orbitals are represented by five boxes, ▢▢▢▢▢, one each for $d_{x^2-y^2}$, d_{xz}, d_{z^2}, d_{yz}, d_{xy}, and the f orbitals by seven boxes. A spin quantum number of $+\frac{1}{2}$ is indicated by the symbol ↑ and $-\frac{1}{2}$ by ↓. In addition to the above conventions, two rules are required for the application of the box diagram designation to all atoms:

(1) Pauli exclusion principle—No two electrons in an atom have all four quantum numbers alike.

(2) Hund's rule—Electrons will distribute themselves in degenerate orbitals so as to retain parallel spins as much as possible; i.e., electrons do not pair up until they have to.

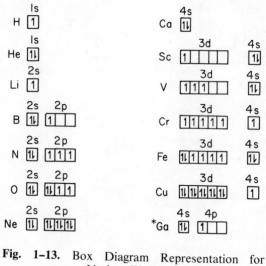

Fig. 1–13. Box Diagram Representation for Various Elements

Figure 1-13 contains several examples of the box diagram representation of atomic structure.

Excluding the principal quantum number, the box diagrams for the outer electrons of all the elements in a given family in the periodic table are identical (e.g., P, As, Sb, and Bi are like N), with the exception of some transition metals.

In forming positive or negative ions from elements other than transition elements, an electron is added to the next orbital to form a negative ion, or the last electron added to form the element is removed to form a positive ion. However, for transition elements the energy sequence obtained by the Aufbau order does not apply. The first electrons removed to form the transition metal cations are the s electrons. The box diagrams for Co, Co^{2+}, and Co^{3+} are illustrated:

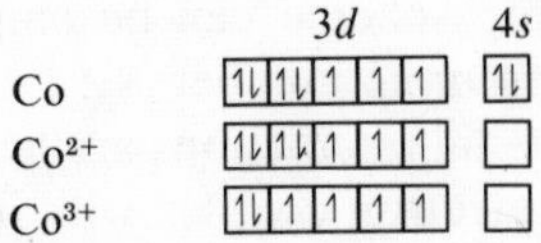

TERM SYMBOLS AND THE VECTOR METHOD

An additional complication encountered in many-electron systems arises from the large number of ways the electrons can be added to a set of orbitals. A few of the possibilities for arranging two electrons in a set of p orbitals are:

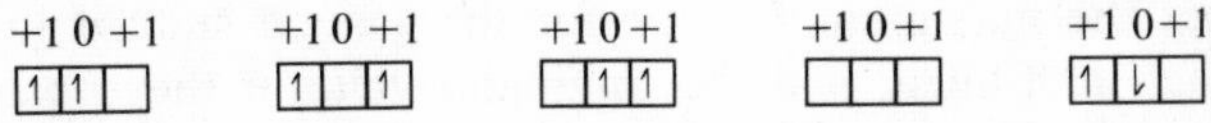

Some of these states would be higher energy states in an atom and some combinations are degenerate. Interelectronic repulsions vary for the different electron arrangements, being larger for two electrons in the same orbital than for electrons in different orbitals. As a result of different types of interelectronic interactions, which are absent in a single-electron system, many more nondegenerate states exist in a many-electron system than in a single-electron system. Furthermore, the concepts of spin and orbital angular momentum for the individual electrons lose significance in a many-electron system. These properties of the individual electrons are coupled together to produce a single resultant angular momentum for the entire multielectron atom. This resultant momentum is described by the quantum number J. "Term symbols" are used to indicate both the electronic configuration and the resultant angular momentum of an atomic state.

In order to determine J, two schemes are used to describe the coupling of all the angular momenta in the atom. These schemes are referred to as LS (or Russell-Saunders) coupling and jj coupling. The LS coupling scheme is used when spin-orbital interactions are relatively small. The individual orbital angular momenta of the electrons couple to produce a resultant angular momentum indicated by the quantum number L for the state. The individual electron spin moments also couple to give a resultant spin momentum described by the quantum number S. The L and S values determine the value of the resultant angular momentum J, which can take on quantized positive values ranging from $|L - S|$ to $|L + S|$ (consecutive values are separated by 1). The $|\ |$ indicate that the absolute value of $|L - S|$ is employed (i.e., no regard is paid to the sign and $J \geq 0$). The LS coupling scheme can be employed for all atoms except those that have high atomic numbers ($Z > 30$). The jj coupling scheme is used when spin orbital interactions are large. The spin angular momentum of an individual electron couples with its orbital momentum to give an individual j for that electron. The individual j's couple to produce a resultant J for the atom.

The rules for determining the term symbol for the ground state according to the LS coupling scheme can be summarized:

(1) Maximize the spin multiplicity (S); i.e., electrons occupy degenerate orbitals so as to retain parallel spins as long as possible (Hund's rule).

(2) Maximize orbital angular momentum (L); i.e., fill the orbitals with the highest positive m values first.

(3) Select the maximum J value for the ground state if the subshell is more than half-filled, and the minimum value if the subshell is less than half-filled.

The rules for determining the term symbol for the ground state of an atom, assuming LS coupling, are best indicated by an example. The box diagram for carbon is:

$$2p$$
$$1s \quad 2s \quad +1\ 0\ -1$$

and the term symbol to be determined is $^3P_0$. The value of the L quantum number is obtained by adding the m_l values for all the electrons in incomplete orbitals. For example, in carbon $L = +1 + 0 = 1$. The quantum number l for an individual electron is treated as a vector with component m_l in the direction of the applied field. The vector sum L will have a maximum component equal to the sum of the individual components

m_l. The value for the S quantum number is the sum of the spin quantum numbers ($m_s = \pm\frac{1}{2}$) for each unpaired electron, e.g., for carbon $S = \frac{1}{2} + \frac{1}{2} = 1$ (the absolute values of L and S are employed). Complete subshells contribute nothing to L or S because the sum of the m_s and m_l values for a filled s, three filled p, or five filled d orbitals is zero. The value of L is indicated in the term symbol by the letters S, P, D, F, G, H, and I for L values corresponding to 0, 1, 2, 3, 4, 5, and 6, respectively. This is similar to describing l values of orbitals as s, p, d, f, etc. Thus, the P in the term symbol of carbon indicates $L = 1$. The number in the upper lefthand corner corresponds to the spin multiplicity of the state and is given by the formula:

$$2\Sigma m_s + 1 \qquad \text{or} \qquad 2S + 1 \qquad\qquad (1\text{-}20)$$

This is three for carbon and corresponds to the degeneracy resulting from all the different possible orientations of the total electron spin moment. Since $S = 1$, the spin multiplicity is three, and there are three orientations of the spin moment in a magnetic field: parallel, perpendicular, and opposed to the external field. This is similar to the alignment of the orbital moments as indicated for the d orbitals in Fig. 1-4. The values for J (as given by $|L - S|, \ldots, |L + S|$) are $|L - S| = 1 - 1 = 0$, $|L + S| = 1 + 1 = 2$, so $J = 0, 1, 2$ (one being the only integer needed to complete the series). Whenever the subshell involved is less than half-filled, the state with minimum J is lowest energy, while maximum values of J are lowest energy when the subshell is more than half-filled. There will be only one J value for a half-filled shell because L will be zero: $|L + S| = |0 + S| = |L - S| = |0 - S| = S$. Since carbon has only two electrons with a capacity of six in the p-set, the value $J = 0$ is lowest in energy. The term symbol $^3P_0$ results for the ground state of carbon.

The box diagram for the ground state of V^{3+} is

$$+2 +1 0 -1 -2$$
$$\boxed{\uparrow}\boxed{\uparrow}\boxed{\ }\boxed{\ }\boxed{\ }$$

with term symbol $^3F_2$ ($L = 3$, $S = 1$, $J = 4, 3, 2$). An excited state for this species is represented by: $\boxed{\uparrow\downarrow}\boxed{\ }\boxed{\ }\boxed{\ }\boxed{\ }$ which has the term symbol $^1G_4$ ($L = 4$, $S = 0$, $J = 4$). Because of interelectronic interactions, the energies of many of the V^{3+} states are different.

For nitrogen with a box diagram $\boxed{\uparrow}\boxed{\uparrow}\boxed{\uparrow}$ $L = 0$, $S = 3/2$, $J = 3/2$ and the term symbol $^4S_{3/2}$ results. Note that there is only one J value in this case with $L = 0$ for $|L + S| = |L - S| = 3/2$.

For practice, one can determine the following term symbols for the ground state of the element in parentheses: $^3P_2$ (S), $^2P_{3/2}$ (Cl), $^3F_2$ (Ti), $^7S_3$ (Cr), $^3F_4$ (Ni), $^3P_0$ (Si), $^4S_{3/2}$ (As), $^4I_{9/2}$ (Pr).

TERM SYMBOLS FOR EXCITED STATES

In the previous section, rules were presented for determining the term symbol for the ground state of an atom. If the L value is other than zero, this ground state is orbitally degenerate. For the V^{3+} ion (d^2), the ground state term symbol $^3F_2$ indicates that $L = 3$. There are seven quantized positions for this total orbital angular momentum, L, in a magnetic field, and these have the components: $m_L = 3, 2, 1, 0, -1, -2, -3$. The quantity m_L can be treated as the sum of the m_l values for the individual electrons. Thus, included in this F state are seven combinations of m_l values, producing the m_L values in Fig. 1-14. To

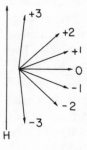

Fig. 1-14. The m_L Values Included in an F Term Symbol

convert this to a box diagram representation, the following configurations would be degenerate and would be included along with others in the ^3F state, for their m_L values are $+3, +2,$ and -2.

The rules in the previous section indicated how to calculate the maximum m_L value, which determines the term symbol of the ground state.

The following procedure can be employed to determine which states are degenerate and to indicate the total number of different states. The procedure to determine the energy states of V^{3+}, a d^2 configuration, will be illustrated. In this case, all the different possible ways in which two electrons can be arranged with parallel spins in the d orbitals are

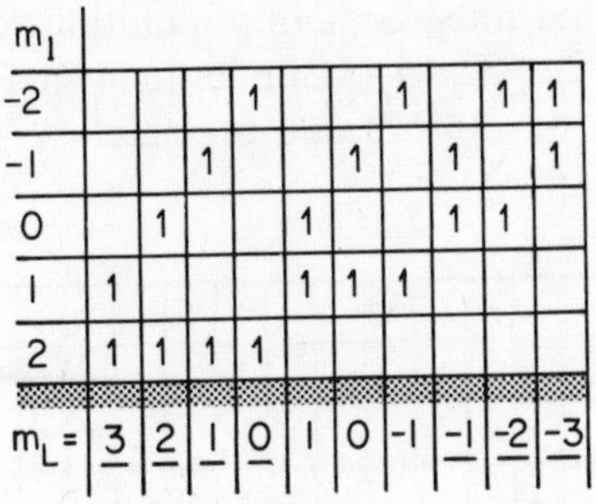

m_l										
-2				1			1		1	1
-1			1			1		1		1
0		1			1			1	1	
1	1				1	1	1			
2	1	1	1	1						
$m_L =$	3	2	1	0	1	0	-1	-1	-2	-3

Fig. 1–15. Possible Arrangement of Two Electrons with Parallel Spin in the Five d Orbitals

indicated by the "pigeon hole" diagram illustrated in Fig. 1-15. In this diagram, each vertical rectangle illustrates a box diagram configuration.

The rules for constructing such a pigeon hole diagram are as follows:

(1) Use one horizontal row for each value of m_l.

(2) In a given column, place the first electron with spin *up*.

(3) The other electrons in a given column are placed in rows above that of the first electron. This avoids duplication of configurations.

(4) In subsequent columns, systematically place the electrons in higher rows until all possibilities have been exhausted.

(5) The Pauli exclusion principle must be obeyed.

The resultant m_L which represents the sum of the m_l values is indicated in the bottom row. The highest m_L value was determined in the previous section, and this produced the F in the term symbol. It also indicates that m_L values of 3, 2, 1, 0, −1, −2, −3 are the degenerate components of this ground state. For counting purposes, configurations corresponding to these m_L values are underlined in Fig. 1-15. Three configurations, +1, 0, −1, are left over, and these must comprise an excited ^3P state. (Recall $L = 1$ for P with m_L components +1, 0, −1.) Electron interactions account for the energy differences of the P and F states. These two states each contain $m_L = +1$, $m_L = 0$, and $m_L = −1$. It is impossible to assign a particular box diagram configuration with these m_L values to the ^3P or ^3F state, but this problem need not concern us here.

Next, consider the possible box diagram configurations of the d^2 singlet state ($S = 0$) corresponding to paired electrons (Fig. 1-16). The maximum m_L value indicates that the lowest energy singlet excited state is a ^1G state and must contain orientations corresponding to $m_L = $ 4, 3, 2, 1, 0, −1, −2, −3, −4 (as underlined in Fig. 1-16). This leaves a ^1D state (+2, +1, 0, −1, −2) and a singlet ^1S state (0). In summary,

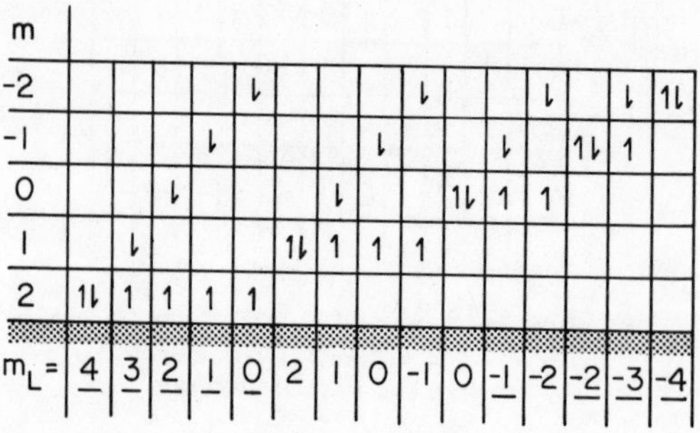

m															
-2					↓				↓			↓		↓	1↓
-1				↓				↓			↓		1↓	1	
0			↓				↓			1↓	1	1			
1		↓				1↓	1	1	1						
2	1↓	1	1	1	1										
$m_L=$	4	3	2	1	0	2	1	0	-1	0	-1	-2	-2	-3	-4

Fig. 1–16. Possible Arrangement of Opposite Spin Electrons in the d Orbitals

all possible d^2 states for V^{3+} are: ^3F, ^3P, ^1G, ^1D, and ^1S. An extension of these considerations permits calculation of other excited states, e.g., d^1s^1, d^1p^1, etc.

By this procedure we have considered all possible arrangements of two electrons in the d orbitals and have divided these arrangements up to produce all the possible nondegenerate states.

EXERCISES

1. a. How many different sets of quantum numbers are available for electrons with:
   (1) $n = 3$?
   (2) $n = 3, l = 2$?
   (3) $n = 2, l = 0$?
   (4) $n = 2, l = 0$?
   b. What notation (s, p, d, or f) is used to describe the electrons in (2), (3), (4) above?
2. a. Are the electrons in $n = 3, l = 2$ all degenerate?
   b. Are the above electrons degenerate in a magnetic field? Why?
   c. What is the physical evidence in support of your answer to 2b?
   d. What quantum number describes the orientations of orbitals in a magnetic field?
3. List all of the elements with valence electrons having the following quantum numbers:
   a. $n = 2, l = 1$.
   b. $n = 3, l = 0$.
   c. $n = 2, l = 2$.
   d. $n = 3, l = 2$.

4. Why has copper a smaller radius than potassium?
5. Using s, p, d, and f terminology, describe the electronic arrangement in: Na, K, Mn, Cu, P.
6. Draw the box diagrams for: P, As, Cl, S, U, Co, Ni, Ni^{2+}.
7. Indicate the term symbol for the lowest energy state corresponding to the following electron configurations: d^8, d^6, and $d^7 s^1$.
8. Indicate the term symbols for all states corresponding to different d-electron arrangements in the following: d^3 and d^7.

REFERENCES CITED

1. C. A. Coulson, "Valence," p. 40, Oxford, London, 1952.
2. G. Herzberg, "Atomic Spectra and Atomic Structure," p. 148, Dover, New York, 1944.

2 *Bonding*

IN THIS CHAPTER, we will be mainly concerned with covalent bonding. Small sections at the end contain very brief treatments of electrostatic and hydrogen bonding. Two approaches will be employed to describe the nature of covalent bonds, the valence bond and the molecular orbital descriptions. Both of these descriptions make use of the variation principle, and this principle will be discussed before covalent bonding.

THE VARIATION PRINCIPLE

The Schrödinger equation (1-13) can be rearranged to produce equation (2-1):

$$[-(h^2/8\pi^2m) \nabla^2 + V]\psi = E\psi \qquad (2\text{-}1)$$

where the terms in the brackets make up the Hamiltonian operator which is abbreviated by the symbol H (an operator is an instruction to carry out a specific mathematical operation). Accordingly, equation (2-1) is often abbreviated as:

$$H\psi = E\psi \qquad (2\text{-}2)$$

The Hamiltonian is a total energy operator; i.e., it is a specific mathematical operation which, when carried out upon ψ, gives a value for the energy of the system described by ψ. The general equation (2-3) results by multiplying both sides of (2-2) by ψ and integrating over all the coordinates involved:

$$E = \int \psi H \psi \, d\tau / \int \psi^2 d\tau \qquad (2\text{-}3)$$

where $d\tau$ is the volume element, and the wave functions are assumed

30

to be real. In principle, the energy, E, of a system can be calculated with this equation if the wave function ψ and potential energy, V, of the Hamiltonian are known.

To illustrate the use of these equations, the energy of the ground state for the hydrogen atom will be determined by this procedure. As mentioned in Chapter 1, this problem can be solved by a direct solution of the differential equation (1-13). The potential energy term for the hydrogen atom, $V = -e^2/r$, is accurately known and can be substituted in (2-1). The form of the resulting differential equation suggests that a function of the type $\psi = \exp(-ar)$, where a is some unknown constant, will be a solution. For a particular value of a, $\exp(-ar)$ can be substituted for ψ in equation (2-3) and an energy $E(1)$ calculated. This guess at ψ is referred to as a trial wave function and as a result of the direct solution in Chapter 1, we know this is a good guess in this case. The Variation Principle states that if ψ is not a true solution (i.e., an eigenfunction) of (2-1), then this calculated $E(1)$ will be greater than the energy of the true wave function of the system. We shall use this principle to evaluate a of the trial wave function for the hydrogen atom. By using a different value of a, a new energy $E(2)$ can be calculated. If this energy $E(2)$ is lower than $E(1)$, then the second choice of a has given a trial wave function which is closer to the true wave function than the first trial function was. The energy of an approximate wave function is lower and closer to the true energy as the wave function is closer to the true wave function. This means that the lowest energy that can be calculated by varying a in the trial wave function $\psi = \exp(-ar)$ corresponds to that value of a which makes ψ best resemble the true wave function.

A systematic way to carry out variations is to choose an approximate ψ which contains one or more variable parameters and then to minimize the calculated energy (equation 2-3) with respect to these parameters. This is done by setting the derivatives of E with respect to each of the parameters equal to zero. The resulting equations are called the *secular equations*. With the normalization requirement, these give the values of the parameters in the approximate ψ which lead to the lowest energy. The minimum energy calculated by this procedure will be closer to the true energy of the system the more nearly the approximate ψ resembles the true wave function of the system. In the case of the hydrogen atom, we have assumed the wave function to be of the form $\psi = \exp(-ar)$, where r is the distance of the electron from the nucleus and a is the adjustable parameter which is to be determined for a minimum energy.

The Hamiltonian can be obtained from equation (2-1) by properly representing the potential energy term for this system i.e., $V = -e^2/r$.

The resulting equation for H is transformed to polar coordinates using the relationship:

$$\nabla^2 = [(1/r^2)(\partial/\partial r)][r^2(\partial/\partial r)]$$

This operation leads to

$$\nabla^2\psi = (1/r^2)(\partial/\partial r)[r^2(\partial/\partial r)]\exp(-ar)$$
$$= (1/r^2)\{-r^2[-a^2\exp(-ar)] + [a\exp(-ar)](-2r)\}$$
$$= (a^2 - 2a/r)\exp(-ar)$$

Since $H = -(\mathbf{h}^2/8\pi^2 m)\nabla^2 + V$, equation (2-3) becomes

$$E = \frac{\displaystyle\int^{\infty}\exp(-ar)[(\mathbf{h}^2/8\pi^2 m)(a^2 - 2a/r)\exp(-ar) - (e^2/r)\exp(-ar)]4\pi r^2\,dr}{\displaystyle\int_0^{\infty}\exp(-2ar)\,4\pi r^2\,dr}$$

where $4\pi r^2\,dr = d\tau$. Performing the integrations gives:

$$E = (\mathbf{h}^2 a^2/8\pi^2 m) - e^2 a \qquad (2\text{-}4)$$

The minimum energy of the system is obtained by taking the first derivative of E with respect to a and setting this quantity equal to zero. Setting the derivative of equation (2-4) equal to zero yields:

$$a = 4\pi^2 m e^2/\mathbf{h}^2 \qquad (2\text{-}5)$$

and substituting equation (2-5) back into (2-4) produces the value for the minimum energy in terms of fundamental constants:

$$E_{\min} = -2\pi^2 m e^4/\mathbf{h}^2 \qquad (2\text{-}6)$$

This result is identical to that obtained in Chapter 1 because the correct trial wave function was selected.

The extension of these calculations to a molecule becomes more difficult because of the difficulties involved in defining ψ of equation (2-3). To demonstrate the variation procedure, the simple system H_2^+ will be treated. The ground state trial wave function ψ^0 which will be used to attempt to obtain the energy of this system is given by equation (2-7)

$$\psi^0 = C_1\phi_A + C_2\phi_B \qquad (2\text{-}7)$$

where ϕ_A and ϕ_B represent the wave functions for an electron on atom A and atom B, respectively.

The problem is to evaluate C_1 and C_2 and hence define the minimum energy structure. This is a rather trivial but illustrative example, because we know from the symmetry of the molecule that $C_1 = C_2$. Substituting (2-7) into (2-3) and utilizing the equality $\int \varphi_A H \varphi_B d\tau = \int \varphi_B H \varphi_A d\tau$, the following equation for the energy of this system results:

$$E = \frac{C_1^2 \int \varphi_A H \varphi_A \, d\tau + 2C_1 C_2 \int \varphi_A H \varphi_B \, d\tau + C_2^2 \int \varphi_B H \varphi_B d\tau}{C_1^2 \int \varphi_A^2 \, d\tau + 2C_1 C_2 \int \varphi_A \varphi_B \, d\tau + C_2^2 \int \varphi_B^2 \, d\tau} \qquad (2\text{-}8)$$

This equation, (2-8), though difficult to solve, is simpler than a first glance would indicate. The integrals $\int \varphi_A H \varphi_A d\tau$ and $\int \varphi_B H \varphi_B d\tau$ are referred to as *Coulomb integrals* and represent the interaction energy between the electron and the respective nuclei. In some cases, these energies can be estimated from the ionization energies of the atoms. The integrals $\int \varphi_A^2 d\tau$ and $\int \varphi_B^2 d\tau$ are equal to one (see equation 1-16; the normalization requirement). The quantity $\int \varphi_A \varphi_B d\tau$ is referred to as the *overlap integral,* and this will be discussed in detail shortly. The quantity $\int \varphi_A H \varphi_B d\tau$ is referred to as the *exchange integral.* The integrals in the numerator are negative and those in the denominator positive. A large negative number for E corresponds to a stable system.

We have expressed the energy of equation (2-7) by (2-8) in order to determine the combination of coefficients C_1 and C_2 that will give the lowest energy structure for the trial wave function. This is done by the variation procedure which involves differentiation of (2-8) with respect to C_1 to produce an equation which is set equal to zero to obtain the minimum energy. This is followed by differentiation of (2-8) again, this time with respect to C_2 to produce a second equation which is also set equal to zero, i.e., $\partial E / \partial C_1 = 0$ and $\partial E / \partial C_2 = 0$. The resulting equations are the secular equations, and for the general case of n variable parameters in ψ^0 there will be n such equations,

$$\psi^0 = C_1 \varphi_a + \ldots + C_n \varphi_n \qquad (2\text{-}9)$$

If we had accurate expressions for the wave functions and H, the secular equations, of which there are two in our example, could be solved with the normalization equation for the two unknowns C_1 and C_2, yielding the best values for these coefficients in equation (2-7) to describe the wave function for the actual structure of the molecule. The result using the trial wave function (2-7) and the accurate Hamiltonian is $C_1 = C_2$.

The calculated energy is very close to the experimental energy, indicating that a good trial wave function (equation 2-7) was selected. Since the actual structure is always lower in energy than an approximate description, energies calculated by this method will always be equal to or higher than the true value, depending on how good the selected trial wave function is.

The entire derivation for H_2^+ is discussed more completely in Day and Selbin[1]. For more complicated molecules, it is necessary to make approximations for ψ^0, and a valence bond or molecular orbital approach can be employed. In some approximate solutions of complex molecules, simplified forms of the Hamiltonian are often utilized. The treatment of the hydrogen molecule has been clearly indicated in the Day and Selbin text by use of an accurate Hamiltonian and valence bond and molecular orbital estimates of the wave function. The reader is referred to texts by W. Kauzmann and A. Streitwieser[2] for a discussion of approximation procedures in other molecules.

TREATMENTS OF THE HYDROGEN MOLECULE

The hydrogen molecule is a simple system consisting of two electrons attracted by two nuclei. By labeling the two nuclei H_A and H_B and numbering the two electrons 1 and 2, the following Schrödinger equation (2-10) can be written for this molecule:

$$\nabla^2\psi + (8\pi^2 m/h^2)[E + e^2/r_{A-1} + e^2/r_{B-1} + e^2/r_{A-2} + e^2/r_{B-2} - e^2/R_{A-B} - e^2/r_{1-2}]\psi = 0 \quad (2\text{-}10)$$

In this equation r_{A-1} is the distance between H_A and electron 1; r_{B-1} is the distance between H_B and electron 1; r_{A-2} and r_{B-2} represent similar distances from electron 2; R_{A-B} is the distance between the two nuclei; and r_{1-2} is the electron–electron distance. All terms within the brackets except E represent the potential energy, V, of the system. The first four terms containing e^2 represent the attraction between the electrons and nuclei, and the last two terms represent the repulsions between the two nuclei and between the two electrons. In general, a wave equation can be written for any system by properly representing the potential energy term of equation (1-13). Equation (2-10) cannot be solved directly so the variation method is used.

In the valence bond (VB) method, the molecule is considered to be made up by bringing isolated atoms together and allowing them to interact. There is a theorem stating that if φ_A and φ_B are the wave functions for two isolated, noninteracting atoms, with energies E_A and E_B, the wave function for the noninteracting system as a whole can be written as a product, $\psi = \varphi_A \varphi_B$, with energy $E = E_A + E_B$. Consequently in the valence bond approach, the trial wave functions for the molecule used in the variation procedure will be made up of products of atomic wave functions with variable coefficients.

For the hydrogen molecule we will choose the following set of functions with which to make up the trial wave function ψ^0:

$$\psi_1 = \varphi_A(1)\ \varphi_B(2) \qquad\qquad (2\text{-}11)$$

$$\psi_2 = \varphi_A(2)\ \varphi_B(1) \qquad\qquad (2\text{-}12)$$

$$\psi_3 = \varphi_A(1)\ \varphi_A(2) \qquad\qquad (2\text{-}13)$$

$$\psi_4 = \varphi_B(1)\ \varphi_B(2) \qquad\qquad (2\text{-}14)$$

where ψ_1 is the wave function for electron 1 on H_A ($\varphi_A(1)$) and electron 2 on H_B (see Fig. 2-1) and ψ_4 is a wave function for both electrons on H_B.

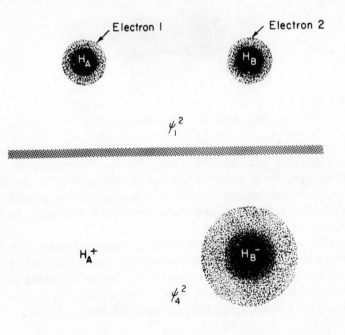

Fig. 2-1. Structures Corresponding to $\psi_1{}^2$ and $\psi_4{}^2$

The trial function, ψ^0, will be expressed as a linear combination of these product functions,

$$\psi^0 = N(C_1\psi_1 + C_2\psi_2 + C_3\psi_3 + C_4\psi_4) \tag{2-15}$$

where N is the normalization constant and the coefficients C_1, C_2, C_3, and C_4 indicate the weight to be given to each of the ψ_n's. The trial wave function is substituted into equation (2-3), and differentiating with respect to C_1, C_2, C_3, and C_4, yields four secular equations which when solved produce the values for these coefficients.

The interaction of the ψ_n's in equation (2-15) is called resonance. The result of resonance is that the energy calculated for ψ^0 will be lower than the energies of any of the individual ψ_n's in (2-15). Conceptually, resonance indicates that the actual structure is represented by none of the structures corresponding to the ψ_n terms in equation (2-15) but rather by an intermediate one, ψ^0, that has some character of each of the individual ones. The structure corresponding to ψ^0 is indicated in Fig. 2-2.

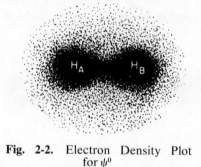

Fig. 2-2. Electron Density Plot
for ψ^0

Covalent bonding increases the charge density between the two nuclei and the bonding force results from the attraction of both electrons by both nuclei. In the ground state wave function, the coefficients C_1 and C_2 are equal to each other, and much larger than C_3 and C_4, which are also equal: $C_1 = C_2 >>> C_3 = C_4$.

The difference between the application of the valence bond and the molecular orbital theories is in the formulation of the trial wave function. To a first approximation, molecular orbital theory assumes that the hydrogen molecule is represented by adding one electron to the molecular orbitals of H_2^+. Consequently the trial wave function is of form:

$$\psi^0{}_{MO} = a\varphi_A + b\varphi_B$$

This molecular orbital trial wave function consists of a linear combination of hydrogen atomic orbitals and is referred to as the LCAO approximation. As formulated above, ψ^0_{MO} corresponds to the wave function employed in the discussion of the application of the variation principle of H_2^+.

ELECTRON EXCHANGE INTERACTION

The phenomenon of *electron exchange interaction* is somewhat like resonance and is a concept that is not related to bonding but one that we will need to use in later chapters. This effect can be demonstrated by considering the electronic structure for the first excited state of He. Two possible ways in which two electrons can be arranged in $1s$ and $2s$ orbitals with their spins parallel are:

$1s$ $2s$ $1s$ $2s$

$\boxed{\uparrow}\boxed{\uparrow}$ and $\boxed{\uparrow}\boxed{\uparrow}$ (one arrow is dotted to distinguish the electrons)

In effect, there are two similar energy solutions to the Schrödinger equation for this helium excited state corresponding to these two possibilities. A resonance type approach can be employed by taking linear combinations of the two possibilities. The resulting stabilization is said to result from exchange interaction. Electron exchange interaction is most effective when the electron spins are parallel. Consequently the first excited state in helium (i.e., the lowest energy electronic excited state) is one in which the two electron spins are parallel.

APPLICATIONS OF VALENCE BOND THEORY

THE GENERAL MOLECULE XY — ELECTRONEGATIVITY

Qualitative formulation of ground state wave functions, ψ^0, and the corresponding charge clouds will be discussed for a series of general molecules X—Y in which the electronegativity differences between the two atoms X and Y vary. Electronegativity is a qualitative concept defined as the ability of an atom to attract the bonding electrons.[*] The structure of a diatomic molecule containing a single bond can be des-

---

*For a detailed discussion of electronegativity see: H. O. Pritchard and H. A. Skinner, *Chem. Revs.*, **55**, 745 (1955); R. P. Iczkowski and J. L. Margrave, *J. Am. Chem. Soc.*, **83**, 3547 (1961); J. Hinze and H. H. Jaffe, *ibid.*, **84**, 540 (1962); L. Pauling. "Nature of the Chemical Bond," 3rd ed., Cornell, Ithaca, N.Y., 1960.

cribed by an equation identical with (2-15) where ψ_1, ψ_2, ψ_3, and ψ_4 have the same general form as in the discussion of the H_2 molecule (equations 2-11 through 2-14). The relative magnitudes of the coefficients of equation (2-15) for the molecule BrCl are: $C_1 = C_2 >>> C_3 > C_4$ where ψ_3 refers to $Br^+ :Cl^-$. Since chlorine is more electronegative than bromine, C_3 is greater than C_4. The difference in electronegativity of Br and Cl is not very great and the bonding is essentially covalent ($C_1 = C_2 >>> C_3$). The resulting charge cloud for the valence electrons is illustrated in Fig. 2-3a.

For the molecule Li^+Cl^- (in the gas phase), the difference in electronegativity of the two atoms is very large and the bonding is essentially ionic. Accordingly, the coefficients for (2-15) are $C_3 >> C_1 = C_2 >> C_4$ where ψ_3 refers to Li^+Cl^-. The resulting charge cloud for the valence electrons is illustrated in Fig. 2-3b. A whole series of intermediate situations exists which depend upon the electronegativity difference between X and Y. In future discussion, equation (2-15) will be abbreviated: $\psi^0 = a\psi_{cov} + b\psi_{el}$ where ψ_{cov} represents ψ_1 and ψ_2 and ψ_{el} is the more important electrostatic form. The amount of ionic character in the bond is described by the coefficient b.

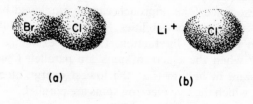

(a) (b)

Fig. 2-3. Electron Density Plots for BrCl and LiCl

More Complicated Molecules — Resonance

In the preceding section, the bonding in diatomic molecules was discussed in terms of a linear combination of ionic and covalent wave functions, i.e., resonance of ionic and covalent forms. In more complicated molecules containing only single bonds (e.g., CH_4) the molecule is often factored for qualitative discussion into individual bonds consisting of two atoms (e.g., four C—H bonds) and treated as above. When this is done, an approximation referred to as *perfect pairing* is often introduced. This approximation assumes that the bonding is localized (in the above example in the C—H bond) and there is no interaction between the adjacent bonds or non-nearest-neighbor atoms, e.g., no H—H bonding in CH_4. This assumption is fairly good[3] for CH_4 but is apt to be poor for less symmetrical and more complex molecules. The perfect pairing approximation is a good one for many applications, but the existence of this assumption should be recognized when complex structures are described in terms of localized single bonds.

In many molecules containing double and triple bonds it is possible to write several structures for a molecule, as in N_2O:

$$\overline{N}{=}N{=}\overline{O} \quad \text{and} \quad |N{\equiv}N{-}\overline{O}|$$

Resonance is taken into account in these cases by describing the wave function of the molecule as a linear combination of the wave functions for these valence bond structures. The N_2O molecule can be represented as a resonance hybrid of these two forms. This is in agreement with the experimental finding that the N—N distance in N_2O is intermediate between a double- and triple-bond distance, and the N—O distance is intermediate between a single- and double-bond distance.

Five forms are illustrated in Fig. 2-4 for the benzene molecule. $\psi^0 = C_1\psi_1 + C_2\psi_2 + C_3\psi_3 + C_4\psi_4 + C_5\psi_5$, where $C_1 = C_2 >>> C_3 = C_4 = C_5$.

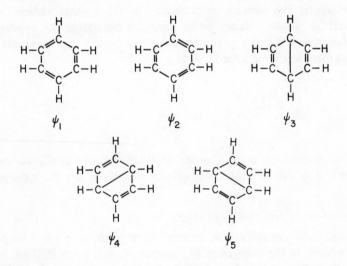

Fig. 2-4. Some Valence Bond Structures for Benzene

Resonance forms ψ_3, ψ_4, and ψ_5 are less favorable from an energy stand-point because of the weak, long bond in these structures. In the actual structure all C—C bonds in benzene are equivalent, and the bond distance is intermediate between that of a single bond and that of a double bond.

It is important to emphasize that the actual structure, ψ^0, does not oscillate back and forth between the forms ψ_1, ψ_2, etc., but is a single hybrid structure.

In applying resonance theory to more complicated molecules, the various forms are written by intuition employing the following rules:

(1) Each form must contain the same number of unpaired electrons.

(2) The relative positions of the atoms in the various forms must be the same.

(3) The contributing forms must be of comparable energy, e.g., in the N_2O molecule the structure, $\overline{N}\!\!=\!\!N\!\!-\!\!\overline{O}|$, would be so unstable that it could make only negligible contribution to the ground state, for the central atom has only six electrons.

When applying the concept of resonance to the consideration of more complicated molecules, one must consider all possible structures that conform to the above requirements. Requirement (3) is often the most difficult one to evaluate.

In the beginning of this section we discussed the perfect pairing approximation. The interaction neglected by this approximation can be accounted for in the valence bond approach by adding the appropriate resonance forms to the ground state description. For example, the following form would be added to CH_4:

$$
\begin{array}{c}
H \\
\diagdown \\
H\!\!-\!\!\overset{\displaystyle C}{\underset{\displaystyle H}{|}}\diagdown H
\end{array}
$$

Since this represents a very unstable (high energy) configuration, its contribution to the ground state will be negligible for most purposes.

THE OVERLAP OF ATOMIC ORBITALS

An important consideration in the description of a bond based on atomic orbitals is the overlap of the atomic orbitals since this affects the magnitude of the $\int \varphi_A H \varphi_B d\tau$ and $\int \varphi_A \varphi_B d\tau$ terms in the variational expression for E (equation 2-8). There are some very important consequences of this principle. Consider the molecule hydrogen selenide, H_2Se. Selenium has an atomic structure: ⊞ ⊞⊞⊞. In the molecule H_2Se, two atomic p orbitals on selenium, which are at right angles to each other, overlap the stable 1s orbitals of the two hydrogen atoms. The structure of the resulting molecule is indicated in Fig. 2-5. The region of overlap (shaded area of Fig. 2-5) represents the bonding electron density being shared by

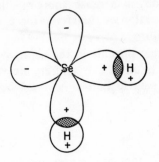

Fig. 2-5.   Overlap of the Bonding
Orbitals in H_2Se

the two atoms. The extent of overlap is expressed quantitatively by the overlap integral, S:

$$S = \int \varphi_A \varphi_B \, d\tau \qquad (2\text{-}16)$$

where φ_A and φ_B are the atomic orbital wave functions for the atoms A and B joined by a covalent bond. In those regions where either φ_A or φ_B approaches zero, the integral approaches zero and there is no bonding in this area. Only in those regions where both φ_A and φ_B are appreciable does the above integral become significant. With greater overlap, the value for the overlap integral is larger, and the bond is stronger. The overlap concept requires that the bonds lie in a direction in which there will be maximum overlap with the atomic orbitals employed. As a consequence of this principle of maximum overlap, the shape of the molecule will suggest which atomic orbitals of the atom determining the geometry (e.g., Se in H_2Se) should be used to describe the bonding.

The quantitative use of equation (2-16) again involves substitution of accurate wave functions into the equation and evaluation of the integral. Values for the overlap integrals, S, of Slater-type orbitals have been tabulated for a variety of bond types.[4] The value of S is presented as a function of internuclear distance and effective nuclear charge. As will be discussed shortly, different overlaps are obtained for σ and π bonds, and both types are reported.

It is interesting to point out that the overlap integral appears in the denominator of equation (2-14) and the bond strength should decrease (i.e., the energy of the system would be a smaller negative number) as the magnitude of this integral increases. However, as this integral becomes larger, the exchange integral increases more rapidly, and the bond strength increases. As a simplification we shall relate increased overlap to increased bond strength in the future.

Whenever two atomic orbitals in the same atom are substituted into equation (2-16), e.g., $1s$ and $2s$, $1s$ and $2p$, etc., the integral has a value of zero. Orbitals are said to be *orthogonal* whenever the result of this integration is zero.

HYBRID ORBITALS

Strict application of the above concepts to the methane molecule leads to an incorrect answer. By inspecting the box diagram for carbon, $\boxed{1\!\uparrow}$ $\boxed{1\!\uparrow\,1\!\uparrow\,\,}$, one might expect carbon to form the compound CH_2. By promoting an electron the following excited structure represented by C^* is obtained: $\boxed{1\!\uparrow}$ $\boxed{1\!\uparrow\,1\!\uparrow\,1\!\uparrow}$. Four hydrogen atoms could combine with carbon to produce CH_4 with an "expected" structure consisting of three hydrogen atoms, all at right angles to each other (from overlap of the p_x, p_y, and p_z orbitals), and a fourth hydrogen atom at the apex of a trigonal pyramid as far away from the others as possible. Since the s orbital is nondirectional, this location of the fourth hydrogen atom would minimize H—H repulsions. Instead, all four bonds in CH_4 are equivalent, and the four hydrogen atoms are tetrahedrally located about carbon (i.e., the H—C—H angles are all 109°28′). Orbitals with this geometry can be obtained by combining the four orbitals (one s, three p) in such a way as to produce four equivalent hybrid sp^3 orbitals (i.e., each orbital consists of 25 per cent s and 75 per cent p character). The linear combination of the s and three p atomic orbitals to produce four equivalent, tetrahedral sp^3 hybrids is indicated mathematically by the following equations:

$$
\begin{aligned}
(\varphi_{sp^3})_1 &= \tfrac{1}{2}(\varphi_{2s} + \varphi_{2p_x} + \varphi_{2p_y} + \varphi_{2p_z}) \\
(\varphi_{sp^3})_2 &= \tfrac{1}{2}(\varphi_{2s} + \varphi_{2p_x} - \varphi_{2p_y} - \varphi_{2p_z}) \\
(\varphi_{sp^3})_3 &= \tfrac{1}{2}(\varphi_{2s} - \varphi_{2p_x} - \varphi_{2p_y} + \varphi_{2p_z}) \\
(\varphi_{sp^3})_4 &= \tfrac{1}{2}(\varphi_{2s} - \varphi_{2p_x} + \varphi_{2p_y} - \varphi_{2p_z})
\end{aligned}
\tag{2-17}
$$

The constants again satisfy the normalization requirement. Each orbital

*A discussion of the derivation of these equations for the hybrids is found in L. Pauling, "The Nature of the Chemical Bond," 3rd ed., Cornell, Ithaca, N.Y., 1960.

has a capacity of two electrons and is a hybrid of all four of the $2s$ and $2p$ atomic orbitals.

Boron trichloride can be treated in a similar fashion by considering the atomic structure of boron in the ground state (⬚ ⬚⬚⬚) and in the activated (⬚ ⬚⬚⬚) state. The s and two p orbitals can be hybridized to produce three equivalent sp^2 hybrid orbitals which lie in a plane and are separated by an angle of $120°$ (see Fig. 2-6). The linear combination of

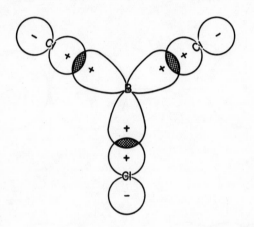

Fig. 2-6. Overlap of sp^2 Boron Orbitals with p Chlorine Orbitals in BCl_3

these orbitals is expressed* mathematically by equations (2-18). Each sp^2 orbital is a hybrid consisting of one-third s character and two-thirds p character.

$$(\varphi_{sp^2})_1 = (1/\sqrt{3})\varphi_{2s} + (\sqrt{2}/\sqrt{3})\varphi_{2p_x}$$
$$(\varphi_{sp^2})_2 = (1/\sqrt{3})\varphi_{2s} - (1/\sqrt{6})\varphi_{2p_x} - (1/\sqrt{2})\varphi_{2p_y} \qquad (2\text{-}18)$$
$$(\varphi_{sp^2})_3 = (1/\sqrt{3})\varphi_{2s} - (1/\sqrt{6})\varphi_{2p_x} + (1/\sqrt{2})\varphi_{2p_y}$$

An sp hybrid consists of one-half s and one-half p character. The mathematical equations (2-19) used to represent this linear combination are:

$$(\varphi_{sp})_1 = (1/\sqrt{2})(\varphi_{2s} + \varphi_{2p_x})$$
$$(\varphi_{sp})_2 = (1/\sqrt{2})(\varphi_{2s} - \varphi_{2p_x}) \qquad (2\text{-}19)$$

Mercury in $HgCl_2$ is said to employ essentially *sp* hybrids in bonding the chlorines, since the bonds are linear.

It is possible to present a physical picture for equations (2-19), i.e., the linear combination of φ_{2s} and φ_{2p_x} orbitals to produce *sp* hybrid orbitals. The orbitals φ_{2s} and φ_{2p_x} are represented in Fig. 2-7a. The signs of the wave function in the various regions (Chapter 1) are indicated for these orbitals. In Fig. 2-7b, the linear combination of these two orbitals to produce $(\varphi_{sp})_1$ is indicated. The positive regions of the angular

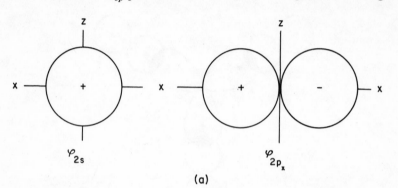

(a)

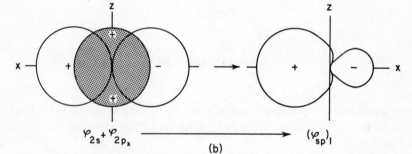

(b)

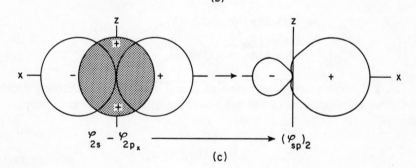

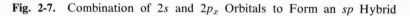

(c)

Fig. 2-7. Combination of 2s and $2p_x$ Orbitals to Form an *sp* Hybrid

plot of φ_{2s} cancel the negative part of the p orbital and reinforce the positive part of the p orbital, producing the hybrid $(\varphi_{sp})_1$. Multiplication of the p orbital by minus one changes the signs of the lobes and $(\varphi_{sp})_2$ of Fig. 2-7c results from this linear combination. This pictorial representation clearly indicates that the two sp hybrid orbitals must point in opposite directions, i.e., form a linear molecule. In an sp^2 hybrid, the resulting orbitals will lie in the x–y plane, for by convention the p_x and p_y orbitals are used. Since p_x, p_y, and p_z orbitals are employed to form sp^3 hybrids, these orbitals will point in three dimensions.

Table 2-1 contains a summary of the hybrids discussed above plus some common ones employing d orbitals.

TABLE 2-1. SOME COMMON HYBRID ORBITALS

Type	Geometry	Examples
sp	linear, 180°	$HgCl_2$
sp^2	planar, 120°	BCl_3, $GaCl_3$
sp^3	tetrahedral, 109°28′	CH_4, $GeCl_4$
dsp^2	square planar, 90°	$Ni(CN)_4^{2-}$, $Cu(NH_3)_4^{2+}$
d^2sp^3	octahedral	$Co(NH_3)_6^{3+}$, $Fe(CN)_6^{3-}$

HYBRIDS INVOLVING d ORBITALS*

The following box diagram describes the electronic structure of Fe^{3+}:

$$3d \qquad 4s$$
$$\boxed{1}\,\boxed{1}\,\boxed{1}\,\boxed{1}\,\boxed{1} \quad \boxed{\ }$$

In the complex $Fe(CN)_6^{3-}$, six pairs of electrons from the cyanide ions form polar covalent bonds, and the following box diagram describes the configuration of iron(III) in the complex:

$$3d \qquad 4s \qquad 4p$$
$$\boxed{1\downarrow}\,\boxed{1\downarrow}\,\boxed{1}\,\boxed{\cdot\cdot}\,\boxed{\cdot\cdot} \quad \boxed{\cdot\cdot} \quad \boxed{\cdot\cdot}\,\boxed{\cdot\cdot}\,\boxed{\cdot\cdot}$$

The dots represent electron pairs from the cyanide ion (i.e., $:C{\equiv}N\,|$). Electrons are paired up and d^2sp^3 hybrid orbitals are utilized for the covalent contribution to the bonding in this molecule. There are ap-

---

*In Chapter 3 an alternate explanation, ligand field theory, is presented for the bonding in metal ion complexes. A more complete discussion of the valence bond explanation is available: D. H. Busch, *J. Chem. Educ.*, **33**, 376, 498 (1956).

preciable contributions to the ground state from an ionic structure with the same number of unpaired electrons.

In $FeF_6{}^{3-}$, the iron(III) interactions with the fluoride ions are weak (less heat is evolved in bond formation) and the energy to pair up the electrons is not supplied. The box diagram for iron(III) in the complex is:

The bonding is essentially electrostatic and any slight covalent contributions to the bonding come from an sp^3d^2 hybrid; i.e., the 4s, 4p, and 4d orbitals are involved. The hybrid is octahedral and the $FeF_6{}^{3-}$ complex is described as an *outer orbital* or ionic complex. By contrast 3d, 4s, and 4p orbitals are used in the *inner orbital* complex, $Fe(CN)_6{}^{3-}$. Sulfur hexafluoride, SF_6, is an example of a compound with polar covalent bonds in which the hybridization is sp^3d^2. The gaseous PCl_5 molecule (Fig. 2-8) has a trigonal bipyramid structure, and phosphorus is sometimes said to employ "dsp^3" hybrids to bond the chlorines. The apical chlorines have three equivalent chlorine atoms *cis* (as neighbors) and have a single chlorine in the *trans* (opposite) position. The equatorial chlorine atoms have two near neighbors, two chlorine atoms farther away (the apical atoms), but none in the *trans* position. Since the five bonds in any trigonal

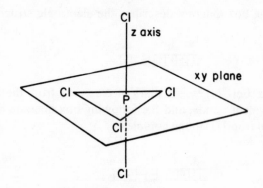

Fig. 2-8. The Structure of PCl_5

bipyramid cannot be equivalent, the "dsp^3" hybrid can be described as two hybrids: (1) an sp^2 hybrid bonding the equatorial chlorines and (2) a pd hybrid (from p_z and $d_z{}^2$) bonding the apical chlorines. This problem will be considered in more detail in a later section.

ENERGETICS OF HYBRID BOND FORMATION

A convenient way to factor the energy terms involved in hybridization is:

(1) Promotion of the ground state atom to the excited configuration.
(2) Hybridization of the excited configuration.
(3) Bond formation with the other atoms in the molecule.

Promotion for carbon and iron(III) is indicated by:

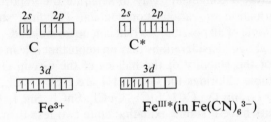

Energy is required to promote the atom to a hybridized excited configuration, but when much stronger bonds are formed by using hybrids, some of the energy gained from bonding can be expended for the excitation. When overlap is greater with a hybrid orbital than with a pure atomic orbital, a more stable system results by using hybrid bonds than would result by forming bonds without hybridization. Fig. 2-9 illustrates

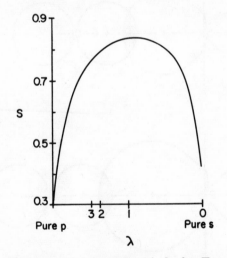

Fig. 2-9. Overlap Integral, S, for Two Similar Hybrids $\psi_s + \sqrt{\lambda}\psi_p$. (From C. A. Coulson, p. 199, "Valence," Oxford, London, 1961.)

the relative magnitude of the overlap integral for two identical atoms employing identical hybrids consisting of s and p orbitals. The amount of p character is indicated by λ in the hybrid, e.g., $\lambda = 2$ for sp^2 and $\lambda = 3$ for sp^3. As a result of more effective overlap the hybrids form stronger bonds than pure s or pure p orbitals.

It is important to emphasize that the steps, excitation, hybridization, and bonding, do not imply a mechanism for forming molecules. They are merely a convenient way to separate the important energy terms in the formation of various compounds. The final structure will be the most stable of all possibilities that can be formulated.

The above considerations play an important role in a qualitative explanation of the stability of the halides of the Group III and IV elements. The stable chlorides for Group III are BCl_3, $AlCl_3$, $GaCl_3$, $InCl_3$, $TlCl$ and for Group IV, CCl_4, $SiCl_4$, $GeCl_4$, $SnCl_4$, $SnCl_2$, $PbCl_2$. The heaviest elements have a stable oxidation state two less than the maximum even though the orbitals are closer and promotion is easier than in the light elements.

The radial part of the wave function indicates that the orbital is more diffuse in the heavy element and in a given volume element ψ_{Tl} or ψ_{Pb} will

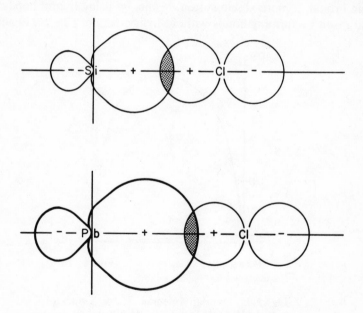

Fig. 2-10.   Effect of Orbital Size on Overlap

be smaller than ψ_B or ψ_{Si}. As a result the overlap integral for the central element and chlorine will be smaller and the bond weaker in the compounds of the heavy elements than in the lighter elements. This effect is illustrated in Fig. 2-10. Repulsions of the $4f$ electrons of lead and nonbonding chlorine electrons also cause a decrease in bond strength. As a result of less effective overlap, the heavy atom forms a more stable compound by reacting and leaving the lone pair of electrons intact in the s orbital. Consequently, the most stable chlorides for thallium and lead are TlCl and $PbCl_2$. The actual structure which results is more stable (lower in energy) than any other possible structure. Thermodynamic data and promotion energies which substantiate these conclusions have been reported.[5]

NONEQUIVALENCE OF ORBITALS

In many "tetrahedral" molecules the bond angles are distorted slightly from the normal 109°28′ angle, e.g., in CH_3Cl the H—C—H angles are 110°20′. The hybrid bonding of carbon to the hydrogens in CH_3Cl may be described as $s + \sqrt{\lambda}p$ where the amount of p character is given by $\lambda < 3$. A λ value slightly greater than three describes the hybrid used for the C—Cl bond. The sum of the s orbital contribution in the four bonds must be one and the sum of the p orbitals three. Increasing s character in a hybrid increases the angle ($sp^3 < sp^2 < sp$), while increasing p character (decreasing s) decreases the angle.

This effect is even more pronounced in molecules containing lone pairs of electrons. Table 2-2 contains some data on bond angles of some Group V and VI hydrides. The bonding in ammonia can be described as

TABLE 2-2. BOND ANGLES IN SOME HYDRIDES

H_2O	104·5°	NH_3	107·3°
H_2S	92·2°	PH_3	93·3°
H_2Se	91·0°	AsH_3	91·8°

an sp^3 hybridized nitrogen accommodating three hydrogens and a lone pair in the four orbitals.* The slight deviation from the tetrahedral angle

---

*It is sometimes difficult for the student to see how nitrogen with a box diagram [↑↓] [↑|↑|↑] can form sp^3 hybrids. One may consider that the $2s$ and $2p$ orbitals of N^{5+} can be hybridized to sp^3 hybrids. A lone pair of electrons is placed in one orbital and three hydride ions are added to the other three hybrid orbitals. This is merely a counting procedure and not a mechanism for forming NH_3. The net effect is to promote lone pair electron density out of the s orbital, since the sp^3 hybrid orbital that accommodates the lone pair has only about 25 per cent s character.

can be accounted for by incorporating a little more than 25 per cent s character into the hybrid containing the lone pair and consequently a little more p character into the hybrids employed to bond the hydrogens. Since only about 25 per cent of the s orbital is used to accommodate the lone pair in ammonia and since the entire orbital is used to accommodate a pair of electrons in the ground state of the nitrogen atom, promotion of some of the electron density out of the nitrogen s orbital has occurred in ammonia. A more stable structure (stronger bonds) results for ammonia when the s electrons are promoted and nitrogen uses hybrid orbitals to bond the hydrogens. In phosphine the bonds with hydrogen are weaker, the promotion energy is not supplied, and the lone pair remains in the low energy s orbital. As a result, the P—H bonding orbitals at the phosphorus atom have a nearly pure p character. With the larger elements in this family, as with phosphorus, the energy of the bond with hydrogen is not increased as much by hybridization as in the case of nitrogen. The larger orbitals are more diffuse and the magnitude of the wave function in the region of overlap is smaller. A smaller overlap integral results; consequently, hybridization does not occur as readily in the larger elements. In certain compounds of the Group V elements in which bond energy is more sensitive to hybridization because bond strengths are greater, we might expect hybrids to be employed in the bonding (e.g., PF_3 where the P—F bond energy is greater than the P—H bond energy, and the F—P—F angle is 104°).

The concept of *isovalent hybridization*, summarized by the following statement, is closely allied to the topics being discussed here. In a hypothetical molecule A—M—B, replacement of B by a more electronegative group, C, causes M to rehybridize in such a manner that more p character is placed in the orbital used to bond C than there is in the orbital to B. As a result more s character is employed in the bond M—A in the molecule A—M—C than in A—M—B. There is, for example, more s character in the hybrid carbon uses to bond the methyl hydrogens in CH_3OH than in CH_3NH_2, because oxygen is more electronegative than nitrogen. Correspondingly, more p character is employed in the C—O bond than in the C—N bond. These considerations explain the H—C—H bond angles in the example CH_3Cl that was first mentioned in this section. A considerable amount of data in support of this postulate has been presented.[6]

Bond angles in many compounds have been explained by considering only electron repulsions.[7] It is proposed that lone pair electrons are "pear shaped" while a bonding electron pair occupies a smaller "sausage shaped" orbital. Thus lone pairs have a greater space requirement than bonding pairs. The structures of H_2O, NH_3, and NF_3 differ from the $90°$ angle because of appreciable lone pair–bonding pair and bonding pair–bonding pair repulsions. A tetrahedral configuration produces minimum repulsion when all four electron pairs are equivalent, as in NH_4^+. Since the lone pairs have a greater space requirement than bonding electron pairs, the bond angles in H_2O and NH_3 are slightly less than tetrahedral. Bonding pair–bonding pair repulsions are less important than lone pair–bonding pair repulsions in molecules containing larger central atoms (H_2S, H_2Se, PH_3, and AsH_3), and angles near $90°$ result. It is proposed that in these larger atoms, bonding pair–bonding pair repulsions do not become important until the angle approaches $90°$.

This author feels that electronic repulsions are certainly important in determining stereochemistry and the best explanation of bond angles consists of a blend of all the proposals described above. Certainly three large groups bound weakly to nitrogen by single bonds will have near tetrahedral geometry because of steric considerations. The hybrids nitrogen employs to bond to these groups is another matter. Hybridization cannot always be deduced from the bond angle. It has been shown that the H—C—H angle in a tetrahedral carbon atom can vary as much as $11°$ from the direction in which the hybrids used in bonding point, without appreciably affecting the overlap integral. It is also reported[8] that the hybridization of the H—C—H bond in CH_2Cl_2 cannot be deduced from the measured angle. This effect will be discussed in more detail in the chapter on nuclear magnetic resonance. Evidence concerning hybridization can be obtained in some cases with this technique.

In the compounds formed by the larger elements the problem of describing hybridization is further complicated by the inclusion of d orbitals in the bonding description. Instead of employing an sp hybrid to describe the bonding in $HgCl_2$, it is proposed[9] that the hybrid should be described as a mixture of $d_{z^2}^n$, s^{1-n}, and p (where n is a fraction). It has also been reported[10] that the phosphorus hybridization in the axial bonds in PF_5 is not pd but there are appreciable contributions from the $3s$ orbital. This would require some d character in the hybrids used to bond the equatorial florines.

The above discussion can best be summarized by a remark of Professor R. S. Mulliken, "I believe the chemical bond is not so simple as some people seem to think."

σ AND π BONDS

A σ bond results from the "head on" overlap of the atomic orbitals, and the resulting bond axis lies in the direction in which the atomic orbitals are pointing (see Fig. 2-11a). In order to form a bond, the orbitals must have the same symmetry relative to the molecular axis (i.e., the bond axis). To have the same symmetry the wave functions for the parts of the orbitals involved in overlap must have the same sign (Fig. 2-11a).

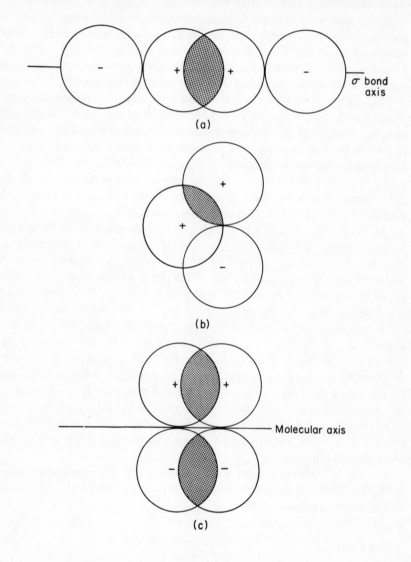

Fig. 2-11. π and σ Overlap of Atomic Orbitals

An example is illustrated in Fig. 2-11b where the orbitals have different symmetries relative to the bonding axis and a bond is not formed. Overlap of the positive s orbital with the negative lobe of the p orbital cancels the bonding contribution from overlap of the s orbital with the positive lobe. For this case the value of the overlap integral, S (equation 2-16), is zero; the orbitals are orthogonal.

Figure 2-11c illustrates two p_y orbitals which overlap laterally to produce a π bond. This should be contrasted with the "head on" overlap of a σ bond. A σ bond is cylindrically symmetrical about the bonding axis, but a π bond is not. In ethylene, the two carbons are joined by a σ sp^2 hybrid bond and a π bond described by the overlap of two p_z orbitals, one from each carbon atom. The π overlap of the two p_z orbitals requires that the $\begin{smallmatrix} H \\ \diagdown \\ \end{smallmatrix}$ C—C $\begin{smallmatrix} \\ \diagup \\ H \end{smallmatrix}$ system be planar. In acetylene, the two carbons are bonded by a σ sp hybrid bond and two π bonds.

APPLICATIONS OF MOLECULAR ORBITAL THEORY

In the valence bond (VB) approach to bonding, it is assumed that electrons in atomic orbitals (often hybridized) overlap to form bonds. Molecular orbital (MO) theory treats the nuclei of the whole molecule as a polycentric nucleus and attempts to construct a system of molecular orbitals characterized by a set of quantum numbers, in a manner similar to the treatment of atomic orbitals in atoms. After the MO's have been constructed, the electrons are added. The Pauli exclusion principle is obeyed. On adding electrons, the lowest energy orbital is filled first and Hund's rule is obeyed. The approximation is often made that the molecular orbitals may be represented by a combination of atomic orbitals. This is referred to as the LCAO (linear combination of atomic orbitals) method for constructing molecular orbitals. In order for the atomic orbitals to interact and form molecular orbitals, the atomic orbitals must (1) have similar energies, (2) overlap appreciably, and (3) have the same symmetry with respect to the bonding molecular axis.

Molecular Orbitals for Homonuclear Diatomic Molecules

The combination of atomic orbitals to produce molecular orbitals for homonuclear diatomic molecules (e.g., H_2, O_2, N_2, etc.) will be discussed first. For the hydrogen molecule, combination of the two $1s$ atomic orbitals from the two hydrogen atoms produces two molecular orbitals (Fig. 2-12). Mathematically, the wave functions φ_A and φ_B for the two identical hydrogen atoms H_A and H_B are combined $(\varphi_A \pm \varphi_B)$ producing two molecular orbitals, $1s\sigma_g$ and $1s\sigma_u$:

$$1s\sigma_g = N(\varphi_A + \varphi_B) \qquad (2\text{-}20)$$
$$1s\sigma_u = N(\varphi_A - \varphi_B) \qquad (2\text{-}21)$$

where N is the normalization constant. (The shapes of these orbitals are shown in Fig. 2-15.)

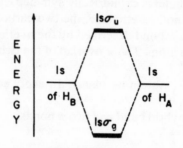

Fig. 2-12. Combination of $1s$ Atomic Orbitals to Produce Molecular Orbitals

The symbols g and u refer to the German words *gerade* and *ungerade*. It is common to use the g and u to label orbitals in an atom. They are also employed to label molecular orbitals in molecules that possess a center of symmetry. The orbital is referred to as *gerade* and is labelled with a g if after starting at any point in the orbital and moving along a straight line through the center of symmetry to an equal distance on the other side of the center one encounters a point where the wave function has the same sign as the starting point. If the wave function changes sign the orbital is *ungerade* and the symbol u is employed. The reader can verify that these criteria have been satisfied in labeling the orbitals in Fig. 2-15 (remember the center of symmetry in a diatomic molecule is midway between the two nuclei). Examination of the p orbital plot in Chapter 1 will make obvious the fact that the p orbitals are *ungerade*.

The molecular orbitals for H_2 are made up of equal parts of the two $1s$ atomic orbitals from H_A and H_B. The MO $1s\sigma_g$ accommodates the pair of bonding electrons in the hydrogen molecule and is referred to as a bonding MO while $1s\sigma_u$ is referred to as antibonding and is often abbreviated as σ^*. Note (Fig. 2-12) that the bonding MO represents a lower energy situation than the original atomic orbitals (equivalent to the H—H bond strength) while the antibonding orbital $1s\sigma_u$ is higher. The extents of the lowering of $1s\sigma_g$ and the raising of $1s\sigma_u$ are identical and increase as the overlap of the two atomic orbitals increases. The charge distribution in the final structure is identical to that described by the valence bond approach.

These qualitative considerations can be made more quantitative by a treatment similar to that previously employed for $H_2{}^+$. For the hydrogen molecule, the molecular orbital wave function is:

$$\psi = a\varphi_A + b\varphi_B$$

where $a = b$. Substituting this wave function into equation (2-10) and solving for the energies of the two molecular orbitals, $\psi_1 = (1/\sqrt{2})(\varphi_A + \varphi_B)$ and $\psi_2 = (1/\sqrt{2})(\varphi_A - \varphi_B)$, one obtains:

$$E_1 = q + \beta \quad \text{and} \quad E_2 = q - \beta$$

where E_1 and E_2 refer to the energies of ψ_1 and ψ_2, respectively, q equals the Coulomb integral, and β the exchange integral. Consequently ψ_1 or σ_g is lowered in energy to the extent that σ_u is raised and the difference in energy of σ_g and σ_u is 2β. The energy of E_1 is lower because the exchange integral, β, is negative.

When electrons are present in the antibonding orbital, these electrons cause repulsion between the two atoms. An electron in $1s\sigma_u$ causes repulsion to compensate the attractive force of an electron in $1s\sigma_g$. Therefore, He_2 with two electrons in $1s\sigma_g$ and two in $1s\sigma_u$ is not a stable molecule. Table 2-3 contains a description of the bonding in molecules and molecule-ions that utilize $1s\sigma_g$ and $1s\sigma_u$ orbitals. Note that the dissociation energy (a measure of bond strength) of $H_2{}^+$ is greater than

TABLE 2-3. MOLECULAR ORBITAL DESCRIPTION
OF SOME DIATOMIC MOLECULES

Entity	Configuration	Bond Order	Dissoc. Energy (ev)
$H_2{}^+$	$1s\sigma_g{}^1$	$\frac{1}{2}$	2.65
H_2	$1s\sigma_g{}^2$	1	4.48
$He_2{}^+$	$1s\sigma_g{}^2\ 1s\sigma_u{}^1$	$<\frac{1}{2}$	~2.5
He_2	$1s\sigma_g{}^2\ 1s\sigma_u{}^2$	0	—

$He_2{}^+$, as would be predicted from the greater repulsion resulting from more electrons in $He_2{}^+$.

The combination of two homonuclear atomic orbitals to produce molecular orbitals is illustrated in Fig. 2-13 for $2s$ and $2p$ atomic orbitals. The principles and equations are similar to those for $1s$. A few important

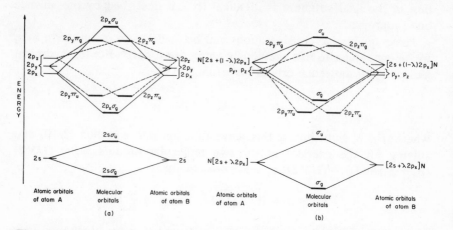

Fig. 2-13. Formation of Molecular Orbitals for Homonuclear Diatomic Molecules from $2s$ and $2p$ Atomic Orbitals (a) No hybridization of atomic s and p orbital (b) Hybridization of atomic s and p orbitals. (Braces indicate degenerate atomic orbitals.)

features of Fig. 2-13a should be discussed. The energies of the individual atomic orbitals are represented on the extreme left and right, and the energies of the molecular orbitals are illustrated in the center. There are two important factors that determine the energy of the molecular orbitals: (1) the initial energy of the atomic orbitals and (2) the extent of overlap of the atomic orbitals. Since φ_{2s} is so much lower in energy than φ_{2p}, both $2s\sigma_g$ and $2s\sigma_u$ are lower in energy than MO's from φ_{2p}. If the p_x orbitals overlap in a σ manner, the p_y and p_z orbitals must overlap in a π manner (Fig. 2-14). Since π overlap is less effective than σ overlap, the energies of $2p_y$ and $2p_z$ are not lowered as much as that of $2p_x$. Accordingly, $2p_y\pi_g$ and $2p_z\pi_g$ are not raised as much as $2p_x\sigma_u$. The energy sequence represented in Fig. 2-13a results.

When the $2s$ and $2p_x$ orbitals used to construct the molecular orbitals are hybridized, a different energy sequence results; see Fig. 2-13b. In this scheme, the low energy σ_g is lower in energy than $2s\sigma_g$ and the higher energy σ_g is higher in energy than $2p_x\sigma_g$. A very important difference is the relative positions of the π orbitals and $2p_x\sigma_g$ compared to the equivalent orbitals in Fig. 2-13b. This latter sequence accounts for the paramagnetism of B_2 and is in accord with most of the spectroscopic data on homonuclear diatomic molecules. In summary then the

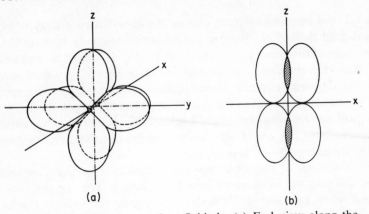

Fig. 2-14. Overlap of p_y and p_z Orbitals. (a) End view along the
σ bond. (b) Front view perpendicular to the σ bond. (For simplicity
only p_z overlap is illustrated; the x axis and σ bond axis coincide.)

energies of the resulting molecular orbitals for homonuclear diatomic
molecules most commonly encountered are:*

$$1s\sigma_g < 1s\sigma_u < 2s\sigma_g < 2s\sigma_u < 2p_y\pi_u = 2p_z\pi_u < 2p_x\sigma_g < 2p_y\pi_g$$
$$= 2p_z\pi_g < 2p_x\sigma_u$$

Table 2-4 contains a MO description of the structure of several molecules
and molecule ions along with their dissociation energies. Notice that the

TABLE 2-4. MOLECULAR ORBITAL DESIGNATION
FOR SOME HOMONUCLEAR DIATOMIC MOLECULES

Species	Molecular Orbital Designation[a]	Dissociation Energy (ev)
Li_2	$KK\ 2s\sigma_g^2$	1.14
Be_2	$KK\ 2s\sigma_g^2\ 2s\sigma_u^2$	> 0
N_2^+	$KK\ 2s\sigma_g^2\ 2s\sigma_u^2\ \pi_u^4\ 2p_x\sigma_g^2$	7.38
N_2^+	$KK\ 2s\sigma_g^2\ 2s\sigma_u^2\ \pi_u^4\ 2p_x\sigma_u^2$	6.35
O_2	$KK\ 2s\sigma_g^2\ 2s\sigma_u^2\ \pi_u^4\ 2p_x\sigma_g^2\ \pi_g^2$	5.08
O_2^+	$KK\ 2s\sigma_g^2\ 2s\sigma_u^2\ \pi_u^4\ 2p_x\sigma_g^2\ \pi_g^1$	6.48
F_2	$KK\ 2s\sigma_g^2\ 2s\sigma_u^2\ \pi_u^4\ 2p_x\sigma_g^2\ \pi_g^4$	1.8
Ne_2	$KK\ 2s\sigma_g^2\ 2s\sigma_u^2\ \pi_u^4\ 2p_x\sigma_g^2\ \pi_g^4\ 2p_x\sigma_u^2$	> 0

[a]KK is an abbreviation for $1\ s\sigma_g^2$ and $1s\sigma_u^2$, π_u for $2p_y\pi_u = 2p_z\pi_u$
and π_g for $2p_y\pi_g = 2p_z\pi_g$.

*A common alternate convention for labeling these orbitals is: KK for $1s\sigma_g$ and $1s\sigma_u$,
$z\sigma$ for $2s\sigma_g$, $y\sigma$ for $2s\sigma_u$, $x\sigma$ for $2p_x\sigma_g$, $w\pi$ for $2p_y\pi_u$ and $2p_z\pi_u$, $v\pi$ for $2p_y\pi_g$ and $2p_z\pi_g$,
$u\sigma$ for $2p_x\sigma_u$. This alternate convention is commonly used for heteronuclear diatomics.
The π_g orbital is often abbreviated as π^*.

removal of a bonding electron causes the dissociation energy of N_2^+ to be less than that of N_2. Removal of an antibonding electron results in a higher dissociation energy for O_2^+ than for O_2. It should be emphasized also that the observed paramagnetism of oxygen is obtained directly from the derived sequence of molecular orbital energies. The spins of the two electrons added to the doubly degenerate oxygen levels $2p_y\pi_g = 2p_z\pi_g$ will remain unpaired (Hund's rule). In the VB system, the expected structure, $\overline{O}{=}\overline{O}$ is not in agreement with the observed paramagnetism, and the structure $|O\overset{\cdots}{\cdots}O|$ is proposed.

The electrons in the molecular orbitals of the species contained in Table 2-4 can be categorized into four classes. The oxygen molecule is used as an example in Table 2-5 to illustrate the various types. The shapes of these molecular orbitals are illustrated in Fig. 2-15.

TABLE 2-5. TYPES OF MOLECULAR
ORBITALS IN O_2

Type	Oxygen Orbitals
Inner shell electrons	$1s\sigma_g^2\,1s\sigma_u^2$
Valence shell nonbonding	$2s\sigma_g^2\,2s\sigma_u^2$
Valence shell bonding	$2p_x\sigma_g^2\pi_u^4$
Valence shell antibonding	π_g^2

MOLECULAR ORBITALS IN HETERONUCLEAR DIATOMIC MOLECULES

When two different kinds of atoms combine to produce molecular orbitals, equation (2-20) becomes:

$$\sigma = N(\varphi_A + \lambda\varphi_B)$$

where N is the normalization constant, and λ is a constant indicating the contribution of φ_B to the MO. If λ is less than unity, the resulting bonding molecular orbital is more like the original atomic orbital, φ_A, rather than being equally constituted from the two atomic orbitals. The molecule HF is an example in which λ is less than one when F is atom A. The resultant MO sequence which arises by combining the hydrogen $1s$ orbital with the fluorine $2p_x$ atomic orbital is:

$$1s^2 \quad 2s^2 \quad \sigma_g^2 \quad 2p_y^2 \quad 2p_z^2 \quad \sigma_u^{0*}$$

The $1s^2$ and $2s^2$ orbitals of fluorine are too low in energy to interact significantly with the hydrogen $1s$ orbital, and, as a result, these are assumed to be identical to the original atomic orbitals of fluorine (i.e., these electrons are localized on the fluorine atom). This result is the

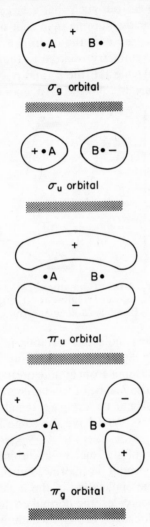

Fig. 2-15. The Shapes of σ_g, σ_u, π_u, and π_g Molecular Orbitals. σ_g and σ_u arise from s orbitals.

same as that in the valence bond approach, where inner electrons make no contribution to the bonding. The bonding molecular orbital σ_g results by overlap of a $2p_x$ orbital (p_x is arbitrarily selected) from fluorine and a $1s$ orbital of hydrogen ($\varphi_F + \lambda\varphi_H$). Since λ is less than one, the resulting molecular orbital is polarized such that a larger fraction of the bonding electron density is near the fluorine than near the hydrogen. The $2p_y$ and $2p_z$ orbitals cannot interact with the hydrogen $1s$ orbital, for they do not have the appropriate symmetry relative to the molecular (bonding) axis (Fig. 2-11). In the molecule HF the p_y and p_z orbitals are essentially the original atomic orbitals of fluorine. An energy level diagram for the

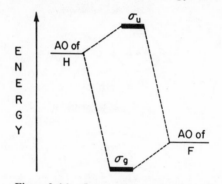

Fig. 2-16. Interaction of Atomic Orbitals of Different Energy to Produce Molecular Orbitals

bonding and antibonding molecular orbitals in HF is indicated in Fig. 2-16. The HF molecule illustrates the very important set of requirements for forming molecular orbitals from atomic orbitals:

(1) The atomic orbitals must be of similar energy.

(2) The atomic orbitals must overlap appreciably.

(3) The atomic orbitals must have the same symmetry relative to the molecular axis.

A better description of the molecular orbitals uses a hybrid orbital rather than a pure $2p_x$ orbital on fluorine, but this has little effect on the above discussion. In the application of the molecular orbital description to more complicated molecules, the normal covalent σ bonds in the molecule are described by localized orbitals which are linear combinations of atomic orbitals.

ELECTRON DEFICIENT MOLECULES

An electron deficient molecule is one in which there are not enough bonding electrons available to join all of the atoms in the molecule together by normal covalent bonds (i.e., electron pair bonds). Diborane,

B_2H_6, is an example. Resonance is invoked in the valence bond description. The structures contained in Fig. 2-17 are involved. Structure (e) is a minor contributor, and other forms similar to (e) have not been indicated.

The molecular orbital description invokes a *three-center bond* to describe the bridge hydrogens. When two atomic orbitals (AO's) overlap to produce molecular orbitals, two molecular orbitals are formed. The

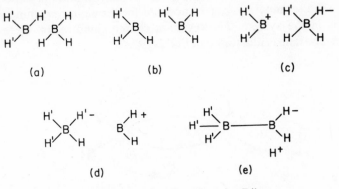

Fig. 2-17. Resonance Structures for Diborane

overlap of three atomic orbitals produces three molecular orbitals, described as *bonding, nonbonding,* and *antibonding.* This type of bond is called a three-center bond. Correspondingly, four AO's overlap to produce four MO's, five AO's produce five MO's, etc. In diborane, the hybridization at the borons is approximately sp^3, and each boron forms normal covalent bonds with two terminal hydrogens. Each bridge bond is a three-center bond that results from the overlap of two sp^3 orbitals

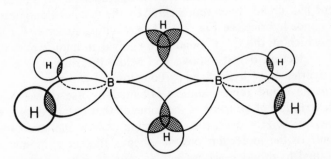

Fig. 2-18. Overlap of the Atomic Orbitals in B_2H_6. Since the boron is hybridized sp^3, the bridge hydrogens and the borons are in a plane perpendicular to the terminal hydrogens.

(one from each boron) and a 1s orbital from hydrogen. The overlap of these orbitals is illustrated in Fig. 2-18. A pair of electrons is added to the bonding molecular orbital that results, and the nonbonding and anti-bonding orbitals are empty. This pair of electrons is said to be delocalized over the three atoms (B—H—B), for the electron pair is in a molecular orbital which is comprised of all three atomic orbitals that form the three-center bond. Another pair of electrons is placed in the three-center bond involving the second bridge hydrogen, and normal covalent bonds to the terminal hydrogens account for the eight remaining valence electrons in the system. The resultant charge cloud of the three-center bonds in diborane is illustrated in Fig. 2-19.

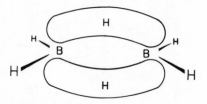

Fig. 2-19. Charge Cloud Representation of the Bridge Bonds in B_2H_6

A Delocalized π-Electron System

Wherever resonance is invoked in the valence bond description of molecular structure, delocalization is employed in the molecular orbital description. The structure of benzene will be described by both methods to illustrate the difference between the two approaches.

Benzene has already been represented by the valence bond description as a resonance hybrid (see Fig. 2-4). The resulting structure for benzene is one in which all the C—C bonds are equivalent and there is a charge cloud of π-electron density above and below the ring. The σ bonding involves overlap of sp^2 hybridized carbon atoms.

The charge cloud representation obtained by use of the molecular orbital description of benzene is the same as that obtained by a valence bond description. However, the description of how the structure arises is different. In the molecular orbital scheme, the six p_z atomic orbitals are combined to produce six molecular orbitals. The energies of these molecular orbitals are indicated in Fig. 2-20. Each MO is represented by a line and has a capacity for two electrons. The six π electrons are fed into the three lowest energy molecular orbitals with their spins paired. Each of the three bonding MO's consists of contributions from all six carbon atoms and the electrons are said to be delocalized over all these carbon atoms; i.e., none of the electrons or electron pairs can be assigned to particular carbon atoms. The resulting charge cloud is illustrated in

π_6

E
N
E π_4 π_5
R
G π_2 ↿⇂ π_3 ↿⇂   **Fig. 2-20**   Energies of the π Molecular Orbitals in Benzene
Y
        π_1 ↿⇂

Fig. 2-21. The mathematical equations illustrating the various combinations of the six AO's, φ_a to φ_f, to produce the six MO's, π_1 to π_6, are:

$$\pi_1 = (1/\sqrt{6})(\varphi_a + \varphi_b + \varphi_c + \varphi_d + \varphi_e + \varphi_f)$$
$$\pi_2 = (1/\sqrt{12})(2\varphi_a + \varphi_b - \varphi_c - 2\varphi_d - \varphi_e + \varphi_f)$$
$$\pi_3 = (\tfrac{1}{2})(\varphi_b + \varphi_c - \varphi_e - \varphi_f)$$
$$\pi_4 = (\tfrac{1}{2})(\varphi_b - \varphi_c + \varphi_e - \varphi_f)$$
$$\pi_5 = (1/\sqrt{12})(2\varphi_a - \varphi_b - \varphi_c + 2\varphi_d - \varphi_e - \varphi_f)$$
$$\pi_6 = (1/\sqrt{6})(\varphi_a - \varphi_b + \varphi_c - \varphi_d + \varphi_e - \varphi_f)$$

These molecular orbitals are normalized (neglecting overlap) and are mutually orthogonal.

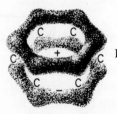

Fig. 2–21. Charge Cloud Picture of the π Electron Density in C_6H_6

The description in MO terminology of a π bond which is localized can be indicated by considering the carbonyl group in acetone. The lone pair electrons on oxygen are in atomic orbitals (approximately sp^2 hybrids). The π electrons are in a π molecular orbital formed by overlap of the p_z atomic orbitals of carbon and oxygen. The σ bonding MO is described as the overlap of carbon and oxygen sp^2 orbitals. There are higher energy π^* and σ^* orbitals which are empty. In summary, the bonding in the carbonyl group can be described as:

$$\sigma^2 \pi^2 \pi^{*0} \sigma^{*0} \qquad \text{(the oxygen lone pair electrons are not indicated)}$$

MOLECULAR ORBITAL DESCRIPTION OF SOME INTERHALOGEN MOLECULES

In valence bond terminology the covalent contribution to the bonding in I_3^- is described by having the central iodine atom employ $p_z d_{z^2}$ hybrids to bond the two terminal iodines. It has been proposed[11] for I_3^- and also for several other interhalogen compounds, that the bonding can be described by molecular orbital theory utilizing only the p_z orbital of the central atom. According to these arguments, a three-center molecular orbital would arise from the atomic p orbital of the central atom and two atomic orbitals, one from each of the two terminal atoms. Three molecular orbitals would result, and two electrons would be placed in the bonding orbital and two in the nonbonding orbital. It should be pointed out that the absence of a contribution to the bonding from the d orbitals of the central atom has not been experimentally proved or disproved. Since d_{z^2} has appropriate symmetry and does overlap the bonded atoms, some contributions to the bonding from this orbital are expected and the extent to which this occurs determines the difference between the three-center MO description and the pd hybrid description.

QUALITATIVE COMPARISON OF THE VALENCE BOND AND MOLECULAR ORBITAL APPROACHES

The valence bond and molecular orbital theories have the following features in common:

(1) The resultant electron distributions for a given molecule are similar.

(2) In both descriptions of a normal covalent bond the essential interaction is the sharing of the bonding electron density by both nuclei and concentration of electron density between the nuclei.

(3) In both descriptions orbitals of the bonded atoms must overlap and have appropriate symmetry about the molecular axis in order to form a bond.

(4) σ and π bonds are distinguished.

The essential differences between the two approaches are encountered in the procedures employed in the mathematical calculations involved. In addition, the concept of resonance, utilized in the VB theory, has as its counterpart delocalization in the MO theory. The term delocalization energy is employed instead of resonance energy. The VB concept of partial ionic character:

$$\psi_{VB}{}^0 = a\psi_{cov} + b\psi_{ionic}$$

is taken into consideration in MO theory by the coefficient λ, i.e., $\varphi_A + \lambda\varphi_B$ (recall the discussion of HF).

Molecular orbital theory is more convenient for the description of excited states in molecules. The electronic transitions that occur in the visible and ultraviolet region of the spectra involve these states and can be simply described. For example, absorption of radiation can cause the following transition to occur in acetone:

$$\sigma^2\pi^2\pi^{*0} \xrightarrow{h\nu} \sigma^2\pi^1\pi^{*1}$$

(the two lone pair electrons on oxygen in nonbonding orbitals are not represented). This is described as a $\pi \to \pi^*$ transition. The excited state (indicated on the right-hand side of the arrow) is not so easily described in valence bond terminology.

ELECTROSTATIC BONDING*

Interactions in the general category of electrostatic bonding can be subdivided into the following types: (1) ionic, (2) ion-dipole, (3) dipole-dipole, (4) dipole–induced dipole, and (5) London dispersion.

IONIC BONDING

Ionic bonding results from the attraction of charges on cations and anions. According to the Coulomb law, the energy of attraction, E, between a cation and an anion is given by the equation:

$$E = -q_1q_2/r \tag{2-22}$$

where q_1 and q_2 are the charges on the ions, and r is the distance between the centers of the two ions. At close interionic distances a repulsive

*For a more nearly complete discussion of electrostatic bonding see: J. A. A. Ketelaar, "Chemical Constitution," Elsevier, New York, 1953; J. O. Hirschfelder, C. F. Curtiss, and R. B. Bird, "Molecular Theory of Gases and Liquids," Wiley, New York, 1954.

force arises from the overlap of the electron clouds of the cation and anion. This repulsive energy is proportional to $1/r^9$ and thus becomes very important at small distances. The equilibrium internuclear distance $r°$, is that distance at which an energy minimum exists because of an equilibrium between the attractive and repulsive forces.

The above discussion applies to a pair of ions in the gas phase. The interactions in a crystal lattice are of the same type, but now one must consider the interaction of the ions with all the neighbors in the lattice. The relative sizes of the ions partially determine the packing arrangement which in turn affects r and the energy. For a given crystal type, the packing and other effects are accounted for by a constant referred to as the Madelung constant.

ION-DIPOLE

This type of bonding results from the attraction between a charged ion and the oppositely charged end of a dipole of a neutral molecule. The potential energy of interaction, E, of an ion of charge e, with a molecule which has a permanent dipole μ, properly aligned for maximum attraction, is given by the equation:

$$E = -e\mu/r^2 \tag{2-23}$$

As a result of this attraction the neutral molecule is polarized and a larger dipole moment is induced in it than the original permanent dipole. The additional energy gained by polarization is given by the equation:

$$E = \alpha e^2/r^4 \tag{2-24}$$

where α, the polarizability of the molecule, is a measure of the ease with which the electron cloud of the molecule can be distorted. Polarizability is determined experimentally from the refractive index or, more exactly, the molar refraction. The application of equation (2-24) is complicated by the fact that the polarizability of a molecule varies along the different axes and the value α obtained from the molar refraction in solution is the average polarizability.

In arriving at equation (2-23) it is assumed that the dipole is properly aligned and its moment can be considered as located at a point. The moment can be considered a point charge accurately only when the length of the dipole l is considerably smaller than the distance, r, between the charge and the dipole. When these requirements are not met, the energy E of the interaction is given by the equation:

$$E = \frac{(ee^0 l \cos \theta)}{r^2 - (l^2/4) \cos \theta} \qquad (2\text{-}25)$$

All terms are defined in Fig. 2-22 except e, the magnitude of the electrostatic charge on the dipole, and e^0 the charge on the ion. When the interaction energy per mole is greater than kT (for small values of r), the species are not free to assume any position and equation (2-23) applies. In the rest of this treatment only strong interactions will be considered.

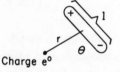

Charge e^0

Fig. 2-22. Charge-Dipole Interaction with the Dipole Properly Oriented

DIPOLE-DIPOLE

The energy of interaction of two properly oriented dipoles is given by the equation:

$$E = -2\mu_1\mu_2/r^3 \qquad (2\text{-}26)$$

where μ_1 and μ_2 are the dipole moments of molecules 1 and 2, respectively. The orientation of the dipoles should be linear, i.e., $+ - + -$. The length of the dipoles must be less than the distance between them for (2-26) to hold.

DIPOLE–INDUCED DIPOLE

Subject to the geometrical requirements mentioned above, the interaction energy is given by:

$$E = -2\alpha\mu^2/r^6 \qquad (2\text{-}27)$$

where μ is the permanent dipole moment and α is the polarizability of the molecule in which the dipole is induced.

LONDON DISPERSION

These forces can be described by considering an argon atom as an example. In any finite period of time the electron cloud in this atom would be spherical. If an instantaneous picture of the atom could be taken, the position of the electrons would be nonspherical and a dipole moment would exist. This instantaneous dipole induces a similar instantaneous dipole in a neighboring argon atom. The net effect is a tendency to synchronize the electron motion in both atoms, and this results in an interaction between the two atoms. For two different molecules this interaction energy is approximated by the expression:

$$E = -\tfrac{3}{2}(\alpha_1\alpha_2/r^6)[I_1I_2/(I_1 + I_2)] \qquad (2\text{-}28)$$

where I_1 and I_2 the respective ionization potentials of molecules 1 and 2.

In addition to charge asymmetry of the dipole type a molecule may also possess a quadrupole moment, $-^+_+-$. Table 2-6 summarizes the dependence on r of this and the above-mentioned electrostatic interactions.

TABLE 2-6. DEPENDENCE OF INTERACTION ENERGY ON DISTANCE FOR VARIOUS
ELECTROSTATIC INTERACTIONS

	Ion	*Dipole*	*Quadrupole*
Ion	r^{-1}	r^{-2}	r^{-3}
Dipole	r^{-2}	r^{-3}	r^{-4}
Quadrupole	r^{-3}	r^{-4}	r^{-6}

At very close distances a molecule held together by strong covalent forces may have contributions to the overall energy from quadrupole and other electrostatic interactions.

HYDROGEN BONDING

COVALENCE AND POLARIZABILITY

When two atoms or ions are involved in bond formation which is largely electrostatic, there are two approaches to the qualitative description of the bonding that give the same charge picture. In one description the wave function for the ground state, ψ^0, has largest contributions from a purely ionic wave function and smaller contributions from a covalent state (see Fig. 2-3 and the discussion thereof).

$$\psi^0 = a\psi_{A^+B^-} + b\psi_{B:A(cov)}$$

Here, $a >> b$; the larger b, the larger the distortion of the electron cloud of B^-. In this discussion, the amount of covalent character in a bond will depend on the relative magnitudes of a and b.

In a second description, the same final structure can be arrived at by an electrostatic approach which includes polarization of atoms A and B. For example, Li^+Cl^- (see Fig. 2-3) is described as an ionic interaction with the lithium ion polarizing the chloride ion.

There is no experimental method of distinguishing between these two descriptions or the relative contribution of each interaction in a bond. In the discussion of hydrogen bonding, we will be concerned with the amount of distortion of the charge cloud for various systems and demonstrate how these two descriptions are employed.

THE HYDROGEN BOND

It is often found that a hydrogen atom bonded to an electronegative atom is attracted rather strongly to another atom containing lone pairs of electrons (for example, H_3N:---H—O—H or F---H---F$^-$). The interaction is often weak compared to ordinary chemical bonds (3 to 10 kcal/mole compared to about 50 kcal/mole for a normal single covalent bond), but it has a pronounced effect on the physical and chemical properties of many systems.

According to the currently accepted model, hydrogen bonding is no longer considered to be purely electrostatic. Significant contributions from covalency or polarizability are now included. The following evidence has been offered by Coulson[13] in support of this proposal:

(1) The increase in intensity of the O—H stretching vibration in the infrared spectra of hydrogen-bonded adducts compared to the intensity of nonhydrogen-bonded adducts cannot be explained by an electrostatic model.

(2) There is no correlation between hydrogen bond strength as measured by the enthalpy of adduct formation and the dipole moment of the base. For a purely electrostatic interaction such a relationship is to be expected*.

*This is not the case if the geometry of the molecule is such that the overall moment is a poor criterion for the lone pair moment of a donor. The lone pair moment is difficult to evaluate, but the large number of exceptions found employing the overall moment support a lack of correlation.

The lack of correlation is illustrated by the following results:

The enthalpy of formation of the phenol–$(CH_3)_3N$ adduct is $-5 \cdot 8$ kcal/mole, and the dipole moment of $(CH_3)_3N$ is $0 \cdot 7$ D. The enthalpy of formation of the acetonitrile adduct is $-4 \cdot 2$ kcal/mole, and the dipole moment of acetonitrile is $3 \cdot 44$ D.

A similar lack of correlation exists between the overall dipole moment of the Lewis acids SO_2 and phenol and their enthalpies of interaction[14] with a reference base. Although both SO_2 and phenol have high dipole moments ($1 \cdot 6$ and $1 \cdot 5$ D, respectively), the enthalpy of formation of adducts of SO_2 and phenol with N, N-dimethylacetamide are $-3 \cdot 4$ and $-6 \cdot 4$ kcal/mole, respectively. The stronger interaction with phenol is attributed to polarizability or covalence in the hydrogen bonding interaction, while the SO_2 interaction is more electrostatic[14].

In valence bond terminology, the ground state for the hydrogen-bonded adduct can be represented as: $\psi^0 = a\psi_1 + b\psi_2 + c\psi_3$, where important contributing forms are:

$$\psi_1 \quad A{-}H \qquad B \qquad \text{(London dispersion)}$$
$$\psi_2 \quad A^-{-}H^+ \quad B \qquad \text{(electrostatic)}$$
$$\psi_3 \quad A^- \quad HB^+ \qquad \text{(covalent)}$$

For weak interactions $b \gg c$, and for strong interactions such as in HF_2^- $b \sim c > a$.

In the molecular orbital description, three molecular orbitals (bonding, nonbonding, and antibonding) are formed from a combination of the two

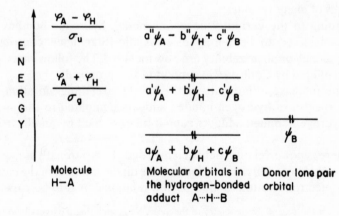

Fig. 2-23. Molecular Orbital Representation of the Hydrogen Bond B---H—A (for a Strong Interaction)

lone pair orbitals on A and B and the $1s$ orbital on hydrogen. Four electrons are added to the bonding $(a\varphi_A + b\varphi_H + c\varphi_B)$ and nonbonding $(a'\varphi_A + b'\varphi_H - c'\varphi_B)$ molecular orbitals that result. The energy levels of the resulting molecular orbital sequence are qualitatively indicated in Fig. 2-23. For simplicity, the interaction is described by considering the formation of the adduct from a donor molecule B and the molecule A—H. The magnitude of the coefficients of the atomic wave functions vary with the nature and extent of the interaction. For strong interactions, as in HF_2^-, all three atoms make appreciable contributions to the molecular orbitals (as indicated in Fig. 2-23) and the two pairs of electrons are delocalized over the three atoms. When the interaction of B with H is weak, because B is a weak base, a pair of electrons is added to a low energy MO which is essentially the donor molecule and the second pair is placed in a higher energy MO which is essentially the A—H bond.

EXERCISES

1. Draw structural formulas for each of the following: NH_3, S_2Cl_2, H_2O_2, NH_4^+, NO_3^-, SF_6, ICl_3, CO, SO_3^{2-}, NO.
2. a. Draw possible resonance structures for the following: HNO_3, HN_3, H_3PO_4, $CH_3C(O)N(CH_3)_2$ (*N,N*-dimethylacetamide).
   b. Indicate formal charges on the above structures.
3. Draw structures, indicate the geometry and the hybrid bonds employed by the central atom in the σ bonds of the following: $GeCl_4$, SO_2, PF_5, $Co(NH_3)_6^{2+}$, NO_2^-, SbH_3, SO_3^{2-}, I_3^-, SCl_2, $TlCl_3$.
4. a. Using the molecular orbital designation, indicate the structure of: F_2, NO, O_2^{2-}, O_2, NO^+.
   b. Which will have the highest bond energy?
      (1) O_2, O_2^-, or O_2^{2-}.
      (2) NO, NO^+, or NO^-.
5. a. Will the bonding molecular orbital in the BrF molecule more closely resemble the AO of fluorine or bromine?
   b. Will λ in the expression $\psi^0 = \psi_F + \lambda\psi_{Br}$ be less or more than one?
6. Consider the molecule LiH and describe its structure using molecular orbital terminology. Indicate the energy of the various orbitals by drawing a figure similar to Fig. 2-16. What criterion is employed to determine if ψ_{Li} (for the bonding electron) or ψ_H is lower in energy? Can the $2p_x$ orbital of Li be employed in the bonding? Why?
7. Draw a sequence of molecular orbitals similar to that in Fig. 2-23 for the following example: The hydrogen bonding in A—H—B is weak because A is not very electronegative even though B is a very strong base. Indicate the relative contribution of $\psi_{A—H}$ and ψ_B to the different orbitals.
8. Using valence bond terminology, explain why the Pb—Cl bond strength is less than the Si—Cl bond strength. How would you qualitatively account for this difference with a molecular orbital description?

9. In the compounds MCl_4 in which would you expect to find the most s character in the hybrid employed by the chlorine atom: Si—Cl, Ge—Cl, Sn—Cl?

10. Employing arguments developed by Bent (see D in General References), indicate in which compound the C—H orbitals will be closest to sp^3: CH_3F, $(CH_3)_2O$, $(CH_3)_3N$, $(CH_3)_3B$.

11. The compound KNO is reported to be a white diamagnetic solid which is insoluble in all solvents tried. Is the diamagnetism expected from the MO sequence derived for NO^- by assuming $\lambda \sim 1$ (i.e., applying the homo-nuclear sequence)? Explain this discrepancy.

12. Using the arguments developed in Chapter 2 under the section on non-equivalence of orbitals, which structure would you expect for ClF_3: the one with two electron pairs *trans* in the *pd* orbital or the one with two electron pairs *cis* in equatorial positions? Explain.

13. What structure would you predict for SF_4?

14. Would there be a greater or lesser tendency for the central atom to employ d orbitals in the σ bonds to the halogens in $SiCl_4$ compared to $PbCl_4$? Explain.

15. Is the extent of π bonding greater in the $\geqslant$Si—O—H bond or in the $\geqslant$Pb—O—H bond? Explain.

REFERENCES CITED

1. M. C. Day and J. Selbin, "Theoretical Inorganic Chemistry," Reinhold, New York, 1962.
2. W. Kauzman, "Quantum Chemistry," Wiley, New York, 1944; A. Streit-wieser, "Molecular Orbital Theory for Organic Chemists," Wiley, New York, 1961.
3. M. Karplus and D. H. Anderson, *J. Chem. Phys.*, **30**, 6 (1959).
4. R. S. Mulliken, C. A. Rieke, D. Orloff, and H. Orloff, *J. Chem. Phys.*, **17**, 1248 (1949).
5. R. S. Drago, *J. Phys. Chem.*, **62**, 353 (1958).
6. H. A. Bent, *Chem. Revs.*, **61**, 275 (1961).
7. R. J. Gillespie, *J. Am. Chem. Soc.*, **82**, 5978 (1960).
8. N. Muller and D. E. Pritchard, *J. Chem. Phys.*, **31**, 1471 (1959).
9. L. E. Orgel, *J. Chem. Soc.*, **1958**, 4186.
10. F. A. Cotton, *J. Chem. Phys.*, **35**, 228 (1961).
11. R. E. Rundle, *Record Chem. Progr.*, **23**, 195 (1962); E. H. Wiebenga, E. E. Havinga, and K. H. Boswijh, *Advan. Inorg. Chem. Radiochem*, **3**, 133 (1961).
12. G. C. Pimentel and A. L. McClellan, "The Hydrogen Bond," W. H. Freeman, San Francisco, 1960.
13. C. A. Coulson, *Research (London)*, **10**, 149–59 (1957).
14. M. D. Joesten and R. S. Drago, *J. Am. Chem. Soc.*, **84**, 2037 (1962); R. S. Drago and D. A. Wenz, *ibid.*, **84**, 526 (1962).

GENERAL REFERENCES

A. For introductory treatments of the topics in Chapters 1 and 2 see:
   F. A. Cotton and G. Wilkinson, "Advanced Inorganic Chemistry," Inter-science, New York, 1962.

C. A. Coulson, "Valence," 2nd ed. Oxford, London, 1961.

M. C. Day and J. Selbin, "Theoretical Inorganic Chemistry," Reinhold, New York 1962.

H. B. Gray "Electrons and Chemical Bonding," W. A. Benjamin, New York, 1964.

K. B. Harvey and G. B. Porter, "Introduction to Physical Inorganic Chemistry," Addison Wesley, Reading, Mass., 1963.

G. Herzberg, "Atomic Spectra and Atomic Structure," Dover, New York, 1944.

J. Linnett, "Wave Mechanics and Valency," Wiley, New York, 1960.

L. Pauling, "Nature of the Chemical Bond" Cornell, Ithaca, New York, 1960.

O. K. Rice, "Electronic Structure and Chemical Bonding," McGraw-Hill, New York, 1940.

B. For treatments more advanced than those in A, see:

R. Daudel, R. Lefebvre, and C. Moser, "Quantum Chemistry," Interscience, New York, 1959.

H. Eyring, J. Walters, and G. E. Kimball, "Quantum Chemistry," Wiley, New York, 1944.

W. Kauzmann, "Quantum Chemistry," Academic, New York 1957.

L. Pauling and E. B. Wilson, "Introduction to Quantum Mechanics," McGraw-Hill, New York, 1935.

J. C. Slater, "Quantum Theory of Atomic Structure," Vol. I, McGraw-Hill, New York, 1960.

C. For a discussion of molecular orbital theory see:

C. J. Ballhausen and H. B. Gray "Introductory Notes on Molecular Orbital Theory," W. A. Benjamin, New York, 1965.

J. D. Roberts, "Molecular Orbital Calculations," W. A. Benjamin, New York, 1961.

A. Streitwieser, "Molecular Orbital Theory for Organic Chemists," Wiley, New York, 1961.

D. The reference by H. A. Bent, *Chem. Revs.*, **61**, 275 (1961), is highly recommended.

3 *Ligand Field and Molecular Orbital Description of Bonding in Complexes*

THE SCOPE of this discussion will be limited to those points necessary for a qualitative understanding of the material presented later on the spectra and magnetism of complexes. Several excellent references are available for a more exhaustive treatment.*

LIGAND FIELD THEORY

With ligand field theory, we can provide a simple model for the description of the bonding in transition metal complexes and indicate what effect the ligands have on the degeneracy of the five d orbitals of the metal. As will be seen in this and subsequent chapters, consideration of the latter phenomenon aids in understanding and lends some degree of predictability to the structure, spectra and magnetic properties of these complexes.

SHAPES AND POSITIONS OF THE ORBITALS

It is essential to the understanding of ligand field theory that the orientation of the five d orbitals be clearly seen. In Fig. 3-1, the orbitals are placed in cubes to aid in visualizing their relative positions. The x, y, and z axes extend through the centers of the faces of the cube and the orbitals $d_{x^2-y^2}$ and d_{z^2} lie along these axes and point toward centers of the six faces of the cube. The d_{xz}, d_{yz}, and d_{xy} orbitals bisect the twelve edges and lie in the xz, yz, and xy planes, respectively. For clarity, d_{yz} is not illustrated.

SIX-COORDINATE COMPLEXES

In a gaseous transition metal ion, the five d orbitals are degenerate. In many six-coordinate complexes, six ligands are located on the corners of a regular octahedron. Since the labeling of the axes in a metal ion is

*See General References at the end of this chapter.

arbitrary, we can arbitrarily designate d_{z^2} and $d_{x^2-y^2}$ as the orbitals toward which the six ligands point when coordinated in an octahedral manner. (An octahedral field of electron density is said to result.) Note then (Fig. 3-1) that d_{xy}, d_{yz}, and d_{xz} point between the ligands. The ligands are Lewis bases, and their electron density is pointed directly toward d_{z^2} and $d_{x^2-y^2}$. As a result, these two orbitals become less favorable

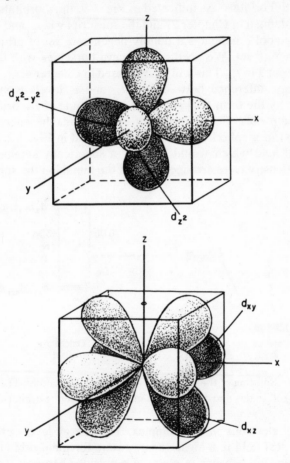

Fig. 3-1. Orientation of the d Orbitals

positions (from an energy standpoint) for the metal ion to utilize for its own d electrons because of the electronic repulsions that would occur between the electron pair of the ligand and the d electrons of the metal ion in these orbitals. An energy level diagram (Fig. 3-2) illustrates that

$d_{x^2-y^2}$ and d_{z^2} are higher in energy than the orbitals d_{xy}, d_{yz}, and d_{xz}, which point in between the ligands in an octahedral complex. The five d orbitals are not all degenerate in the complex ion but split into one set of triply and a second set of doubly degenerate levels. The group of orbitals d_{xy}, d_{yz}, and d_{xz} are often referred to as the t_{2g} (or sometimes $d\epsilon$) orbitals. The two orbitals $d_{x^2-y^2}$ and d_{z^2} are referred to as the e_g (or sometimes $d\gamma$) orbitals. As indicated in Fig. 3-9, the d orbitals are gerade orbitals (as defined in Chapter 2) and the subscript g in t_{2g} and e_g indicates this. The symbol e indicates a doubly degenerate set of orbitals and t a triply degenerate set. We need not concern ourselves with the meaning of the subscript 2 in t_{2g}. This will be discussed in Chapter 4.

The energy difference between the t_{2g} and e_g levels is symbolically represented by the term $10Dq$ or Δ. The magnitude of Dq or Δ varies for different complexes. For purposes of comparison, the energy levels of the same ion in a spherical field are represented in Fig. 3-2. This is the hypothetical field which would result if a spherically symmetrical shell of electron density were arranged around the metal ion the same distance

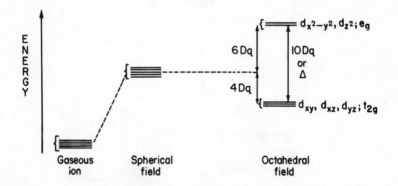

Fig. 3-2.   Splitting of the d Orbitals in an Octahedral Field. The braces, $\{$, in this and other figures indicate degenerate orbitals.

away as the electrons in the complex. The energy level corresponding to the spherical field is a higher energy state for the d orbitals than that in the gaseous ion because of electron repulsions between the metal ion electron density and the spherical field of negative charge. In an actual complex a spherical field is never obtained. Metal electron-ligand electron repulsions are decreased by a splitting of the orbitals into t_{2g} and e_g sets. The splitting occurs in such a way as to result in an average energy for the five d orbitals which is equal to that in the spherical field. Two orbitals are raised ($6Dq$ each) and three are lowered ($4Dq$ each) with respect to the energy of the d orbitals in the hypothetical spherical field. When the d orbitals are split by the ligands, the average energy after splitting must remain the same as that of the spherical field before splitting.

These concepts can be made clearer by considering some specific complexes. Two different types of complexes formed by iron(III) will be considered first. Since iron(III) has five d electrons, it is commonly referred to as a d^5 case. In the first example to be considered, a poorly coordinating ligand (for example F^-) is attached to the metal ion, producing what is described as a *weak ligand field*. The other situation results when a strongly coordinating ligand (for example CN^-) is attached to Fe^{III}, producing a *strong ligand field*. The energy difference between t_{2g} and e_g levels (the magnitude of Δ or $10Dq$) will increase as the coordinating ability of the ligand increases. This occurs because the metal-ligand distance is shorter for strongly coordinating ligands than for weak ones, causing greater repulsion between the electrons of the ligand and the metal electrons in $d_{x^2-y^2}$ and d_{z^2} orbitals. These energy differences for weak and strong field complexes are illustrated in Fig. 3-3.

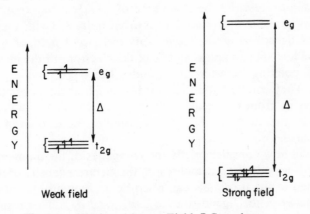

Fig. 3-3. Weak and Strong Field d^5 Complexes

Now that we have a simple model for the magnitude of the splitting, let us consider the effect of this splitting on the d electron configuration. In placing the five electrons into the d orbitals, two *opposing* effects must be considered: (1) The lower energy orbitals will be filled first, and (2) the electrons have a tendency not to pair (Hund's rule). The latter effect is caused by greater repulsion between two electrons in the same orbital than between one each placed in two degenerate orbitals. The spins of these two unpaired electrons in degenerate orbitals are parallel because *exchange interaction* leading to stabilization occurs between electrons of the same spin.*

In FeF_6^{3-} the magnitude of Dq is not very great, a weak ligand field results, and Hund's rule is obeyed (Fig. 3-3). In the strong field created by cyanide ions, the magnitude of Dq is large, t_{2g} is lowered appreciably (e_g is raised) and a lower energy situation for the system results from the pairing of electrons in t_{2g} than would result from occupation of the higher energy e_g orbitals, d_{z^2} and $d_{x^2-y^2}$ (Fig. 3-3). This is equivalent to saying that in the strong field case, the interaction of the ligands with the d_{z^2} and $d_{x^2-y^2}$ orbitals is so strong that these orbitals are unfavorable ones in which to place the d electrons of the metal. The magnetism that would result for the two complexes described above is identical with that predicted by the valence bond theory where sp^3d^2 and d^2sp^3 hybrids are involved (Chapter 2).

The two types of complexes have been described with no reference as yet to hybrid orbitals or covalent bonding. In this model the bonding is essentially electrostatic, and electron repulsions (not hybridization) determine whether or not electrons pair up. The following terms have been used to describe the same kind of complex: *low spin, spin paired, strong field,* and *inner orbital.* This is to be contrasted with a second kind of complex described as *high spin, spin free, weak field,* or *outer orbital.*

In the low spin complex, all five of the electrons of the metal ion are in orbitals pointing between the ligands. The $d_{x^2-y^2}$ and d_{z^2} orbitals are vacant. They can be hybridized for bonding and can accommodate electron density from the ligand allowing some covalence in the metal ion–ligand interaction.** In the cyanide complex the amount of covalence is appreciable.

We will now consider briefly the energetics of the interaction of metal ions with ligands. In a complex ion, the electron density of the metal ion contained in the d orbitals can often be accommodated by orbitals that point between the ligands (i.e., d_{xy}, d_{yz}, and d_{xz}). This results in an increase in the attraction of the positive metal ion for the ligand relative to the attraction that would result in the absence of rearrangement of these electrons (i.e., in a spherical field) because the rearrangement decreases the effectiveness with which the electrons of the metal ion shield

---

*For example, letter two electrons in two different d orbitals as a and b. Two identical structures are represented as $d_{xy}{}^a$; $d_{xz}{}^b$ and $d_{xy}{}^b$; $d_{xz}{}^a$. The energy of the system is lowered by exchange or resonance type interaction. This effect is manifested in the energy of the first excited state for helium where the configuration $1s^1 2s^1$ with both spins parallel is a lower energy state than that in which the spins are opposite (see Chapter 2).

**Crystal field theory does not consider covalency in the metal ion-ligand bond and differs from ligand field theory in this respect.

the positive nuclear charge of the ion from the ligand electron density. This added attraction is referred to as *crystal field stabilization energy* (CFSE). A zinc(II) ion in a complex cannot rearrange its electron density, for the d orbitals are all filled. For this reason it has no CFSE. On the other hand, octahedral Co^{III} (a d^6 case) can accommodate all the d electrons of the metal in t_{2g} orbitals that point between the ligands. Hence, Co^{III} has a large CFSE.

The following counting procedure can be employed to calculate the magnitude of the CFSE for octahedral complexes. Every electron from the metal placed in a t_{2g} orbital stabilizes the system by $-4Dq$ (where the minus sign represents stabilization) compared to the spherical field. Each electron in e_g destabilizes the system by $+6Dq$. By simply counting the electrons in the t_{2g} and e_g orbitals and weighting them as above ($-4Dq$ for each t_{2g} electron and $+6Dq$ for each one in e_g), Table 3-1 can be constructed. The tetrahedral case will be discussed later.

TABLE 3-1. CFSE FOR COMPLEXES[a]

d^n	High Spin (HS) Octahedral Complexes	Low Spin (LS) Octahedral[b] Complexes	Tetrahedral Complexes (High Spin)
d^1	-4	-4	-6
d^2	-8	-8	-12
d^3	-12	-12	-8
d^4	-6	-16	-4
d^5	0	-20	0
d^6	-4	-24	-6
d^7	-8	-18	-12
d^8	-12	-12	-8
d^9	-6	-6	-4
d^{10}	0	0	0

[a] The above treatment of CFSE is a crude simplification of a more complex problem. As will be seen in Chapter 6, interelectronic repulsions tend to split the d levels into various states and the simple d-level splitting used to calculate CFSE cannot be used to interpret the spectra or give accurate energies as implied in Table 3-1 (especially for the d^2 and d^7 weak field cases). Excited states of appropriate symmetry can mix with the ground states in effect placing electron density in the e_g level giving rise to a different CFSE than that in Table 3-1. The pairing energies discussed later in this section are also likely to be 10 to 20 per cent high, for they were determined from data on the gaseous metal ions; as will also be seen in Chapter 6, this produces a high value. Consequently, this treatment should be regarded as approximate.

[b] For d^1, d^2, d^3, d^8, d^9, and d^{10} the electronic arrangement in the d levels is identical for strong field and weak field ligands. Dq is different.

It is interesting to note that the values for CFSE in Table 3-1 have been employed to explain the deviations that occur in the heats of formation of transition metal hydrates.[1] Heats of formation are greater than expected (stronger interactions) for all the divalent cations of the first transition series except Mn^{II}, and the magnitude of the deviation for each ion parallels its CFSE as summarized in Table 3-1. It is proposed that for metal ions with large CFSE values there is poorer shielding of the nuclear charge, and a stronger interaction of water with the metal ion results.

The crystal field stabilization energies listed in Table 3-1 can be employed along with the pairing energies, P, (i.e., the energy required to pair two electrons in an orbital) to predict whether a high spin or low spin complex will result. Consider d^4 high spin and d^4 low spin complexes. The energy for the high spin complex is $-6Dq$ ($E = -6Dq$), while that for the low spin complex is $-16Dq$ plus the energy, P, required to pair two electrons; $E = -16Dq + P$. For Mn^{3+} (d^4), P is about 28,000 cm^{-1}. For a Dq of 2100 cm^{-1}, as would be obtained for six coordinated water ligands, the energy of the high spin state is lower.

$$E_{HS} - E_{LS} = -6Dq + 16Dq - P = 10Dq - P = 21,000$$
$$- 28,000 = -7000 \text{ cm}^{-1}$$

The negative sign indicates that the high spin complex is a lower energy, more stable complex than the low spin one.

For a d^5 complex the energy for a high spin complex is zero and that for a low spin complex is $E = -20Dq + 2P$. The term $2P$ appears in the latter case because four electrons must be paired. By similar reasoning, the equations: $E = -4Dq + P$, $E = -24Dq + 3P$, $E = -8Dq + 2P$, $E = -18Dq + 3P$, can be derived, respectively, for d^6 high spin, d^6 low spin, d^7 high spin, d^7 low spin octahedral complexes. Approximate pairing energies for various metal ions and Dq values for various ligands are presented in Table 3-2.

Let us consider some complexes of copper(II), a d^9 case. The three electrons in e_g could be arranged so as to lead to two different possible configurations, i.e., $(d_{z^2})^2(d_{x^2-y^2})^1$ or $(d_{z^2})^1(d_{x^2-y^2})^2$. In the former case we would expect more repulsion between metal ion and ligand electrons along the d_{z^2} axis than along $d_{x^2-y^2}$ because there is more electron density in d_{z^2}. In the latter case, similar reasoning would predict four long bonds along $d_{x^2-y^2}$ and two short ones along d_{z^2}. In practice, this latter type of distortion is very rare although there is no good theoretical explanation for its instability. Known examples include solid crystals of the ions

TABLE 3-2. PAIRING ENERGIES AND Dq VALUES
FOR VARIOUS METAL IONS AND LIGANDS

d-Electron Configuration	Metal Ion	P	Ligand	Dq	Predicted Spin State
d^4	Mn^{3+}	28,000	$6H_2O$	2100	high spin
	Cr^{2+}	23,500	$6H_2O$	1390	high spin
d^5	Mn^{2+}	25,500	$6H_2O$	850	high spin
	Mn^{2+}		$6Cl^-$	750	high spin
	Mn^{2+}		3en	1010	high spin
	Fe^{3+}	30,000	$6F^-$	1400	high spin
	Fe^{3+}		$6H_2O$	1430	high spin
d^6	Fe^{2+}	17,600	$6H_2O$	1040	high spin
	Fe^{2+}		$6CN^-$	3140	low spin
	Co^{3+}	21,000	$6H_2O$	1820	high spin
	Co^{3+}		$6F^-$	1300	high spin
	Co^{3+}		$6NH_3$	2290	low spin
	Co^{3+}		$6CN^-$	3350	low spin
d^7	Co^{2+}	22,500	$6H_2O$	930	high spin
	Co^{2+}		$6NH_3$	1010	high spin

CuF_4^{2-}, CrF_3^-, and CuF_3^-. The more common distortion involves lengthening of the bonds along d_{z^2}. Under these circumstances, the e_g and t_{2g} levels no longer constitute degenerate sets, and splitting of the d orbitals occurs as indicated in Fig. 3-4.

Distortions of the above type, from octahedral or tetrahedral symmetry are summarized by the *Jahn-Teller theorem* which states that if a subshell (t_{2g} or e_g) is neither filled, half-filled, nor empty, a distortion will occur to remove any possible degeneracy. When the shell is neither empty, half-filled, nor filled, there is more than one possible degenerate configuration for the electron arrangement (as explained above). The orbital energies split to remove this degeneracy. A more stable distorted complex results because metal ion electrons do not repel ligand electron density as much as in the undistorted structure. A reasonably precise statement of the Jahn-Teller theorem is as follows: Any nonlinear molecule possessing orbital degeneracy in a given symmetrical arrangement of its nuclei will distort from this arrangement so as to remove the degeneracy. Since the distortion is opposed by the primary bonding forces in the metal-ligand bond, distortion will occur until a minimum in the net energy of the attractive and repulsive forces is obtained. As a result only slight distortions (often not experimentally detectable) may occur when possible degenerate arrangements exist in a low energy subshell; t_{2g} in an octahedron and e_g for a tetrahedron, because these electrons are not pointing at the ligands. Significant distortions occur when degenerate configurations exist in the high energy subshell consisting of orbitals pointing towards the ligands. For example, for d^4 and d^9 ions ($t_{2g}^3 e_g^1$ and

Fig. 3-4. The d Levels in a Weak-field Tetragonal Copper(II) Complex

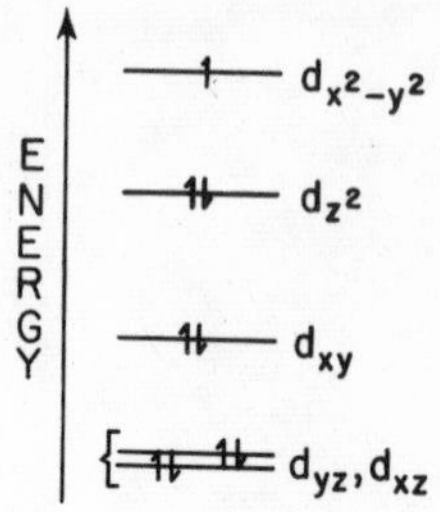

$t_{2g}^6 e_g^3$, respectively) with weak field ligands, tetragonal complexes result. Tetragonal complexes also result for strong field ligands with d^7 and d^9 ions ($t_{2g}^6 e_g^1$ and $t_{2g}^6 e_g^3$, respectively).

Six-coordinate nickel(II) in the presence of four strong field ligands and two weak field ligands produces tetragonal complexes but not because of Jahn-Teller distortion. In this case varying electron repulsions between the nonequivalent ligands and electrons of the metal ion can split d_{z^2} and $d_{x^2-y^2}$ enough so that the d-electron configuration represented in Fig. 3-5 results. A diamagnetic tetragonal complex is formed.

Fig. 3-5. Electronic Arrangement for Tetragonal Ni^{II} with Four Strong and Two Weak-field Ligands

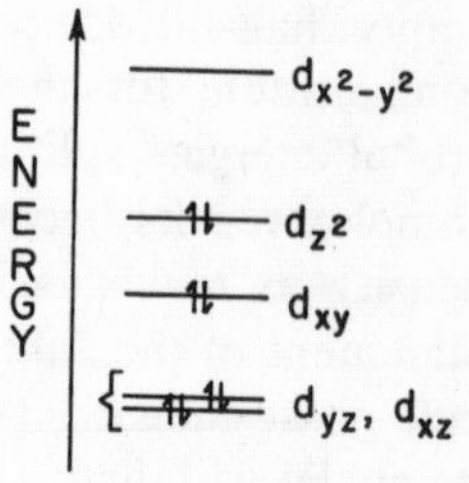

FOUR-COORDINATE COMPLEXES

In the presence of a very strong field ligand, those metal ions that produce tetragonal complexes with weak field ligands (e.g., Cu^{II}) often form square planar four-coordinate complexes. The splitting of the d

orbitals for a square planar copper(II) complex is represented in Fig. 3-6. In a square planar complex, the electron density of the metal in d_{z^2} repels solvent or anions very strongly and hence there is no bonding in this position. The ligands are bonded so strongly along $d_{x^2-y^2}$ and are so close to the metal that they repel the electrons of the metal in the neighboring d_{xy} orbital and cause it to be raised in energy. The d_{yz} and d_{xz} orbitals are least affected by ligand electron density and are lowest in energy in the square planar complex. It has been argued[2] that repulsion between the ligand electron density and the metal ion electron density in the d_{z^2} orbital occupying space in the xy plane (about 33 percent of the d_{z^2} electron density is in the "doughnut") raises the energy of d_{z^2} above that of d_{xz} and d_{yz}.

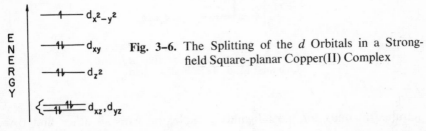

Fig. 3–6. The Splitting of the d Orbitals in a Strong-field Square-planar Copper(II) Complex

There are many examples of tetrahedral transition metal ion complexes. The splitting of the d orbitals in a tetrahedral field is represented in Fig. 3-7. This splitting can be understood by considering that a tetrahedral complex can be placed in a cube so that the four ligands occupy opposite corners of the cube (on any face of the cube there are two ligands in opposite corners). A detailed analysis of the distances from the ligands to the various d orbitals indicates that d_{xy}, d_{yz}, and d_{xz} are closest to the ligands and highest in energy while $d_{x^2-y^2}$ and d_{z^2} are farthest away and lowest in energy. The magnitude of Δ is always small for tetrahedral complexes, and these complexes are always high spin. The following two features favor but do not assure formation of a tetrahedral structure: (1) a very large, easily polarized ligand which either places a large amount of electron density on the metal or introduces a steric effect, both making six coordination unlikely, and (2) a symmetrical shell of nonbonding d electrons in a tetrahedral field, for example, d^0, $eg^2 e_{g2} t_{2g}^3$, $e_g^4 t_{2g}^3$, and d^{10}.

Comparison of the CFSE values for various tetrahedral complexes with the CFSE values for high spin octahedral complexes indicates why the d electron configurations listed in (2) are favorable for tetrahedral complexes (see Table 3-1).

Except for d^1 and d^6, CFSE definitely favors octahedral complexes. In addition, Dq' is always smaller than Dq; in general Dq' being about $\frac{4}{9}Dq$. Thus, d^2, d^5, and d^7 complexes are often octahedral. In the absence of effects listed above in (1), octahedral complexes will be favored over

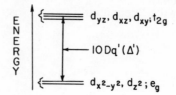

ENERGY

$d_{yz}, d_{xz}, d_{xy}; t_{2g}$

10 Dq' (Δ')

$d_{x^2-y^2}, d_{z^2}; e_g$

Fig. 3-7. Splitting of the d Orbitals in a Tetrahedral field

tetrahedral ones for most ligands complexing with all other first row transition metal ions.

Equations for the energy of tetrahedral configurations can be derived as was previously done for octahedral geometry by employing the CFSE values in Table 3-1 and subtracting the pairing energies. Using the data in Table 3-2 for the pairing energies and recalling that $Dq' \sim \frac{4}{9} Dq$, the energy of the tetrahedral complex can be compared with those of the high spin and low spin octahedral complexes.

Tetrahedral nickel(II) complexes are not as common as was believed in the past*. The tetrahalonickelate(II) anions are among the examples of tetrahedral nickel complexes. The data in Table 3-1 indicate that octahedral complexes of Ni^{II} are stabilized by $-12Dq$ as compared with $-8Dq'$ for tetrahedral complexes. Therefore, most paramagnetic nickel(II) complexes are six-coordinate. Tetrahedral coordination with nickel(II)

---

*In the initial application of valence bond theory to the description of the structure of complexes it was thought that all paramagnetic four-coordinate nickel complexes were tetrahedral. In addition, many tetragonal paramagnetic complexes (e.g., $Ni(NH_3)_4Cl_2$) were incorrectly assumed to be tetrahedral.

TABLE 3-3. CONFIGURATIONS AND GEOMETRIES OF SOME COMMON COMPLEXES[a]

	High-Spin Complexes				Low-Spin Complexes			
Number of Nonbonding d Electrons	Unpaired Electrons	Configuration	Shape	Example	Unpaired Electrons	Configuration	Shape	Example
1	1	t_{2g}^1	possibly a v. slightly distorted octahedron	$Ti(H_2O)_6^{3+}$				
2	2	t_{2g}^2	possibly a v. slightly distorted octahedron	$V(H_2O)_6^{3+}$				
		e_g^2	tetrahedron	FeO_4^{2-}				
3	3	t_{2g}^3	regular octahedron	Cr^{III} complexes				
4	4	$t_{2g}^3 e_g^1$	tetragonal		2	t_{2g}^4	v. slightly distorted octahedron	$Cr(CN)_6^{4-}$
5	5	$t_{2g}^3 e_g^2$	regular octahedron	FeF_6^{3-}	1	t_{2g}^5	slightly distorted octahedron	$Fe(CN)_6^{3-}$
		$e_g^2 t_{2g}^3$	tetrahedron	$FeCl_4^-$				
6	4	$t_{2g}^4 e_g^2$	slightly distorted octahedron	$Fe(H_2O)_6^{2+}$	0	t_{2g}^6	regular octahedron	Co^{III} complexes
7	3	$e_g^4 t_{2g}^3$	tetrahedron	$CoCl_4^{2-}$	1	$t_{2g}^6 e_g^1$	tetragonal or square planar	Co^{II} complexes
		$t_{2g}^5 e_g^2$	slightly distorted octahedron	$Co(H_2O)_6^{2+}$				
8	2	$t_{2g}^6 e_g^2$	regular octahedron	$Ni(H_2O)_6^{2+}$	0	$t_{2g}^6 e_g^2$	tetragonal or square planar	Ni^{II} complexes
9	1	$t_{2g}^6 e_g^3$	square planar or tetragonal	Cu^{II} complexes				

[a] R. Gillepsie, and R. S. Nyholm, *Quart. Revs.* 11, 339 (1957).

is favored for very large ligands which are easily polarized.* As predicted by the Jahn-Teller theorem there will be distortion from pure tetrahedral geometry in these complexes.

SUMMARY OF THE d-LEVEL SPLITTINGS

The splitting of the d orbitals for the various geometries considered above is summarized in Fig. 3-8. Table 3-3 contains a summary of the geometries of some common complexes. A procedure for determining the crystal field splitting diagrams for these and other structures has been reported.[3]

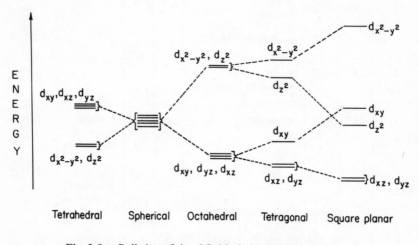

Fig. 3-8.   Splitting of the d Orbitals for Various Geometries

LIGAND FIELD STRENGTHS—COLORS OF COMPLEXES

Transition metal ion complexes have unfilled d orbitals. The energy required to excite an electron in these complexes from a t_{2g} to an e_g orbital is often in the range of energy of visible light. Absorption of light can, therefore, induce these electronic transitions, and the colors of many of the metal ion complexes arise from this effect. As the magnitude of Δ increases, the energy of the radiation necessary to cause the transition also increases and the color of the absorbed light changes. Examination of the visible and ultraviolet spectra gives a measure of Δ. The

---

* See R. S. Nyholm, *Proc. Chem. Soc.* 1961, 273, for a discussion of factors favoring tetrahedral structure.

procedure for calculating Δ is outlined in Chapter 6. The following sequence of ligand field strengths was derived from spectroscopic measurement of Δ and is referred to as the spectrochemical series.

$$I^- < Br^- < Cl^- < OH^- < F^- < H_2O < C_5H_5N < NH_3$$
$$< H_2NC_2H_4NH_2 < NO_2^- < \text{orthophenanthroline} < CN^-$$

A discussion of the factors that effect the magnitude of Δ is contained in Chapter 6.

The chemistry of metal ion complexes would be greatly simplified if we could list the ligands in order of increasing field strength for all metal ions and divide them into weak field or strong field categories. This would allow prediction of the electron arrangment in all d^4, d^5, d^6, d^7, and d^8 complexes. Unfortunately, this is not possible. Ligands that produce low spin complexes with one metal ion often produce high spin complexes with others because of the variations in the pairing energies and Dq values. The problem is thus one of becoming familiar with the chemistry of the various ions and then making guesses based upon previous experience. Accurate predictions can often be made by comparing the results from simple calculations of pairing energies and CFSE's for octahedral and tetrahedral complexes.

THE MOLECULAR ORBITAL THEORY OF BONDING IN COMPLEXES

Although the molecular orbital approach has many advantages for the description of bonding in complexes, it is unfortunately the most cumbersome to utilize. This theory will, however, be discussed for the following reasons:

(1) The valence bond and ligand field descriptions are not of sufficient accuracy to describe all phenomena. Experimental evidence is available to indicate that d electrons of the metal ion are often delocalized onto the ligands. Molecular orbital theory best explains how this results.

(2) The effects which covalency and π bonding in the metal-ligand link have on the energies of filled and empty orbitals are best described by the molecular orbital approach. These effects are of importance in understanding the spectra of complexes. Excited states are more simply and accurately described by this method.

(3) General principles for qualitatively constructing molecular orbitals can be illustrated very well with complexes.

As discussed in Chapter 2, it is important to consider symmetry and overlap criteria in combining orbitals to produce molecular orbitals. The symmetries of the d and p orbitals are illustrated in Fig. 3-9. The sign of the wave function for an s orbital is positive in all regions so this is a gerade orbital referred to as a_{1g}. The a indicates* the absence of degeneracy. The triply degenerate set of ungerade p orbitals is referred to as t_{1u}. Recall that the d_{xy}, d_{yz} and d_{xz} orbitals are referred to as t_{2g} and the $d_{x^2-y^2}$ and d_{z^2} orbitals are referred to as e_g.

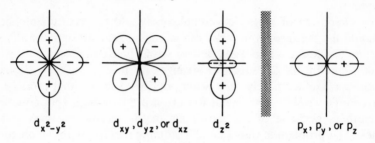

$$d_{x^2-y^2} \qquad d_{xy}, d_{yz}, \text{ or } d_{xz} \qquad d_{z^2} \qquad p_x, p_y, \text{ or } p_z$$

Fig. 3-9.   Symmetries of the d and p Orbitals

Before combining the metal ion orbitals with the ligand orbitals, we shall first consider combinations of ligand orbitals with one another to produce sets of composite ligand orbitals. These composite orbitals are then combined with the appropriate metal orbitals, according to certain rules, to produce a set of molecular orbitals into which the electrons are added. These operations will be explained by considering an example.

Consider the square planar complex tetramminecopper (II). The lone pair ligand electron density directed toward Cu^{II} is in an sp^3 hybrid orbital for each of the four ammonia molecules, and we will refer to these as σ_1, σ_2, σ_3, and σ_4 orbitals. (Note that for simplicity, the VB description of the ligand is employed.) The set of composite ligand molecular orbitals is obtained by group theoretical procedures for a square planar arrangement and this set pertains to any complex with this symmetry. The four σ orbitals which result (a_{1g}, e_u, b_{1g}) are illustrated in Fig. 3-10.

There are two sets of ligand orbitals that look very much alike and are not related to each other by -1: $(\sigma_1 - \sigma_3) \pm (\sigma_2 - \sigma_4)$. These are a set of doubly degenerate levels and are designated by e_u.

---

*More will be said about the information conveyed by these symbols in Chapter 4. For the time being, simply consider these as labels that convey the degeneracy and g or u nature of the orbitals. Pay no attention to the superscript numbers or the fact that a_{1g} and b_{1g} (to be introduced shortly) both convey the same message with regard to the above information.

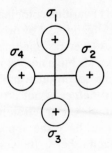

$$\sigma_1 + \sigma_2 + \sigma_3 + \sigma_4$$
$$a_{1g}$$

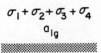

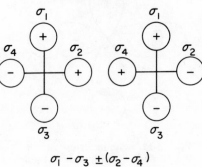

$$\sigma_1 - \sigma_3 \pm (\sigma_2 - \sigma_4)$$
$$e_u$$

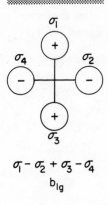

$$\sigma_1 - \sigma_2 + \sigma_3 - \sigma_4$$
$$b_{1g}$$

Fig. 3-10. Possible Combinations of Ligand Orbitals to form Composite Sets

We have now described: (1) various combinations of the ligand electron pairs to produce composite ligand sets of orbitals and (2) the symmetry of the metal ion orbitals. As yet no bonding MO's have been formed because the metal ion and ligands have not yet been combined. In combining metal and ligand orbitals to produce molecular orbitals, symmetry and overlap are important. Whether or not orbitals overlap is determined from the geometry of the complex. For tetramminecopper(II), the orbitals $d_{x^2-y^2}$ and b_{1g} of the ligand set have the appropriate symmetry for combination and also overlap each other in the complex (Fig. 3-11). The two

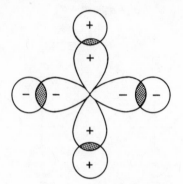

Fig. 3-11. Symmetries of the $d_{x^2-y^2}$ and b_{1g} Ligand Orbitals. Showing Overlap

molecular orbitals which result (B_{1g} and B_{1g}^{*}) are diagrammed in Fig. 3-12. The d_{xy} orbital will not form molecular orbitals, for it does not overlap with the ligands, but the ligand orbital a_{1g} and the metal d_{z^2} and 4s all

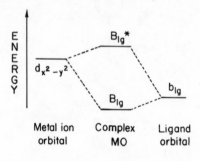

Metal ion orbital   Complex MO   Ligand orbital

Fig. 3-12. Combination of the Metal Ion and Ligand Orbitals to Form the B_{1g}^{*} and B_{1g} Molecular Orbitals in the Complex

combine for they have appropriate symmetry and overlap. Their combination to produce three molecular orbitals is illustrated in Fig. 3-13.

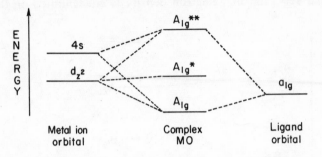

Fig. 3-13. The Combination of a_{1g}, $4s$, and $d_z{}^2$ Orbitals

Since the a_{1g} set of ligand orbitals lie in the xy plane, there is little overlap with d_{z^2} and as a result the nonbonding orbital A_{1g}^* is essentially the same as d_{z^2}. The e_u orbitals have the appropriate symmetry for overlap with the p_x and p_y orbitals. The resulting molecular orbitals are indicated in Fig. 3-14. Each E_u molecular orbital level is doubly degenerate and has a capacity for four electrons. The p_z orbital is not utilized

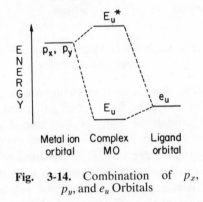

Fig. 3-14. Combination of p_x, p_y, and e_u Orbitals

because its σ overlap with ligands in the xy plane is essentially zero. The complete sequence of energy levels for this square planar complex is indicated in Fig. 3-15. The d orbitals are all degenerate in the free ion but are drawn separate in the figure for clarity. The d_{xy} orbital gives a higher energy molecular orbital than the e_g orbital (from d_{xz} and d_{yz}) because of repulsions from ligand electron density (cf. ligand field theory for square planar complexes).

In tetramminecopper(II), the eight bonding electrons occupy A_{1g}, B_{1g} and E_u molecular orbitals. Their energies are close to the energy of the ligand sets, and this electron density is concentrated on the ligand

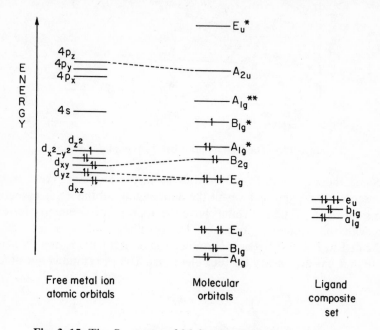

Free metal ion atomic orbitals

Molecular orbitals

Ligand composite set

Fig. 3–15. The Sequence of Molecular Orbitals for Tetramminecopper (II) Complexes

rather than the metal. The metal d electrons are in E_g, B_{2g}, A_{1g}^*, and B_{1g}^* molecular orbitals of which the first four (E_g, B_{2g}, and A_{1g}^*) are essentially metal ion orbitals containing eight of the nine d electrons. The B_{1g}^* orbital contains one electron. Because of the low energy (high ionization potential) of the ligand electron density, the bonding molecular orbitals are composed essentially of the ligand orbitals with small metal ion contributions, mainly from $d_{x^2-y^2}$, $4s$, $4p_x$, and $4p_y$ orbitals. Note the similarity of this description to that of valence bond theory using dsp^2 hybrids. The E_g level is essentially d_{xz} and d_{yz}, the B_{2g} is essentially d_{xy} and A_{2u} is essentially the p_z atomic orbital.

In this model the color of the complex is due to electronic transitions to empty molecular orbitals whose energies are determined in part by the ligand. As the ligand is varied the energies of the levels are sometimes interchanged and the relative positions are determined experimentally from the spectrum of the complex.

When an unpaired d electron of the metal ion is in a molecular orbital which consists of metal ion and ligand orbitals, the electron is delocalized on the ligand. Such is the case for the odd electron in B_{1g}^*. This is supported by electron spin resonance studies which indicate that the odd electron in certain Cu^{II} complexes spends some of its time on the ligand.

The effect of π bonding on the molecular orbital sequence can be illustrated by considering monomeric cupric chloride. The structure is linear. Ligand combinations produce a composite set of two orbitals: $\oplus - \oplus$, σ_g and $\oplus - \ominus$, σ_u. Combination of σ_g from the ligand set, with $d_{x^2-y^2}$ and the s orbital of the metal ion produces molecular orbitals σ_g, σ_g^* and σ_g^{**}. Combination of σ_u of the ligand set and p_z produces the molecular orbitals of the complex σ_u and σ_u^*. This sequence of σ orbitals is illustrated in Fig. 3-16.

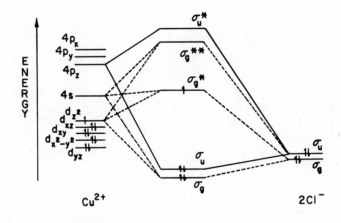

Fig. 3-16. σ Molecular Orbitals in $CuCl_2$

The other d and p orbitals of the metal ion not involved in σ bonding would be essentially unchanged in the complex. If, however, the ligand has filled p orbitals, these can overlap with empty metal ion orbitals to form π bonds. Similarly, if the ligand has empty d orbitals (ϕ_3P, Et_2S, etc.), these can form bonds by interacting with electrons in filled d levels of the metal. The net effect is to raise and lower the initial energies of the ligand or metal orbitals to an extent which depends on the amount of overlap and the energy of the orbitals. This complicates the problem of determining the relative energies of the various molecular orbitals and requires that the final sequence of levels be determined from experimental data. These effects also cause difficulty in making spectral assignments.

A complete description[4] of $CuCl_2$ is indicated in Fig. 3-17. In this diagram the copper atom is combined with chlorine atoms (this is equivalent to combining Cu^{2+} and $2Cl^-$), and all of the valence electrons of copper and chlorine are included.

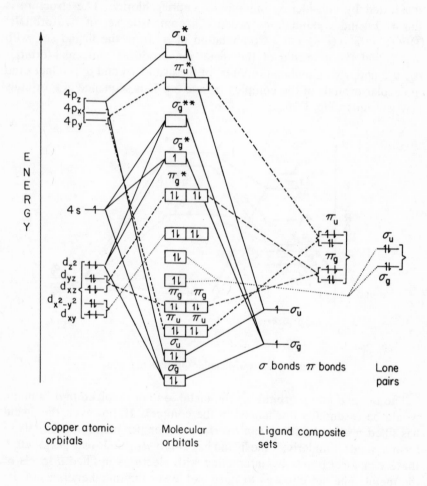

Fig. 3-17. A More Complete Molecular Orbital Description of $CuCl_2$. The energy scale for the ligand orbitals has been greatly expanded for clarity so differences in σ, π, and lone pair energies are exaggerated. The two chlorine atoms have 14 electrons.

EXERCISES

1. Draw a cube and locate a tetrahedron in it as described in the Chapter. Explain how the splittings in Fig. 3-7 arise.
2. Indicate the splitting of the d-levels and the number of electrons in each level for each of the following complexes:
   a. $Ni(NH_3)_6^{2+}$ (paramagnetic).
   b. $trans$-$Ni(NH_3)_4Cl_2$ (paramagnetic, tetragonal, Δ for $NH_3 > Cl^-$).
   c. $Ni(CN)_4^{2-}$.
   d. $trans$-$Ni(CN)_4(H_2O)_2^{2-}$.
   e. $Cu(NH_3)_4^{2+}$.
   f. $NiCl_4^{2-}$ (tetrahedral).
   g. $Mn(acac)_3$ (acac = acetylacetonate).
   h. $Cr(CN)_6^{3-}$.
   i. FeO_4^{2-} (tetrahedral).
   j. $CuCl_4^{2-}$ (tetrahedral).
   k. $Co(NH_3)_6^{2+}$.
3. Of the complexes in a, f, g, h, i, j, and k above, which would you expect to be distorted?
4. Compare the CFSE in $Co(NH_3)_6^{2+}$ and $Co(NH_3)_6^{3+}$.
5. a. Calculate the relative energies as a function of Dq and P for both the high spin (HS) and low spin (LS) octahedral and HS tetrahedral aquo complexes of Co^{II} and Fe^{II}. On the basis of these calculations state which configuration is the most energetically favorable for each of these ions.
   b. On the basis of the CFSE's $alone$, predict which ion should show the greater tendency to form tetrahedral complexes.
   c. Is this prediction upheld by the calculations made above and if not, why?
6. In an octahedral complex, one triply degenerate set of composite orbitals can be represented as $\oplus\!-\!\ominus\!-\underline{x}$, $\oplus\!-\!\ominus\!-\underline{y}$, and $\oplus\!-\!\ominus\!-\underline{z}$. Which set of metal ion orbitals can interact with these?

A second doubly degenerate set is:

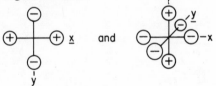

Which metal ion orbitals can overlap with these? A third set is:

Which metal ion orbital can overlap with this orbital? Why doesn't d_{xy}, d_{xz}, or d_{yz} interact with any of these sets in a σ manner?

7. Combine the results of 6 (above) to prepare a schematic diagram similar to Fig. 3-15. Ignore π bonding and guess at the relative energies of the molecular orbitals by employing qualitative overlap considerations and the initial energies of the metal ion levels.

REFERENCES CITED

1. F. Basolo and R. G. Pearson, "Mechanisms of Inorganic Reactions," pp. 34–87, Wiley, New York. 1958.
2. L. E. Orgel, "An Introduction to Transition Metal Ion Chemistry: Ligand Field Theory," Wiley, New York, 1960.
3. A. L. Companion and M. A. Komanynsky, J. Chem. Educ., 41, 257 (1964).
4. A. D. Liehr, J. Chem. Educ., 39, 135 (1962).

GENERAL REFERENCES

C. J. Ballhausen, "Introduction to Ligand Field Theory," McGraw-Hill, New York (1962).
C. J. Ballhausen and H. B. Gray, "Introductory Notes on Molecular Orbital Theory," Benjamin, New York, 1965.
F. Basolo and R. G. Pearson, "Mechanisms of Inorganic Reactions," pp. 34–87, Wiley, New York, 1958.
F. A. Cotton, J. Chem. Educ., 41, 466 (1964).
F. A. Cotton and G. Wilkinson, "Advanced Inorganic Chemistry," Wiley, New York (1962).
H. B. Gray, "Electrons and Chemical Bonding," Benjamin, New York, 1964.
H. B. Gray, J. Chem. Educ., 41, 2 (1964).
J. Griffith and L. E. Orgel, Quart. Revs., 11, 381–3 (1957).
L. E. Orgel, "An Introduction to Transition Metal Ion Chemistry: Ligand Field Theory," Wiley, New York, 1960.
L. E. Sutton, J. Chem. Educ., 37, 498 (1960).

PART II

Spectroscopic Methods

NOW THAT some fundamental considerations concerning bonding have been reviewed, we shall begin discussion of the topics which provided the motivation for writing this text book—spectroscopic methods. The level of presentation is a compromise between a theoretical approach and one dealing only with applications. Applications are included for it is realized that the chemist concerned with synthesis frequently reasons by analogy in his research. It is hoped that the applications discussed here will stimulate analogous applications of these physical methods to other inorganic systems. The theory is presented to make the limitations of such applications clear. The author feels that the theory presented in this text constitutes an absolute minimum for the intelligent use of these spectroscopic methods by chemists concerned with synthesis.

4 Symmetry and the Character Tables

INTRODUCTION

IF A MOLECULE has two or more orientations in space that are indistinguishable, the molecule possesses *symmetry*. Two possible orientations for the hydrogen molecule can be illustrated in Fig. 4-1 only by labeling the two equivalent hydrogen atoms in this figure with prime and double prime marks. Actually the two hydrogens are indistinguishable, the two orientations are equivalent and the molecule has symmetry. The two orientations in Fig. 4-1 can be obtained by rotation of the molecule through 180° about an axis through the center of and perpendicular to the hydrogen-hydrogen bond axis. This rotation is referred to as a

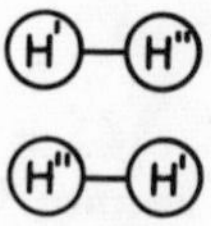

Fig. 4-1 Equivalent Orientations for H_2

symmetry operation, and the rotation axis is called a *symmetry element.* The terms symmetry element and symmetry operation should not be confused or used interchangeably. The symmetry element is the line, point, or plane about which the symmetry operation is carried out. A simple test can be performed to verify the presence of symmetry. If you were to glance at a molecular structure, turn your back and have someone perform a symmetry operation, you would not, on once again examining the molecule, be able to determine that a change had been made.

In the area of structural chemistry it is becoming customary to describe the structures of molecules in terms of the symmetry the molecules possess. Spectroscopists have described molecular vibrations and struc-

99

tures in these terms for many years. The intelligent application of spectroscopy to the problem of structure determination requires a knowledge of symmetry properties. A qualitative treatment will be employed and we shall be concerned mainly with the description of the symmetry of an isolated molecule, the so-called *point symmetry*. Point symmetry refers to the set of operations transforming a system about a common point, which usually turns out to be the center of gravity of a molecule.

SYMMETRY ELEMENTS

There are five types of symmetry elements which will be considered for point symmetry: (1) the center of symmetry (inversion center), (2) the rotation axis, (3) the mirror plane, (4) the rotation-reflection axis, and (5) the identity.

THE CENTER OF SYMMETRY, OR INVERSION CENTER

A molecule is said to possess a center of symmetry if reflection of each of the atoms in the molecule through this center results in its coming into coincidence with an identical atom. If oxygen atom, A, of the hyponitrite ion (Fig. 4-2) is moved through the inversion center, an equal distance to the opposite side, it comes into coincidence with another oxygen atom.

Fig. 4-2. The Center of Symmetry in the Hyponitrite Ion

The same arguments must apply to atom B and also to both nitrogen atoms if the molecule is to possess a center of symmetry. Neither of the two structures indicated in Fig. 4-3 nor any other tetrahedral molecule possesses an inversion center. Other examples of molecules or ions which should be examined for the presence of an inversion center are 1, 4-dioxane, tetracyanonickellate(II), *trans*-dichloroethylene, and *trans*-dichlorotetrammine cobalt(III). The molecule HCCl=CHBr (*cis* or *trans*) does not possess a center of symmetry because the symmetry operation on bromine or hydrogen does not result in coincidence. All points in the molecule must be inverted simultaneously in this operation, if the molecule as a whole is to possess this symmetry element. The symbol used to indicate an inversion center (center of symmetry) is *i*.

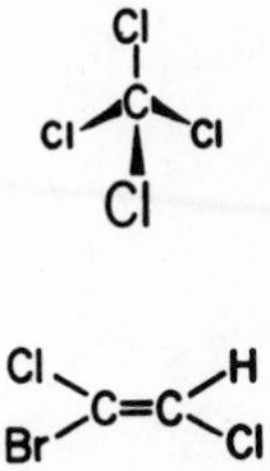

Fig. 4-3. Absence of a Center of Symmetry in CCl_4 and $HCCl{=}CBrCl$

THE ROTATION AXIS

If an imaginary axis can be constructed in a molecule around which the molecule can be rotated to produce an *equivalent* (i.e., indistinguishable from the original) orientation, this molecule is said to possess a rotation axis. The symmetry element, previously discussed for the hydrogen molecule, is a rotation axis. This element is often referred to as a proper rotation axis. It may be possible to carry out several symmetry operations around a single rotation axis. If the molecule can occupy *n* different equivalent positions about this axis, the axis is said to be of order n. For example, consider the axis through the center of the boron atom in BCl_3 perpendicular to the plane of the molecule. Rotation about this axis two times through an angle of 120° each time produces two equivalent orientations. Taken with the initial orientation, we have the three different equivalent orientations illustrated in Fig. 4-4. The order, *n*, of this axis is three, for three rotations are needed to return to the original position. The molecule is said to possess a threefold rotation axis, indicated by the symbol C_3. Rotation of the molecule through $2\pi/n$, i.e., 120°, produces equivalent orientations, and *n* operations produce the starting configuration referred to as the *identity*. It should be clear that an axis through the center and perpendicular to the plane of a benzene ring is a sixfold axis, C_6. Since $n = 6$, rotation by 60° (360°/6) six times produces the six equivalent orientations. Further examination of the BCl_3 molecule indicates the lack of a center of symmetry and the presence of the three additional twofold rotation axes, C_2, illustrated in Fig. 4-5. One, arbitrarily selected, is labeled C_2 and the other two are labeled C'_2 and C''_2. The highest-fold rotation axis is referred to as the *principal axis* and is labeled C_n. The symbol $C_3{}^2$ is employed to indicate a rotation of 240° around a C_3 axis. The $C_3{}^2$ operation is identical to a counterclockwise rotation of 120° which is indicated as $C_3{}^-$. A rotation

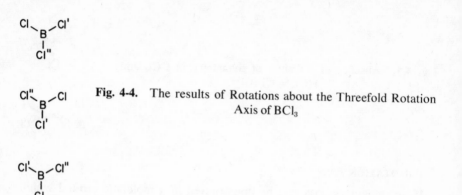

Fig. 4-4. The results of Rotations about the Threefold Rotation Axis of BCl_3

axis of order n generates n operations, i.e., C_n, $C_n{}^2$, $C_n{}^3$, ..., $C_n{}^{n-1}$, $C_n{}^n$. Furthermore, the operation $C_4{}^2$ is equivalent to C_2, $C_6{}^2$ is equivalent to C_3, and $C_n{}^n$ is the identity. If the molecule contains several C_n (i.e.,

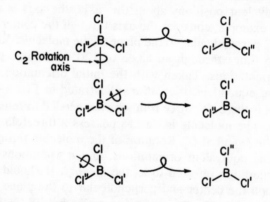

Fig. 4-5. The Results of Rotations about the Three Twofold Rotation Axes in BCl_3. The 180° rotation of the left produces the result on the right.

highest order) rotation axes, the principal one is usually selected as the one colinear with a unique molecular axis. If all of the C_n axes are equivalent, any one may be chosen as the principal axis. If $n = 1$, the molecule must be rotated 360° to produce an equivalent and in this case identical orientation. Consequently, the molecule is said to possess no symmetry if no other elements are present. In Fig. 4-6, a rotation axis is illustrated

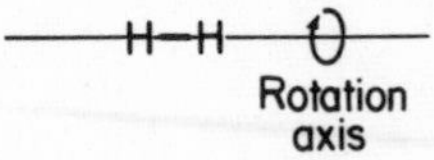

Fig. 4-6.   The C_∞ Axis in H_2

H—H   ()
Rotation
axis

for the H_2 molecule for which $n = \infty$. The C_2 rotation axes are not illustrated but are perpendicular to the bond axis and centered between the two hydrogen atoms. It should also be obvious that benzene possesses six twofold axes which lie in the plane of the benzene molecule. Three pass through pairs of opposite carbon atoms and three through the center of C—C bonds. The molecule ClF_3 is illustrated in Fig. 4-7. The two lone electron pair orbital axes, the flourine atom nearest the chlorine and the chlorine lie in a plane. The other two flourine atoms and the chlorine are in a plane perpendicular to the plane containing the lone pair orbital axes. This molecule has only one rotation axis, the C_2 axis illustrated in Fig. 4-7. The reader should verify the absence of symmetry along the axes indicated by dashed lines. Lone pair electron orbitals are not considered in determining the symmetry of a molecule.

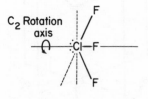

Fig. 4-7.   The Symmetry
Axis in ClF_3

THE MIRROR PLANE OR PLANE OF SYMMETRY

If in a molecule there exists a plane which separates the molecule into two halves that are mirror images of each other, the molecule possesses the symmetry element of a *mirror plane*. This plane cannot lie outside the molecule but must pass through it. Another way of describ-

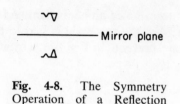

───────────────── Mirror plane

Fig. 4-8. The Symmetry Operation of a Reflection Plane (σ)

ing this operation involves selecting a plane, dropping a perpendicular from every atom in the molecule to the plane, and placing the atom at the end of the line formed by extending this line an equal distance to the opposite side of the plane. If an equivalent configuration is obtained after this is done to all the atoms, the plane selected is a mirror plane. Reflection through the mirror plane is indicated by Fig. 4-8. When the symbol in the bottom half of Fig. 4-8 is reflected through the mirror plane, the symbol on the other side of this plane results. Many rotation axes lie in a mirror plane (see Fig. 4-9, for example) but there are examples where

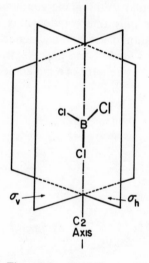

Fig. 4-9. A Mirror Plane in BCl_3

this is not the case. The tetrahedral molecule $POBr_2Cl$ illustrated in Fig. 4-10 is an example of a molecule that contains no rotation axis but does contain a mirror plane. The atoms P, Cl, and O lie in the plane. In general the presence of a mirror plane is denoted by the symbol σ.

In those molecules that contain more than one mirror plane, *e.g.*, BCl_3, the *horizontal plane* σ_h is taken as the one perpendicular to the principal (highest-fold rotation) axis. In Fig. 4-9, the plane of the paper is σ_h and there are then three *vertical planes* (two others, σ_v similar to the one

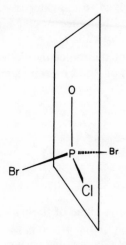

Fig. 4-10. The Mirror
Plane in $POClBr_2$

illustrated) perpendicular to σ_h. When a coordinate axis system is used to describe the molecule, it is usual to identify *the highest n-fold rotation axis as the z axis* and σ_h is then perpendicular to this axis.

Some molecules contain mirror planes containing the principal axis but none of the perpendicular C_2 axes. These planes bisect the angle between two of the C_2 axes (in the *xy* plane) and are referred to as *dihedral planes* and abbreviated as σ_d. Two σ_d planes are illustrated in Fig. 4-13.

THE ROTATION-REFLECTION AXIS; IMPROPER ROTATIONS

This operation involves rotation about an axis followed by reflection through a mirror plane which is perpendicular to the rotation axis or vice

Fig. 4-11. Rotation-Reflection Axis of Symmetry

versa. The result of the two operations produces an equivalent structure. This operation is sometimes referred to as an *improper rotation,* and the rotation-reflection axis is often called an alternating axis. The symbol S is used to indicate this symmetry element. The dotted line in Fig. 4-11 is used to indicate this element in the molecule *trans* dichloroethylene. The subscript two is employed to indicate rotation through 180°. Note that S_2 is actually equivalent to i and, by convention, is usually called i. Higher order, improper axes are called S_n.

A particular orientation of the molecule methane has been illustrated in Fig. 4-12. Open circles or squares represent hydrogen atoms in a

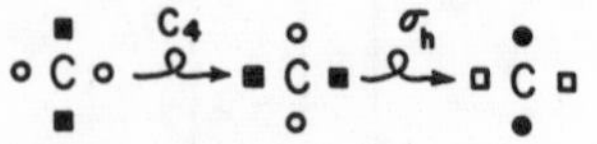

Fig. 4-12. Effect of the Operations C_4 and σ Perpendicular to C_4 on the Hydrogens of CH_4

plane parallel to but above the plane of the paper, and the solid squares or circles are those below the plane of the paper. The plane of the paper is the reflection plane, and it contains the carbon atom. The C_4 operation is straightforward. The operation of reflection, σ, moves the hydrogens below the plane to above the plane and vice versa. This is indicated by changing the solid squares to open squares and the open circles to solid circles. However, since all four hydrogens are identical, the initial and final orientations are equivalent. The molecule contains a fourfold rotation-reflection axis, abbreviated S_4. This operation can be repeated three more times, or four times in all. These four operations are indicated by the symbols S_4^1, S_4^2, S_4^3, and S_4^4. The reader should convince himself that S_4^2 is equivalent to a C_2 operation on this axis. It should also be mentioned that the molecule possesses two other rotation reflection axes, and these symmetry elements are abbreviated by the symbols S' and S''. The operation S_4^3 is equivalent to a counterclockwise rotation of 90° followed by reflection. This is often indicated as S_4^-.

THE IDENTITY

In the identity operation no change is made in the molecule. Obviously the result of this operation is not only to produce an equivalent orientation but an *identical* one; i.e., even if similar atoms were labeled with prime, double prime, etc., marks, no change would be detected. All molecules possess this symmetry element, and it is indicated by the symbol E. This operation probably seems trivial at present, but, as will be seen in the section on group theory, this concept is required so that symmetry elements can be treated by this form of mathematics.

Several of the operations described above which produce configurations identical to the starting one are equivalent to the identity, *e.g.*, C_3^3 or C_n^n or S_n^n (if n is even) or S_n^{2n} (if n is odd) or $\sigma^2 = E$.

POINT GROUPS

It is possible to classify all molecules into one of the point groups. Each point group is a collection of all the symmetry operations that can be carried out on a molecule belonging to this group. We shall first present a general discussion in which molecules belonging to some of the very common, simple point groups are examined for the symmetry elements they possess. This will be followed by a general set of rules for assigning molecules to their appropriate point group.

A molecule in the point group C_n has only one symmetry element, an n-fold rotation axis. (Of course, all molecules possess the element E, so this will be assumed in subsequent discussion.) A molecule such as *trans*-dichoroethylene, which has a horizontal mirror plane perpendicular to its C_n rotation axis, belongs to the point group C_{nh}. The point group C_{nv} includes molecules like water and sulfuryl chloride, which have n vertical mirror planes containing the rotation axis, but no horizontal mirror plane (the horizontal plane by definition must be perpendicular to the highest-fold rotation axis). The C_{2v} molecules, H_2O and SO_2Cl_2, contain only one rotation axis and two σ_v planes. The molecule is assigned to the point group that contains all of the symmetry elements in the molecule. For example, H_2O which has a C_2 axis and two vertical planes is assigned to the more symmetric point group C_{2v} rather than to C_2.

The symbol D_n is used for point groups which have, in addition to a C_n axis, nC_2 axes perpendicular to it. Therefore, the D_n point group has greater symmetry (i.e., more symmetry operations) than the C_n group. A D_n molecule which also has a horizontal mirror plane perpendicular to the C_n axis belongs to the point group D_{nh}, and as a consequence will also have n vertical mirror planes. The addition of a horizontal mirror plane to the point group C_{nv} necessarily implies the presence of nC_2 axes in the horizontal plane, and the result is the point group D_{nh}. BCl_3 is an example of a molecule belonging to the D_{3h} point group. In the D_{nh} point groups the σ_h planes are perpendicular to the principal axis and contain all the C_2 axes. Each σ_v plane contains the principal axis and one of the C_2 axes.

D_n molecules may also have σ_d planes which contain the principal, C_n, axis but none of the perpendicular C_2 axes. As mentioned previously, these dihedral planes, σ_d, bisect the angle between two of the C_2 axes. The notation for a D_n molecule containing this symmetry element is D_{nd}. Such a molecule will contain an n-fold axis, n twofold axes perpendicular to C_n, and in addition n (vertical) planes of symmetry bisecting the angles between two twofold axes and containing the n-fold axis. Allene, $H_2C\!=\!C\!=\!CH_2$, is an example of a molecule belonging to the D_{2d} point group. Some of the symmetry elements are illustrated in Fig. 4-13. The two hydrogens on one carbon are in a σ_d plane perpendicular

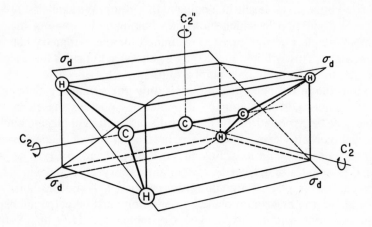

Fig. 4-13. The C_2 Axes and a σ_d Plane in Allene

to the σ_d plane containing the two hydrogens on the other carbon. The C_2 axes (the principal axis being labeled C_2, the others C'_2 and C''_2) and the dihedral planes containing the principal axis are indicated. The two other C_2 axes, C'_2 and C''_2 which are perpendicular to the principal C_2 axis, form 45° angles with the two dihedral planes. (Study the figure carefully to see this. Constructing a model may help.)

Table 4-1 contains the symmetry elements and examples of some of the more common point groups. The reader should examine the examples for the presence of the symmetry elements required for each point group and the absence of others. Remember that the symbol C indicates the molecule has only one rotation axis. The symbol D_n indicates n C_2 axes in addition to the n-fold axis; e.g., the point group D_4 contains a C_4 axis and four C_2 axes.

A more exhaustive compilation of the important point groups is contained in Herzberg[1]. In addition to the point groups listed in Table 4-1, the O_h point group which includes molecules whose structures are perfect octahedra (SF_6, PCl_6^-) is very common.

TABLE 4-1. SYMMETRY ELEMENTS IN SOME COMMON POINT GROUPS

Point Group	Symmetry Elements[a]	Examples
C_1	no symmetry	SiBrClFI
C_2	one C_2 axis	H_2O_2
C_{nh}	one n-fold axis and a horizontal plane σ_h which must be perpendicular to the n-fold axis	trans-$C_2H_2Cl_2(C_{2h})$
C_{2v}	one C_2 axis, and two σ_v planes	H_2O, SO_2Cl_2, $SiCl_2Br_2$
C_{3v}	one C_3 axis, and three σ_v planes	NH_3, CH_3Cl, $POCl_3$
D_{2h}	three C_2 axes all $\perp$, two σ_v planes, one σ_h plane, and a center of symmetry	N_2O_4 (planar)
D_{3h}	one C_3, three C_2 axes $\perp$ to C_3, three σ_v planes, and one σ_h	BCl_3
D_{2d}	three C_2 axes, two σ_d planes, and one S_4 (coincident with one C_2)	$H_2C=C=CH_2$
T_d	three C_2 axes $\perp$ to each other, four C_3, six σ, and three S_4 containing C_2	CH_4, $SiCl_4$

[a] All point groups possess the identity element, E.

It is important to emphasize that although $CHCl_3$ has a tetrahedral geometry it does not have tetrahedral symmetry so it belongs to the point group C_{3v} and not T_d. A tetragonal complex, trans-dichlorotetramine cobalt(III) ion, belongs to the point group D_{4h} (ignoring the hydrogens) and not O_h. Phosphorus pentachloride belongs to the point group D_{3h}, and not to C_{3h}, for it has three C_2 axes perpendicular to the C_3 axis. The structure of monomeric boric acid (assumed to be rigid), illustrated in Fig. 4-14 is an example of C_{3h} symmetry. It has a threefold axis and a σ_h plane but does not have the three C_2 axes or σ_v planes necessary for the D_{3h} point group.

It is helpful but not always possible to classify additional structures by memorizing the above examples and using analogy as the basis for classification instead of searching for all the possible symmetry elements.

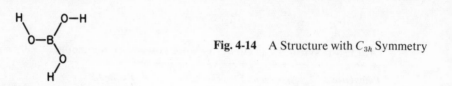

Fig. 4-14   A Structure with C_{3h} Symmetry

The following sequence of steps has been proposed[2] for classifying molecules into point groups and is a more reliable procedure than analogy.

(1) Determine whether or not the molecule belongs to one of the special point groups, $C_{\infty v}$, $D_{\infty h}$, I_h, O_h, or T_d. The group I_h contains the regular dodecahedron and regular icosahedron. Only linear molecules belong to $C_{\infty v}$ or $D_{\infty h}$.

(2) If the molecule does not belong to any of the special groups, look for a proper rotation axis. If any are found, proceed to step (3), if not look for a center of symmetry, i, or a mirror plane, σ. If the element i is present, the molecule belongs to the point group C_i and if a mirror is present, the molecule belongs to the point group, C_s. If no symmetry other than E is present, the molecule belongs to C_1.

(3) Locate the principal axis, C_n. See if a rotation-reflection axis S_{2n} exists which is coincident with the principal axis. If this element exists and there are no other elements except possibly i, the molecule belongs to one of the S_n point groups (where n is even). If other elements are present or if the S_{2n} element is absent, proceed to step (4).

(4) Look for a set of n twofold axes lying in the plane perpendicular to C_n. If this set is found, the molecule belongs to one of the groups D_n, D_{nh}, or D_{nd}. Proceed to step (5). If not, the molecule must belong to either C_n, C_{nh}, or C_{nv}. Proceed to step (6) and skip (5).

(5) By virtue of having arrived at this step, the molecule must be assigned to D_n, D_{nh}, or D_{nd}. If the molecule contains the symmetry element σ_h, it belongs to D_{nh}. If this element is not present, look for a set of $n\sigma_d$'s, the presence of which enable assignment of the molecule to D_{nd}. If σ_d and σ_h are both absent, the molecule belongs to D_n.

(6) By virtue of having arrived at this step, the molecule must be assigned to C_n, C_{nh}, or C_{nv}. If the molecule contains σ_h, the point group is C_{nh}. If σ_h is absent, look for a set of $n\sigma_v$'s which place the molecule in C_{nv}. If neither σ_v or σ_h is present, the molecule belongs to the point group C_n.

GROUP THEORY AND THE CHARACTER TABLES

Group theory is a branch of mathematics that can be applied to certain systems if they meet specific requirements. There are many systems of interest to chemists that can be treated by these techniques including: the description of molecular vibrations; the classification of molecular electronic orbitals; the derivation of selection rules for infrared, Raman, and electronic transitions; the generation of hybrid orbitals and molecular orbitals; the derivation of crystal field splittings; and numerous other applications. The treatment here will provide a brief introduction to the basic concepts necessary to understand the utilization of the character tables in spectroscopy. For a more thorough treatment which leads to a more complete understanding the reader is referred to the text by F. A. Cotton[2] on this subject.

In order that a collection of elements constitute a group (i.e., be subject to group theoretical rules) the following conditions must be satisfied. These conditions are perfectly general but their meaning may be made more clear by applying them to the symmetry elements of the water molecule which belongs to the C_{2v} point group containing the symmetry operations: $E, C_2, \sigma_v, \sigma_v'$.

(1) Taking the product of any two operations in the group or squaring an element must produce an operation of the group. By convention the highest-fold rotation axis is taken as the z axis, i.e., the C_2 axis for the C_{2v} point group, and the three atoms of the water molecule constitute the yz plane which is the mirror plane σ_v'. To take the product of two symmetry operations the corresponding symmetry operations are applied consecutively. Hence, the product of $C_2 \times \sigma_v = \sigma_v'$. Instead of the term product, a more correct term to employ for the above operation is *combination*. It is a simple matter to square all the symmetry operations and to take all possible combinations to show that the result of these combinations is another element in the C_{2v} point group. Some combinations depend upon the order employed, although this is not the case for the above example. For example, in a D_{3h} molecule $C_3 \times \sigma_v \neq \sigma_v \times C_3$. When the result is independent of the order of combination, we say that the symmetry operations commute.

(2) One operation in the group must commute with all the other operations and leave them unchanged. As mentioned previously, this operation is called the identity operation and is abbreviated by the symbol E.

(3) The associative law of combination must hold. The result of combining three elements must be the same if the first element is combined with

the product of the second two, i.e., $\sigma_v(C_2\sigma_v')$, or if the product of the first two is combined with the last element $(\sigma_v C_2)\sigma_v'$.

(4) Every element must have a reciprocal which is also an element of the group. This requires that for every symmetry operation there be another operation which will undo what the first operation did. For any mirror plane, the inverse is the identical mirror plane, e.g., $\sigma \times \sigma = E$. For a proper rotation $C_n{}^m$, the inverse is $C_n{}^{n-m}$; $C_n{}^m \times C_n{}^{n-m} = E$.

Since symmetry operations satisfy the requirements of group theory, the point groups can be treated by group theoretical procedures.

Knowledge of the symmetry properties of transitions or motions in a molecule is essential to the interpretations of spectral data. The effects of the symmetry operations on various properties of a molecule belonging to a particular point group are summarized by *the character table* for that point group. The character table can be derived by group theoretical procedures. We shall not be concerned with the derivation here but simply with the result. The character table for C_{2v} point group is shown in Table 4-2.

TABLE 4-2. CHARACTER TABLE
FOR THE C_{2v} POINT GROUP

C_{2v}	E	C_2	$\sigma_{v(xz)}$	$\sigma'_{v(yz)}$		
A_1	1	1	1	1	z	x^2, y^2, z^2
A_2	1	1	-1	-1	R_z	xy
B_1	1	-1	1	-1	x, R_y	xz
B_2	1	-1	-1	1	y, R_x	yz

To demonstrate its use, we shall consider the effect of the symmetry operations of the C_{2v} point group on a unit vector $\mathbf{X}$ lying along the x axis of an $x, y, z,$ coordinate system, where z is the principal axis (Fig. 4-15). The y and z components of this vector are zero for all operations of the group, so we can say $\mathbf{X}$ transforms independently of y and z. The identity operation, E, does not change the coordinates and we indicate this by the coefficient $+ 1$. This quantity is referred to as the *character* of the E operation on $\mathbf{X}$. As illustrated by the dotted arrow in Fig. 4-15, the C_2 operation changes the components of $\mathbf{X}$ to $-x$, so the character for the C_2 operation on $\mathbf{X}$ is indicated by -1. The operations σ_v and σ_v' on $\mathbf{X}$ have the characters $+1$ and -1, respectively. By looking at the character table, it can be seen that the results $1, -1, 1, -1$ correspond to the row preceded by the symbol B_1. It is said that the vector **X** *transforms* under the symmetry operations of the C_{2v} point group according to species

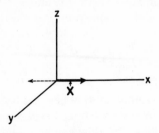

Fig. 4-15. C_2 and σ_v' Operations on the Solid Arrow Producing the Dotted Arrow

B_1. These species are referred to as the *irreducible representations* of the point group. Later we shall have more to say about the symbols for the species and what they signify. For the present, simply consider them as labels for the rows in the character table.

By a set of operations similar to those described for a vector along the x axis, vectors **Z** and **Y** along the z and y axes respectively can be shown to transform as species A_1 and B_2, respectively. The vectors **X**, **Y**, and **Z** are indicated to the right of the character table opposite their symmetry species. The symbols R correspond to rotations. There are three of these R_x, R_y, and R_z corresponding to rotations about the x, y, and z axes. To see how these transform, locate a curved arrow at the center of the coordinate system around the axis indicated by the subscript, e.g., at $z = 0$, and around the z axis for R_z. Although it is not of consequence in this example, by convention the arrow is located so that it is turning clockwise if one were standing at the center of the coordinate system and looking down the axis. The symmetry operations are performed on this arrow, and if the direction in which it points is not changed, the character is $+1$, and if it is changed, the character is -1. It can be seen that R_x, R_y, and R_z transform as species B_2, B_1, and A_2, respectively.

Next let us consider a point in the coordinate system of Fig. 4-15 with coordinates x, y, and z all of which are positive. The operation E leaves the coordinates of the point unchanged, and the sum of the coefficients in the front of x, y, and z equals three. In *this example*, the character is the sum of the coefficients, $+3$. When the arrow lay along the x axis, the sum was one because y and z equaled zero. The C_2 operation transforms the coordinates of x, y, and z into $-\hat{x}$, $-y$, and z. The character of this operation, which is the sum of the coefficients -1, -1, $+1$, is -1. The operation $\sigma_{v(xz)}$ results in x, $-y$, z, or $+1$, and $\sigma'_{v(yz)}$ results in $-x$, $+y$, $+z$, or $+1$. The *total*, or *reducible*, *representation* for these operations can be written:

$$\begin{array}{c|cccc} & E & C_2 & \sigma_v & \sigma'_v \\ \hline \Gamma & 3 & -1 & +1 & +1 \end{array}$$

where Γ is a general symbol used when the symmetry species is not known. A *reducible representation* can be decomposed into the sum of irreducible representations. In this example, this corresponds to the sum of species $A_1, B_1,$ and B_2.

$$\begin{array}{ccccc} (A_1) & 1 & 1 & 1 & 1 \\ (B_1) & 1 & -1 & 1 & -1 \\ (B_2) & 1 & -1 & -1 & 1 \\ \hline (\Gamma) & 3 & -1 & +1 & +1 \end{array}$$

$$\therefore \Gamma = A_1 + B_1 + B_2$$

The irreducible representations in the character table (i.e., A_1, A_2, B_1, and B_2) cannot be decomposed. Since the point described at the beginning of this paragraph has coordinates x, y, and z, it is expected that the reducible representations will consist of the sum of the species for **X**, **Y**, and **Z** vectors. The irreducible representations constituting the reducible representation were visually deduced in the above problem by adding various possible combinations of irreducible representations until the correct result was obtained. In Chapter 7, a general formula is given for determining all the irreducible representations which constitute a reducible representation.

The section on the extreme right of the C_{2v} character table gives the species for square and binary products of the coordinates x, y, and z. The *direct product* of two vectors is obtained by multiplying the species for each, e.g., $\mathbf{XY} = B_1 \times B_2 = A_2$. To perform this multiplication the following procedure is used:

$E(B_1) \times E(B_2) \qquad C_2(B_1) \times C_2(B_2) \qquad \sigma_v(B_1) \times \sigma_v(B_2) \qquad \sigma'_v(B_1) \times \sigma'_v(B_2)$

or

$\quad (1)(1) \qquad\qquad\quad (-1)(-1) \qquad\qquad\quad (1)(-1) \qquad\qquad\quad (-1)(1)$

giving the result

$\qquad +1 \qquad\qquad\qquad +1/ \qquad\qquad\qquad\qquad -1 \qquad\qquad\qquad\quad -1$

The result $+1, +1, -1, -1$, is identical to the irreducible representation A_2; hence, $B_1 \times B_2 = A_2$. In subsequent chapters we shall have occasion to take the direct product of irreducible representations and this procedure will be employed.

Once the symmetry of a molecule is deduced, the appropriate character table can be consulted to describe many properties of the molecule. The asymmetric stretching vibration for the water molecule, belonging to the point group C_{2v}, will be selected as an example. The displacement of the atoms in the molecule can be indicated by arrows as in Fig. 4-16. The symmetry operations are performed on this molecule and if the result leaves the arrows in Fig. 4-16 pointing in the initial direction, the result

Fig. 4-16. Asymmetric Stretching Vibration of the Water Molecule

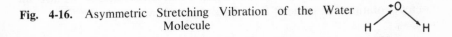

is -1. If the three arrows are pointing in the opposite direction, the result is -1. Performing the symmetry operations in the C_{2v} character table in the order listed produces in this case the irreducible representation $+1, -1, +1, -1$ which is the species B_1 and this notation is employed by infrared spectroscopists to label the vibration. Similarly it can be shown that the symmetric stretch transforms as species A_1.

The character table for the C_{3v} point group (Table 4-3) is more complex than the one for C_{2v}. One obvious difference between this and the previous character table is the number two in front of C_3 and three in front

TABLE 4-3. CHARACTER TABLE FOR THE C_{3v} POINT GROUP

C_{3v}	E	$2C_3$	$3\sigma_v$		
A_1	1	1	1	z	$x^2 + y^2,\ z^2$
A_2	1	1	-1	R_z	
E	2	-1	0	$(x,y)R_xR_y$	$(x^2 - y^2,\ xy)(xz,\ yz)$

of σ_v. The two refers to the fact that there are two C_3 rotations about a given axis which produce a result other than the identity for any molecule in this point group and these two rotations (i.e., rotation through $120°$ and $240°$) constitute a *class*. The three in $3\sigma_v$ indicates these three operations also constitute a class. The members which constitute a class can be determined in a simple way. All the operations of any one class can be converted into any other operation of the same class by a change of the reference coordinates while the figure remains fixed, e.g., on rotation of the coordinates 120°, σ_v becomes σ_v' and on rotation by another 120°, σ_v' becomes σ_v'' in the C_{3v} point group. For present purposes, a class can be treated as a unit and when we consider applications of the character table to spectroscopic problems proper account will be made of the number of elements in the class.

A second difference between the C_{3v} and C_{2v} character tables is the appearance of the symbol E in the species column of the C_{3v} character table. This indicates a doubly degenerate species. Consider the effect of the operation C_3 on a vector lying along the x axis. The result can no longer be represented by plus or minus one but must be described by a combination of x and y coordinates. The same result applies to the $\mathbf{Y}$ vector. A little trigonometry shows that when $\mathbf{X}$ becomes $\mathbf{X}'$ as a result of a C_3 rotation, the value of $\mathbf{X}'$ in the x–y coordinate system is:

$$\mathbf{X}' = \mathbf{X}\cos(2\pi/3) - \mathbf{Y}\sin(2\pi/3) + 0\,\mathbf{Z} = -(1/2)\mathbf{X} - (\sqrt{3}/2)\mathbf{Y}$$

while a similar operation on $\mathbf{Y}$ produces

$$\mathbf{Y}' = \mathbf{X}\sin(2\pi/3) + \mathbf{Y}\cos(2\pi/3) + 0\,\mathbf{Z} = (\sqrt{3}/2)\mathbf{X} - (1/2)\mathbf{Y}$$

The $\mathbf{Z}$ vector is not changed by this operation, so $\mathbf{Z}' = \mathbf{Z}$. Since $\mathbf{X}'$ and $\mathbf{Y}'$ are each functions of x and y, they are inseparable. The character of the C_3 transformation on $\mathbf{X}$ and $\mathbf{Y}$ is the sum of the coefficients of $\mathbf{X}$ in $\mathbf{X}'$ and $\mathbf{Y}$ in $\mathbf{Y}'$. From the above equations this is: $-\frac{1}{2} -\frac{1}{2} = -1$. In this point group the vectors $\mathbf{X}$ and $\mathbf{Y}$ are inseparable and doubly degenerate for together they form the irreducible representations: 2, -1, 0, under the symmetry operations of the C_{3v} point group. The species E can be thought of as two-dimensional in x and y. The vector $\mathbf{Z}$ transforms as species A_1. The identity produces the result 2 for the E species because the sum of the coefficients of $\mathbf{X}$ plus $\mathbf{Y}$ after this operation is two. For any number n in the identity column the species is n-fold degenerate.

Some character tables contain imaginary or complex characters. Whenever complex characters occur, they occur in pairs such that one is the complex conjugate of the other. Together the characters are real and as above the two-dimensional representation is not separable. In the T_d point group, two, triply degenerate species exist, T_1 and T_2, and each of these is constituted of x, y, and z.

It is informative to examine the character table for the T_d point group (Table 4-4) as a review of the above discussion. The symbols across the top represent the symmetry operations characteristic of a tetrahedral molecule. The symmetry operations $6S_4$ constitute a class, and the symbol represents the three alternating axes of the T_d point group (see discussion

TABLE 4-4. CHARACTER TABLE FOR THE T_d POINT GROUP

T_d	E	$6S_4$	$3C_2$	$8C_3$	$6\sigma_d$	
A_1	1	1	1	1	1	
A_2	1	−1	1	1	−1	
E	2	0	2	−1	0	
T_1	3	1	−1	0	−1	R_x, R_y, R_z
T_2	3	−1	−1	0	1	x, y, z

of CH_4 under the section on alternating axes) and the two operations for each axis (i.e., $6S_4$ includes $S_4^1, S_4^3, S_4'^1, S_4'^3, S_4''^1, S_4''^3$). Included in $3C_2$ are the three C_2 axes (recall these $3C_2$ axes are equivalent to $S_4^2, S_4'^2, S_4''^2$); $8C_3$ represents the four C_3 axes with two 120°, rotation operations for each (i.e., $C_3^1, C_3^2, C_3'^1, C_3'^2, C_3''^1, C_3''^2, C_3'''^1, C_3'''^2, C_3''''^1, C_3''''^2$); and $6\sigma_d$ represents the six diagonal planes of symmetry. All tetrahedral molecules possess these symmetry elements. Operations which are identical appear only once (e.g., of the identical operations S_4^2 and C_2 only C_2 is included in the character table). If certain properties (vibrations, etc.) of the tetrahedral molecule are not changed by any of the operations listed in Table 4-2, these properties belong to the species A_1. All the operations in a class need not be carried out because the result for one will be the same for all the elements in the class, e.g., the result for one S_4 is the same for all. Changes corresponding to the species A_2 are listed next. The operations corresponding to species E and T often produce a result which cannot be represented by the changes +1 or −1. The triply degenerate species T_2 is constituted of the vectors X, Y, and Z.

The symbols for the various irreducible representations (species) of the point groups are commonly used for many purposes, e.g., the labeling of vibrations, electronic transitions, and symmetries of molecular orbitals. The following conventions are used to label the irreducible representations. The character tables in the appendix should be referred to when necessary in this discussion.

(1) The symbol A indicates a singly degenerate state which is symmetric about the principal axis, i.e., the character table contains values of +1 under the column for the principal axis for all A species.

(2) The symbol B indicates a singly degenerate state which is antisymmetric about the principal axis; i.e., the value −1 appears under the column for the principal axis for all B species.

(3) The symbols E and T represent doubly and triply degenerate states, respectively. (F is often employed instead of T.)

(4) If the molecule has a center of symmetry (see the C_{2h}, D_{2h}, D_{4h}, and O_h character tables in the appendix) the subscript g is used to indicate symmetry ($+1$) with respect to this center while u indicates antisymmetry (-1).

(5) The subscripts 1 and 2 indicate symmetry or antisymmetry with respect to a rotation axis other than the principal axis. If there is no second axis the subscripts refer to the symmetry about a σ_v plane (e.g., in the C_{2v} group, 1 is symmetric about the xz plane and 2 is antisymmetric).

(6) Prime and double prime marks are employed to indicate symmetry and antisymmetry, respectively, relative to a σ_h plane of symmetry.

The minimum number of symbols beginning with (1) above and proceeding to (6) is used to label all the species in the character table.

Examples of the application of these rules can be obtained by referring to the character tables in Appendix B (the D_{2h} group is an exception). All A species in the D_{3h} group have values of $+1$ in the column for the principal axis, $2C_3$. The species A_1 are symmetric (i.e., have $+1$ values) to $3C_2$ and A_2 species are antisymmetric (-1) to these C_2 axes. The prime species are symmetric ($+$) to the horizontal plane σ_h while the double prime species are antisymmetric ($-$) to this plane. In D_{4h} all A species are symmetric. The u species are antisymmetric ($-$) to the center of symmetry, while the g species are symmetric ($+$). It should now be clear why the symmetric stretch in water is labeled A_1 and the asymmetric is B_1.

In subsequent chapters, applications of the character tables to spectroscopy will be discussed. These applications will give more meaning to the above operations and concepts.

SPACE SYMMETRY

In describing the symmetry of an arrangement of atoms in a crystal (essential to x-ray crystallography), two additional symmetry elements are required: (1) the glide plane and (2) the screw axis, corresponding to translation of a unit through space. A glide plane is illustrated in Fig. 4-17. The group (represented by a comma) is translated a fraction (in this case $\frac{1}{2}$) of a unit cell dimension and is reflected. (A unit cell is the smallest complete representation of the crystal.) The comma must lie in a plane perpendicular to the plane of the page and all of the comma tails must point into the paper.

A screw axis is illustrated in Fig. 4-18. Each position, as one proceeds from the top to the bottom of the axis, represents rotation by 120°. This is a threefold screw axis. Rotations by 90°, 60°, etc., are also possible in other structures. There are 230 possible space groups. These are of importance in x-ray crystallography, and will not be covered here.

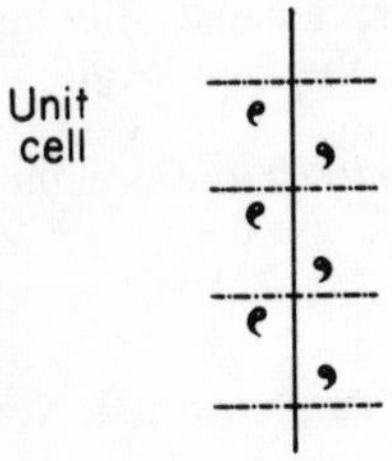

Unit cell

Fig. 4-17. A Glide Plane. (The tails of these commas point into the page.)

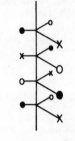

Fig. 4-18. A Screw Axis

EXERCISES

1. Classify the following molecules in the appropriate point groups.

   a. $CoCl_4^{2-}$.   Answer. T_d

   b. $Ni(CN)_4^{2-}$ Answer. D_{4h}

   c. *cis*-$CoCl_4(NH_3)_2^-$ (ignore the hydrogen atoms).   Answer. C_{2v}

   d. C_6H_{12} (chair form), (ignore the hydrogen atoms).   Answer. D_{3d}

   e. $Si(CH_3)_3 \cdot A \cdot B$ (with A and B *trans* in a trigonal bipyramid).   Answer. C_{3v}

   f. PF_3.   Answer. C_{3v}

   g. $(CH_3)_2B \overset{H}{\underset{H}{\diagup\diagdown}} B\ (CH_3)_2$ Answer. D_{2h}

   h. Cl-I-Cl$^-$.   Answer. $D_{\infty h}$

   i. planar *cis*-$PdCl_2B_2$. (B = base)   Answer. C_{2v}

   j. planar *trans*-$PdCl_2B_2$. (B = base)   Answer. D_{2h}

   k. staggered configuration for C_2H_6

   l. ferrocene.

2. a. How does a D_{2d} complex of formula MCl_4^{2-} differ from a T_d complex? (i.e., which symmetry elements differ?)

   b. What important symmetry element is absent in the PF_3 molecule that is present in the D_{3h} point group?

   c. If each Ni—C—N bond in $Ni(CN)_4^{2-}$ was not linear but was bent ($\underset{Ni}{\diagup}\overset{C}{\diagdown}N$) to what point group would this ion belong? What essential symmetry element present in D_{4h} is missing in C_{4h}?   Answer. C_{4h} and σ_h

   d. Indicate which operation is equivalent to the following products of the T_d point group.

     (1) $S_4 \times S_4 = ?$

     (2) $C_3 \times C_2 = ?$

     (3) $\sigma_d \times C_2 = ?$

3. Does $POCl_2Br$ possess a rotation-reflection axis coincident with the P—O bond axis?
4. a. Rotate the molecule in Fig. 4-13, 180° around the S_4 axis, and draw the resulting structure.
   b. Locate the mirror plane, of the S_4 operation and indicate on the structure resulting from part (a) where all the atoms are located after reflection through the plane. Use script letters to indicate the final location of each atom.
   c. Is the result of the operations in (b) equivalent to the initial structure in (a)?

REFERENCES CITED

1. G. Herzberg, "Infrared and Raman Spectra," p. 11, Van Nostrand, New York (1945).
2. F. A. Cotton, "Chemical Applications of Group Theory," p. 38, Wiley, New York (1963).

5 *General Introduction to Spectroscopy*

NATURE OF RADIATION

THERE are many apparently different forms of radiation, e.g., visible light, radio waves, infrared, x rays, and gamma rays. According to the wave model, all of these kinds of radiation may be described as oscillating electric and magnetic fields. Radiation, traveling in the z direction for example, consists of electric and magnetic fields mutually perpendicular to each other and to the z direction. These fields have been represented in Fig. 5-1 for plane-polarized radiation. Polarized radiation was selected

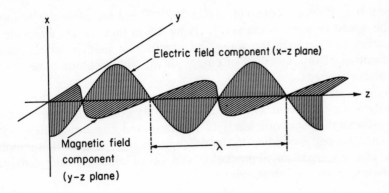

Fig. 5-1. Electric and Magnetic Field Components of Plane Polarized Electromagnetic Radiation

for simplicity of representation, since all other components of the electric field except those in the x–z plane have been filtered out. The wave travels in the z direction with the velocity of light, c (3×10^{10} cm sec^{-1}), and consists of waves with varying electric and magnetic field strengths as indicated by the amplitudes along the x and y axes. The wave length, λ, of the radiation is indicated in Fig. 5-1, and the variation in the magnitude of this quantity characterizes the apparently different forms of radiation listed above. If the radiation consists of only one wavelength it is said to be monochromatic. Polychromatic radiation can be separated into essentially monochromatic beams. For visible, UV or IR radiation, prisms or gratings are employed for this purpose.

Viewed in terms of the corpuscular model, radiation consists of energy packets called photons which travel with the velocity of light. The different forms of radiation have different energies.

In electronic and vibrational spectroscopy our concern will be with the interaction of the electric field component of radiation with the molecular system. This interaction results in the absorption of radiation by the molecule.

In order for absorption to occur, the energy of the radiation must match the energy difference between the quantized energy levels that correspond to different states of the molecule. If the energy difference between two of these states is represented by ΔE, the wavelength of the radiation, λ, necessary for matching is given by the equation:

$$\Delta E = \mathbf{h}c/\lambda \qquad \text{or} \qquad \lambda = \mathbf{h}c/\Delta E \qquad (5\text{-}1)$$

where $\mathbf{h}$ is Planck's constant, 6.623×10^{-27} erg sec molecule^{-1}, and c is the speed of light in cm sec^{-1}, giving ΔE in units of erg molecule^{-1}. Equation (5-1) relates the wave and corpuscular models for radiation. Absorption of one quantum of energy, $\mathbf{h}c/\lambda$, will raise one molecule to the higher energy state.

As indicated by equation (5-1), the different forms of electromagnetic radiation (i.e., different λ) differ in energy. By considering the energies corresponding to various kinds of radiation and comparing these with the energies corresponding to the different changes in state that a molecule can undergo, an appreciation can be obtained for the different kinds of spectroscopic methods.

ENERGIES CORRESPONDING TO VARIOUS KINDS OF RADIATION

Radiation can be characterized by its wavelength, λ, or its frequency, ν. The relationship between these two quantities is given by equation (5-2):

$$\nu\,(\text{sec}^{-1}) = c\,(\text{cm sec}^{-1})/\lambda\,(\text{cm}) \qquad (5\text{-}2)$$

and hence

$$E\,(\text{ergs molecule}^{-1}) = \mathbf{h}\nu = \mathbf{h}c/\lambda \qquad (5\text{-}3)$$

Wavelengths corresponding to various types of radiation are indicated in Fig. 5-2.

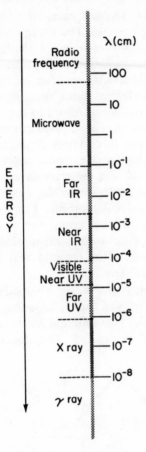

Fig. 5-2. Wavelengths of Various Types of Radiation

The small region of the total spectrum occupied by the visible portion is demonstrated by this figure. The higher energy radiation has the smaller wavelength and the larger frequency (equation 5-3). The following sequence represents decreasing energy:

ultraviolet > visible > infrared > microwave > radio-frequency

ENERGIES FOR ATOMIC AND MOLECULAR TRANSITIONS

In an atom, the change in state induced by the quantized absorption of radiation can be regarded as the excitation of an electron from one energy state to another. In most cases, the change in state is from the ground state to an excited state. The energy required for such excitation is in the range of 60 to 150 kcal mole^{-1}. Calculation* employing equation (5-3) readily shows that radiation in the ultraviolet and visible regions will be involved. Atomic spectra are often examined as emission spectra. Electrons are excited to higher states by thermal or electrical energy and the energy emitted as the atoms return to the ground state is measured.

In molecular spectroscopy, absorption of energy is usually measured. Our concern will be with three types of molecular transitions induced by electromagnetic radiation: electronic, vibrational, and rotational. A change in electronic state of a molecule occurs when a bonding or non-bonding electron of the molecule in the ground state is excited into a higher-energy empty molecular orbital. For example, an electron in a π-bonding orbital of a carbonyl group can be excited into a π^* orbital producing an excited state with configuration $\sigma^2\pi^1\pi^{*1}$. The electron distributions in the two states (ground and excited) involved in an electronic transition are different.

The vibrational energy states are characterized by the directions, frequencies, and amplitudes of the motions that the atoms in a molecule undergo. As an example, two different kinds of vibrations for the SO_2 molecule are illustrated in Fig. 5-3. The atoms in the molecule vibrate

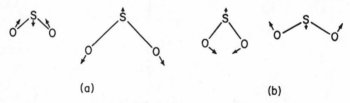

(a)   (b)

Fig. 5-3. Two Different Vibrations for the SO_2 Molecule

*Different units are employed to describe the wavelength (or frequency) in the various spectral regions. The frequency and wavelength are related by (5-2). Wave numbers, $\bar{\nu}$, are expressed in units of cm^{-1} and defined as: $\bar{\nu}$ (cm^{-1}) = $1/\lambda$ (cm). 1 cm = 10^8 Å = 10^4 μ (microns) = 10^7 mμ (millimicrons). To convert wavelength, λ, to wave numbers, $\bar{\nu}$, simply express λ in cm and take the reciprocal. The relationship between energy and wave number is given by:

1 cm^{-1} = 2.858 cal/Avogadro's number of particles = 1.986 × 10^{-16} erg/molecule

These conversion units can be employed or the equation: ΔE (kcal) × λ (Å) = 2.85 × 10^5 can be derived to simplify the calculation of energy from wavelength.

(relative to their center of gravity) in the directions indicated by the arrows, and the two extremes in the vibrational mode are indicated. In the vibration indicated in (a) the sulfur-oxygen bond length is varying, and this is referred to as the *stretching vibration*. In (b), the motion is perpendicular to the bond axis and the bond length is essentially constant. This is referred to as a *bending vibration*. In these vibrations, the net effect of all atomic motion is to preserve the center of gravity of the molecule so there will be no net translational motion. The vibrations indicated in Fig. 5-3 are drawn to satisfy this requirement. Certain vibrations in a molecule are referred to as *normal vibrations* or *normal modes*. These are independent, self-repeating displacements of the atoms which preserve the center of gravity. In a normal vibration, all the atoms vibrate in phase and with the same frequency. It is possible to resolve the most complex molecular vibration into a relatively small number of such normal modes. In Chapter 7, the procedure for calculating the total number of normal modes for different systems will be given. The motion in the different normal modes can be described by a set of *normal coordinates*. These coordinates are uniquely defined to describe most simply the normal vibration but often are complicated functions of angles and distance.

The rotational states correspond to quantized molecular rotation around an axis without any appreciable change in lengths or angles. Different rotational states correspond to different angular momenta of rotation or to rotations about different axes. Rotation about an axis in SO_2, which passes through the sulfur and is midway between the two oxygens, is an example of rotational motion.

In the treatment of molecular spectra, the Born–Oppenheimer approximation is invoked. This approximation proposes that the total energy of a system may be regarded as the sum of three independent energies: electronic, vibrational, and rotational. For example, the electronic energy of the system does not change as vibration of the nuclei occurs. The wave function for a given molecular state can then be described by the product of three independent wave functions: ψ_{el}, ψ_{vib}, and ψ_{rot}.

The relative energies of these different molecular energy states are represented in Fig. 5-4. Rotational energy states are more closely spaced than vibrational states which, in turn, have smaller energy differences than electronic states. The letters v_0, v_1, etc., and v_0', v_1', etc., represent the vibrational levels of one vibrational mode in the ground and first electronic excited states, respectively. *Ultraviolet or visible radiation is commonly required to excite the molecule into the excited electronic states. Lower-energy infrared suffices for vibrational transitions, while pure rotational transitions are observed in the still lower-energy micro-wave and radiofrequency regions.*

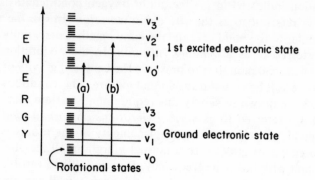

Fig. 5-4.   Energy States of a Diatomic Molecule

Electronic transitions are usually accompanied by changes in vibration and rotation. Two such transitions are indicated by arrows (a) and (b) of Fig. 5-4. In the vibrational spectrum, transitions to different rotational levels also occur. As a result *vibrational fine structure* is often detected in electronic transitions, and *rotational fine structure* is sometimes observed in vibrational transitions.

The energy level diagram in Fig. 5-4 is that for a diatomic molecule. For a polytomic molecule, the individual observed transitions can often be described by diagrams of this type, each representing an electronic transition for a different part of the molecule.

SELECTION RULES

In order for matter to absorb the electric field component of radiation, a requirement in addition to energy matching must be met. The energy transition in the molecule must be accompanied by a change in the elect-rical center of the molecule in order that electrical work can be done on the molecule by the electromagnetic radiation field. Only if this condition is satisfied can absorption occur. Requirements for the absorption of light by matter are summarized in the *selection rules*. Transitions which are possible according to these rules are referred to as *allowed* transitions and those not possible as *forbidden* transitions.

It should be noted, however, that the term "forbidden" refers to rules set up for a simple model and, while the model is a good one, "forbidden" transitions may occur by mechanisms not included in the simple model.

Since the intensity of absorption or emission accompanying a transition is related to the probability of the transition, the more probable transitions giving rise to more intense absorption, forbidden transitions (low probability) give absorptions of very low intensity. The specific selection rules and the less favorable mechanisms pertaining to the various types of spectroscopy will be discussed in the chapters devoted to each type.

GENERAL APPLICATIONS

The following general applications of spectroscopy are very elementary and pertain to both vibrational and electronic spectroscopic methods: (1) determination of concentration, (2) "finger-printing," and (3) determination of the number of species by the use of isosbestic points.

DETERMINATION OF CONCENTRATION

Measurement of the concentrations of species has several important applications. If measured at equilibrium, equilibrium constants can be determined. By evaluating the equilibrium constant at several temperatures, the enthalpy for the equilibrium reaction can be calculated from the van't Hoff equation:

$$\log K = -\Delta H^\circ/2.3RT + C \qquad (5\text{-}4)$$

Determination of the change in concentration of materials with time is the basis of kinetic studies which give information about reaction mechanisms. In view of the contribution of results from equilibrium and kinetic studies to our understanding of inorganic chemistry, the determination of concentrations by spectroscopic methods will be discussed.

The relationship between the amount of light absorbed by certain systems and the concentration of the absorbing species is expressed by the Beer–Lambert law:

$$A = \log_{10} I_0/I = \epsilon c b \qquad (5\text{-}5)$$

where A is the absorbance, I_0 is the intensity of the incident light, I is the intensity of the transmitted light, ϵ is the molar absorptivity (sometimes called extinction coefficient) at a given wavelength and temperature, c is the concentration (usually the molarity), and b is the length of the absorbing system. There are no exceptions to the relationship between absorbance and b (the Lambert law). For a given concentration of a certain substance, the absorbance is always directly proportional to the length of the cell. The part of equation (5-5) relating absorbance and concentration ($\log_{10} I_0/I = \epsilon c$, for a constant cell length) is referred to as Beer's law. Many systems have been found which do not obey Beer's law. The anomalies can be attributed to changes in the composition of the system with concentration (e.g., different degrees of ionization or dissociation of a solute at different concentrations). For all systems, the Beer's law relationship must be demonstrated, rather than assumed, over the entire concentration range to be considered. If Beer's law is obeyed, it becomes a simple matter to use equation (5-5) for the determination of the concentration of a known substance if it is the only material absorbing in a particular region of the spectrum. The Beer's law relationship is tested and ϵ determined by measuring the absorbance of several solutions of different known concentrations covering the range to be considered. For each solution, ϵ can be calculated from:

$$\epsilon = \frac{A\,(1\ \text{cm cell})}{c,\ \text{molarity}} \tag{5-6}$$

For a solution of this material of unknown concentration, the absorbance is measured, ϵ is known (5-6), and c is calculated from equation (5-5). There are some interesting variations on the application of Beer's law. If the absorption of two species should overlap, this overlap can be resolved mathematically and the concentrations determined. This is possible as long as the two ϵ values are not identical at all wavelengths.

First consider the case in which the ϵ values for two compounds whose spectra overlap can be measured for the pure compounds. The concentration of each component in a mixture of the two compounds can be obtained by measuring the absorbance at two different wavelengths, one where both compounds absorb strongly and a second where there is a large difference in the absorption. Both wavelengths should be selected at reasonably flat regions of the absorption curves of the pure compounds, if possible. Consider two such species B and C with wavelengths λ_1 and λ_2. There are molar absorptivities of $\epsilon_{B\lambda_1}$ for B at λ_1, $\epsilon_{B\lambda_2}$ for B at λ_2, and similar quantities $\epsilon_{C\lambda_1}$ and $\epsilon_{C\lambda_2}$ for C. The total absorbance of the mixture at λ_1 is A_1 and at λ_2 is A_2. It follows that:

$$A_1 = x\epsilon_{B\lambda_1} + y\epsilon_{C\lambda_1} \tag{5-7}$$
and
$$A_2 = x\epsilon_{B\lambda_2} + y\epsilon_{C\lambda_2} \tag{5-8}$$

where $x =$ molarity of B and $y =$ molarity of C. The two simultaneous equations (5-7) and (5-8) have only two unknowns, x and y, and can be solved.

In some instances a direct determination of ϵ is prevented by difficulties encountered in isolating the pure compound or by dissociation of a compound in solution. This problem is also easily resolved. For example, consider the equilibrium:

$$D + E \rightleftharpoons F \qquad K = \frac{[F]}{[D][E]} \qquad (5\text{-}9)$$

where F is the only absorbing species at a particular wavelength. Let $[D]_0$ be the initial concentration of D. This can be measured, as can $[E]_0$, the initial concentration of E. The molar absorptivity of F, ϵ_F, cannot be determined, but it is assumed that Beer's law is obeyed. It can be seen from a material balance that:

$$[D] = [D]_0 - [F] \qquad (5\text{-}10)$$
$$[E] = [E]_0 - [F] \qquad (5\text{-}11)$$

The absorbance, A, is related to $[F]$ by:

$$A = [F]\epsilon_F \qquad \text{or} \qquad [F] = A/\epsilon_F \qquad (5\text{-}12)$$

Substitution of (5-10) and (5-11) into (5-9) yields

$$K = \frac{[F]}{([D]_0 - [F])([E]_0 - [F])}$$

or

$$K^{-1} = \frac{([D]_0 - [F])([E]_0 - [F])}{[F]} \qquad (5\text{-}13)$$

Rearranging and substituting A/ϵ_F for $[F]$ (5-12), one obtains:

$$K^{-1} = -([D]_0 + [E]_0) + A/\epsilon_F + ([D]_0[E]_0)(\epsilon_F/A) \qquad (5\text{-}14)$$

All quantities can be measured directly except K^{-1} and ϵ_F. For two different sets of experimental conditions (different values of $[D]_0$ and $[E]_0$) two simultaneous equations can be solved, ϵ_F is eliminated, and K obtained. If several sets of experimental conditions are employed, all possible combinations of simultaneous equations can be considered by a graphical procedure.* For a given $[D]_0$ and $[E]_0$, K^{-1} is plotted as a function of ϵ_F by picking several values of ϵ_F and calculating the values for K^{-1} that correspond to each ϵ_F selected. These results are plotted as illustrated in Fig. 5-5. The procedure is repeated for other initial concentrations, e.g., $[D]_0'[E]_0'$, $[D]_0''[E]_0''$, etc. The intersection of the calculated curves should occur at a point whose value of K and ϵ_F satisfies all the experimental data. This common intersection justifies the Beer's law assumption used in the derivation because it indicates a unique value for ϵ for all concentrations. As a result of experimental error, a triangle usually results instead of a point. Equations have also been derived for systems in which the molar absorptivity of F cannot be measured directly and both D and E have absorptions which overlap that of F[1,2].

The above considerations are general and apply to any form of spectroscopy as long as the absorbance is linearly related to concentration (i.e., equation (5-6) is valid).

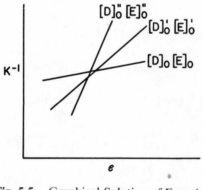

Fig. 5-5.   Graphical Solution of Equation
(5 − 14)

"FINGERPRINTING"

This technique is useful for the identification of an unknown compound which is suspected to be a known compound. The spectra are compared with respect to ϵ values, wavelengths of maximum absorption, and band shapes.

*In many systems $[E]_0$ is small compared to $[D]_0$ and A/ϵ is also small. When these terms are omitted, a linear equation is obtained for (5-14). This system can be treated by the Benesi–Hildebrand procedure: H. A. Benesi and J. H. Hildebrand, J. Am. Chem. Soc., **71**, 2703 (1949).

In addition to this direct comparison, certain functional groups have characteristic absorptions in various regions of the spectrum. For example, the carbonyl group will generally absorb at certain wavelengths in the ultraviolet and infrared spectra. Its presence in an unknown compound can be determined from these absorptions. Often one can even determine whether or not the carbonyl group is in a conjugated system. These details will be considered later when the spectroscopic methods are discussed individually.

Spectroscopic methods provide a convenient way of detecting certain impurities in a sample. For example, the presence of water in a system can easily be detected by its characteristic infrared absorption. Similarly a product can be tested for absence of starting material if the starting material has a functional group with a characteristic absorption that disappears in the reaction. Spectral procedures are speedier and less costly than elemental analyses. The presence of contaminants in small amounts can be detected if their molar absorptivities are large enough.

ISOSBESTIC POINTS

If two substances have absorption bands that overlap, there will be some wavelength at which the molar absorptivities of the two species are equal. If the sum of the concentrations of these two materials in solution is held constant, there will be no change in absorbance at this wavelength as the ratio of the two materials is varied. The invariant point obtained for this system is referred to as the isosbestic point. The existence of one or more isosbestic points in a system provides information regarding the number of species present. For example, the spectra in Fig. 5-6 were obtained[3] by keeping the total iron concentration constant in a system consisting of:

Curve 1	2·1 mole ratio of LiCl to $Fe(DMA)_6(ClO_4)_3$
Curve 2	2·6 mole ratio of LiCl to $Fe(DMA)_6(ClO_4)_3$
Curve 3	3·1 mole ratio of LiCl to $Fe(DMA)_6(ClO_4)_3$
Curve 4	4·1 mole ratio of LiCl to $Fe(DMA)_6(ClO_4)_3$

where DMA is the abbreviation for *N,N*-Dimethylacetamide. Points *A* and *B* are isosbestic points; their existence suggests that the absorption in this region is essentially accounted for by two species. Curve 4 is characteristic of $FeCl_4^-$. A study of solutions more dilute in chloride establishes the existence of a species $Fe(DMA)_4Cl_2^+$ which exists at a $2:1$ ratio of Cl^- to Fe^{III} and absorbs in this region. The isosbestic points indicate that the system can be described by the species $Fe(DMA)_4Cl_2^+$ and $FeCl_4^-$ over the region 2:1 to 4:1 Cl^- to Fe^{III}. The addition com-

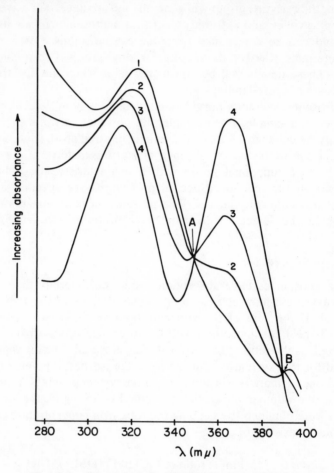

Fig. 5-6. Spectra of the $Fe(DMA)_4Cl_2^+$–LiCl System in N,N–Dimethylacetamide as Solvent

pound $FeCl_3 \cdot DMA$ probably does not exist in appreciable concentration in this system, i.e., at total Fe^{III} concentrations of $2 \times 10^{-4}M$. Curve 4 in this spectrum does not pass through the isosbestic point. Small deviations (e.g., curve 4 at point A) may be due to experimental inaccuracy, changes in solvent properties in different solutions, or a small concentration of a third species, probably $FeCl_3 \cdot DMA$, present in all systems except that represented by curve 4.

The conclusion that only two species are present in appreciable concentrations could be in error if $FeCl_3 \cdot DMA$ or other species were present which had identical molar absorptivities to the above two ions at the isosbestic points. If equilibrium constants for the following equilibrium

$$Fe(DMA)_4Cl_2^+ + 2Cl^- \rightleftharpoons FeCl_4^- + 4DMA$$

are calculated from these different curves at different wavelengths, the possibility of a third species is eliminated if the constants agree.

EXERCISES

1. A series of different molecular transitions require the following energies to occur. Indicate the spectral region in which you would expect absorption of radiation to occur and the wavelength of the radiation.
   a. 0·001 kcal.
   b. 100 kcal.
   c. 30 kcal.
2. Convert the wavelength units in part (a) of exercise (1) to wavenumbers (cm^{-1}).
3. Convert the following wavenumbers to μ and Å:
   a. $3600 \ cm^{-1}$.
   b. $1200 \ cm^{-1}$.
4. Convert $800 \ m\mu$ to cm^{-1}.
5. The ϵ value for compound X is 9000. A solution made up by adding 0·1 gram of X to a liter of water has an absorbance of 0·542. It is known that X reacts according to the equation:

$$X \rightleftharpoons Y + Z$$

   X obeys Beer's law and Y and Z do not absorb in this region. What is the equilibrium constant for this reaction?
6. For the equilibrium

$$A + B \rightleftharpoons C$$

   assume that the ϵ_B can be measured but ϵ_C cannot. Also assume that the absorption bands of B and C overlap and A does not absorb in this region. Derive an equation similar to (5-14) for this system.

REFERENCES CITED

1. R. S. Drago, R. L. Carlson, N. J. Rose, and D. A. Wenz, *J. Am. Chem. Soc.*, **83**, 3572 (1961).
2. M. Joesten and R. S. Drago, *J. Am. Chem. Soc.*, **84**, 2037 (1962).
3. R. L. Carlson, K. F. Purcell, and R. S. Drago, *Inorganic Chem.*, **4**, 15 (1965).

GENERAL REFERENCES

A. The following text is a most highly recommended beginning text on spectroscopy:

  G. M. Barrow, "Introduction to Molecular Spectroscopy," McGraw-Hill, New York, 1962.

B. The following reference sources are recommended for additional reading on the subject matter of this chapter:

  G. M. Barrow, "Physical Chemistry," Chap. 3, McGraw-Hill, New York, 1961.

  G. M. Barrow, "The Structure of Molecules," W. A. Benjamin, New York, 1963.

  J. C. D. Brand and J. C. Speakman, "Molecular Structure," E. Arnold, London, 1960.

  A. E. Gillam and E. S. Stern, "Electronic Absorption Spectroscopy," pp. 1–15, E. Arnold, London, 1957.

  G. Herzberg, "Infrared and Raman Spectra," pp. 13–19, 61–76, Van Nostrand, New York, 1945.

  W. West, "Chemical Applications of Spectroscopy" (vol. 9 of "Technique of Organic Chemistry, A. Weissberger, ed.), 1–70, Interscience, New York, 1956.

  P. J. Wheatley, "The Determination of Molecular Structure," Chap. 2, Oxford, London, 1959.

6 *Electronic Absorption Spectroscopy*

VIBRATIONAL AND ELECTRONIC ENERGY LEVELS IN A DIATOMIC MOLECULE

PRIOR TO a discussion of electronic absorption spectroscopy, the information summarized by a potential energy curve for a diatomic molecule (indicated in Fig. 6-1) will be reviewed. Fig. 6-1 is a plot of E, the total energy of the system, *versus r*, the internuclear distance, and is referred to as a Morse potential energy curve. The Morse potential is one of a number of empirical potentials which have been used to describe diatomic molecules.

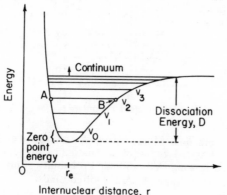

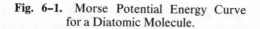
Internuclear distance, r

Fig. 6-1. Morse Potential Energy Curve for a Diatomic Molecule.

As the bond distance is varied in a given vibrational state, e.g., along A–B in the v_2 level, the molecule is in a constant vibrational energy level. At A and B we have, respectively, the minimum and maximum values for the bond distance in this vibrational level. At these points the atoms are changing direction so the vibrational kinetic energy is zero and the total vibrational energy of the system is potential. At r_e, the equilibrium internuclear distance, the vibrational kinetic energy is a maximum and the vibrational potential energy is zero. Each horizontal line represents a different vibrational energy state. The ground state is v_0 and excited states are represented as v_1, v_2, etc. Eventually, if enough energy can be absorbed in vibrational modes, the molecule is excited into the continuum and dissociates. For most compounds, nearly all the molecules are in the v_0 level at room temperature because the energy difference $v_1 - v_0$ is usually much larger than kT (thermal energy).

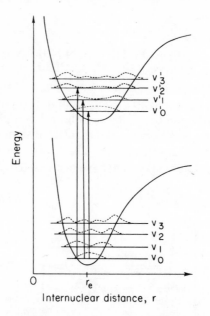

Fig. 6–2. Morse Curves for a Ground and Excited State of a Diatomic Molecule showing Vibrational Probability Functions, ψ_{vib}^2, as Dotted Lines.

Each excited electronic state also contains a series of different vibrational energy levels and may be represented by a potential energy curve. The ground electronic state and one of the many excited electronic states for a typical diatomic molecule are illustrated in Fig. 6-2. Each vibrational level, v_n, is described by a vibrational wave function, ψ_{vib}. For simplicity only four levels are indicated. As previously mentioned (Chapter 1), the square of a wave function gives the probability distribution and in this case ψ_{vib}^2 indicates probable internuclear distances for a particular vibrational state. This function, ψ_{vib}^2, is indicated for the various levels by the dotted lines in Fig. 6-2. The dotted line is not related to the energy axis. The higher this line, the more probable the corresponding internuclear distance. The most probable distance for a molecule in the ground state is r_e while there are two most probable distances corresponding to the two maxima in the next vibrational energy level of the ground electronic state, three in the third, etc.

INTRODUCTION TO ELECTRONIC TRANSITIONS

RELATIONSHIP OF POTENTIAL ENERGY CURVES TO ELECTRONIC SPECTRA

An understanding of electronic absorption spectroscopy requires consideration of three additional principles:

(1) In the very short time required for an electronic transition to take place (about 10^{-15} sec.), the atoms in a molecule do not have time to change position appreciably. This statement is referred to as the *Franck-Condon principle.** Since the electronic transition is rapid, the molecule will find itself with the same molecular configuration and vibrational kinetic energy in the excited state that it had in the ground state at the moment of absorption of the photon. As a result, all electronic transitions are indicated by a vertical line on the Morse potential energy diagram of the ground and excited states (see the arrows in Fig. 6-2), i.e., there is no change in internuclear distance during the transition.

(2) There is no general selection rule which restricts the change in vibrational state accompanying an electronic transition. Frequently transitions occur from the ground vibrational level of the ground electronic state to many different vibrational levels of a particular excited electronic state. Such transitions may give rise to vibrational fine structure in the main peak of the electronic transition.

The three transitions indicated by arrows in Fig. 6-2 could give rise to three peaks. Since nearly all of the molecules are present in the ground vibrational level, nearly all transitions that give rise to a peak in the absorption spectrum will arise from v_0.** Transitions from this ground level (v_0) to v_0', v_1' or   are referred to as $0 \rightarrow 0$, $0 \rightarrow 1$ or $0 \rightarrow 2$ transitions,

*This principle was originally proposed by Franck. It was given a quantum mechanical interpretation and extended by Condon.

**In the gas phase, various rotational levels in the ground vibrational state will be populated and transitions to various rotational levels in the excited state will occur, giving rise to fine structure in the spectrum. This fine structure is absent in solution because collision of the solute with a solvent molecule occurs before a rotation is completed. Rotational fine structure will not be discussed.

respectively. It can be shown[1] that the relative intensity of the various vibrational sub-bands depends upon the vibrational wave function for the various levels. A transition is favored if the probability of the ground and excited states of the molecule are both large for the same internuclear distance. Three such transitions are indicated by arrows in Fig. 6-2. The spectrum in Fig. 6-3 could result from a substance in solution undergoing the three transitions indicated in Fig. 6-2. The $0 \to 0$ transition is the lowest energy–longest wavelength transition. The differences in wavelength at which the peaks occur represent the energy differences of the vibrational levels in the excited state of the molecule. Much information about the structure and configuration of the excited state can be obtained from the fine structure.

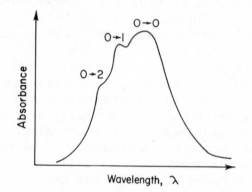

Fig. 6–3. Spectrum Corresponding to the Potential Energy Curves Indicated in Fig. 6–2.

Electronic transitions from bonding to antibonding molecular orbitals are often encountered. In this case the potential energy curve for the ground state will be quite different from that of the excited state because there is less bonding electron density in the excited state. As a result, the equilibrium internuclear distance will be greater and the potential energy curve will be broader for the excited state. Because of this displacement of the excited state potential energy curve, the $0 \to 0$ and transitions to other low vibrational levels may not be observed. A transition to a higher vibrational level becomes more probable. This can be visualized by broadening and displacing the excited state represented in Fig. 6-2.

(3) There is an additional *symmetry requirement* which was neglected for the sake of simplicity in the above discussion. It has been assumed

that this symmetry requirement is satisfied for the transitions involved in this discussion. This will be discussed subsequently in the section on selection rules.

The above discussion pertains to a diatomic molecule, but the general principles also apply to a polyatomic molecule. Often the functional group in a polyatomic molecule can be treated as a diatomic molecule (for example, $\ce{>C=O}$ in a ketone or aldehyde). The electronic transition may occur in the functional group between orbitals which are approximated by a combination of atomic orbitals of the two atoms as in a diatomic molecule. The actual energies of the resulting molecular orbitals of the functional group will, of course, be affected by electronic, conjugative, and steric effects arising from the other atoms. This situation can be understood qualitatively in terms of potential energy curves similar to those discussed for the diatomic molecules. For more complex cases in which several atoms in the molecule are involved (i.e., a delocalized system), a polydimensional surface is required to represent the potential energy curves.

NOMENCLATURE

In our previous discussion we were concerned only with transitions of an electron from a given ground state to a given excited state. In an actual molecule there are electrons in different kinds of orbitals (bonding, nonbonding, π bonding) with different energies in the ground state. Electrons from these different orbitals can be excited to higher-energy molecular orbitals, giving rise to many possible excited states. Thus many transitions from the ground state to different excited states (each of which can be described by a different potential energy curve) are possible in one molecule.

There are several conventions[2,3] used to designate these different electronic transitions. A simple representation introduced by Kasha[2] will be illustrated for the carbonyl group in formaldehyde. This group can be represented in molecular orbital terminology as (see Chapter 2):

$$\sigma^2, \ \pi^2, \ (n_a = n_b)^4, \ (\pi^*)^0, \ (\sigma^*)^0$$

where n_a and n_b are the two nonbonding molecular orbitals containing the lone pairs on oxygen. The relative energies of these orbitals are indicated in Fig. 6-4. The observed transitions are indicated by arrows (1), (2), (3), and (4) and are referred to as $n \rightarrow \pi^*$, $n \rightarrow \sigma^*$, $\pi \rightarrow \pi^*$, and $\sigma \rightarrow \sigma^*$, respectively. The $n \rightarrow \pi^*$ transition is the lowest energy–highest wavelength transition that occurs in formaldehyde and most carbonyl compounds.

Electron excitations can occur with or without a change in the spin of the electron. If the spin is not changed in a molecule containing no unpaired electrons, the excited state and ground state each have a multiplicity of one (see equation 1-20 for determining multiplicity), and these states are referred to as singlets. If the spin of the electron is changed in the transition, the excited state contains two unpaired electrons with identical spin quantum numbers, has a multiplicity of 3, and is referred to as a triplet state.

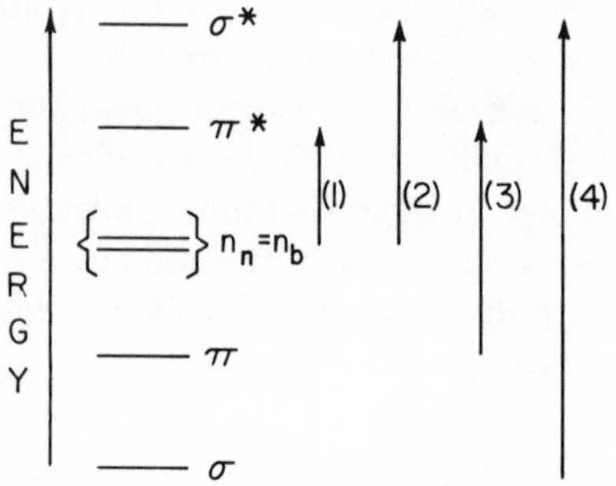

Fig. 6–4. Relative Energies of the Carbonyl Molecular Orbitals in H_2CO.

There are some shortcomings of this simple nomenclature for electronic transitions. It has been assumed that these transitions involve a simple transfer of an electron from the ground state level to an excited state level which is described by placing electrons in the empty molecular orbitals. For many applications this description is precise enough. In many molecules electron-electron interactions complicate the problem when a precise representation is required. Many more transitions are observed than predicted by this simple picture because levels that would otherwise be degenerate are split by electronic interactions. This same effect applied to atoms was discussed in Chapter 1 in the section on term symbols.

In a more accurate[4] system of nomenclature the symmetry, configuration, and multiplicity of the orbitals involved in the transition are utilized in describing the transition. This system of nomenclature can be briefly demonstrated by again considering the molecular orbitals of formaldehyde. The diagrams in Fig. 6-5 qualitatively represent the boundary contours of the molecular orbitals.* The solid line encloses the positive

---

*A discussion of the derivation of the wave functions for orbitals in various molecules is found in the Streitwieser text, Chapters 2-5. See General References.

lobe and the dashed line the negative lobe. The larger π and π^* lobes indicate lobes above the plane of the paper and the smaller ones below the plane. The two lobes actually have identical sizes. To classify these orbitals it is necessary first to determine the overall symmetry of the molecule (Chapter 4), which is C_{2v}. The next step is to consult the C_{2v} character table. Character tables for several common point groups are listed in the appendix. The C_{2v} character table is duplicated here in Table 6-1

TABLE 6-1. CHARACTER TABLE FOR THE C_{2v} POINT GROUP

	E	C_2	$\sigma_{v(xz)}$	σ_v'	
A_1	1	1	1	1	z
A_2	1	1	-1	-1	R_z
B_1	1	-1	1	-1	x, R_y
B_2	1	-1	-1	1	y, R_x

(see Chapter 4). The yz plane is selected to contain the four atoms of formaldehyde. The symmetry operations, E, C_2, $\sigma_{v(xz)}$, $\sigma_v'(yz)$, performed on the π orbital produce the result $+1, -1, +1, -1$. This result is identical to that listed for the species B_1 in the table. The orbital is said to belong to (or to transform as) the symmetry species b_1, the lower case letter being employed for an orbital and the upper case letters being reserved to describe the symmetry of the entire ground or excited state. Similarly, if the n, π^*, σ, and σ^* orbitals of formaldehyde are subjected to the above symmetry operations it can be shown that these orbitals belong to the

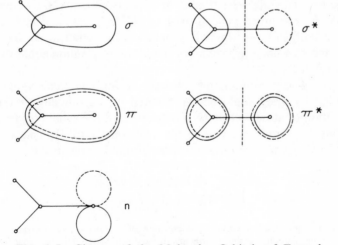

Fig. 6-5. Shapes of the Molecular Orbitals of Formaldehyde.

species b_2, b_1, a_1, and a_1, respectively (the two n orbitals are sp^2 hybrids lying in the yz plane and the p_y contribution to the linear combinations gives b_2 symmetry).

The symmetry species of a state is the product of the symmetry species of each of the electrons. In the state that results from the $n \rightarrow \pi^*$ transition in formaldehyde, there is one unpaired electron in the n orbital with b_2 symmetry and one in the π^* orbital with b_1 symmetry. The row of b_1 is multiplied by the corresponding row of b_2 as follows:

	E	C_2	$\sigma_{v(xz)}$	$\sigma_v'(yz)$	
$b_1 \times b_2 =$	(1)(1)	(−1)(−1)	(1)(−1)	(−1)(+1)	
result $=$	+1	+1	−1	−1	$= A_2$

This is referred to as a *direct product multiplication*. The resulting irreducible representation is of species A_2.* The excited state from this transition is thus described as A_2 and the transition as $A_1 \rightarrow A_2$. A common convention involves writing the high energy state first and labeling the transition $A_2 \leftarrow A_1$. The state multiplicity is usually included so the complete designation becomes $^1A_2 \leftarrow {}^1A_1$. The ground state is A_1 because there are pairs of electrons in each orbital and any orbital symmetry multiplied by itself becomes A_1. Commonly, the orbitals involved in the transitions are indicated and the symbol becomes $^1A_2(n,\pi^*) \leftarrow {}^1A_1$. If the state symmetry species (e.g., A_2 above) is not known, the general term symbol Γ is employed.

If the excited state were doubly or triply degenerate, the symbol E or T would be employed instead of A or B. As mentioned in Chapter 4, A and B both indicate singly degenerate states differing in that A does not change sign under a symmetry operation of rotation about the n-fold axis, but B does.

Instead of representing the orbitals of formaldehyde symbolically, as in Fig. 6-5, they could be represented mathematically by the linear combination of atomic orbitals. We can deduce the symmetry from these equations by simply converting the equations into a physical picture. The following equations describe the formaldehyde π and π^* orbitals:

$$\psi_\pi = N(a\varphi_{pO} + b\varphi_{pC})$$

$$\psi_\pi^* = N(b\varphi_{pO} - a\varphi_{pC})$$

---

*The actual procedure involves multiplication of the orbital symmetries for all the electrons in the carbonyl group. However, all filled orbitals contain two electrons whose product must be A_1, since any symmetry species multiplied by itself is A_1, e.g., $b_1 \times b_1 = A_1$. Thus these electrons have no effect on the final result for the excited state symmetry.

Lettering Sequence for A.O.'s

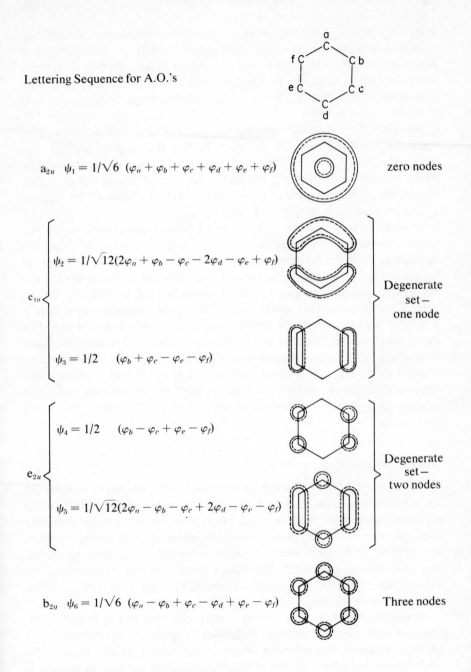

a_{2u} $\psi_1 = 1/\sqrt{6} \ (\varphi_a + \varphi_b + \varphi_c + \varphi_d + \varphi_e + \varphi_f)$ zero nodes

e_{1g}
$\psi_2 = 1/\sqrt{12}(2\varphi_a + \varphi_b - \varphi_c - 2\varphi_d - \varphi_e + \varphi_f)$

$\psi_3 = 1/2 \quad (\varphi_b + \varphi_c - \varphi_e - \varphi_f)$

Degenerate set — one node

e_{2u}
$\psi_4 = 1/2 \quad (\varphi_b - \varphi_c + \varphi_e - \varphi_f)$

$\psi_5 = 1/\sqrt{12}(2\varphi_a - \varphi_b - \varphi_c + 2\varphi_d - \varphi_e - \varphi_f)$

Degenerate set — two nodes

b_{2g} $\psi_6 = 1/\sqrt{6} \ (\varphi_a - \varphi_b + \varphi_c - \varphi_d + \varphi_e - \varphi_f)$ Three nodes

Fig. 6–6.   Shapes of the Benzene Molecular Orbitals.

143

where $\varphi_{p}0$ and $\varphi_{p}C$ are the wave functions for the atomic oxygen and carbon p orbitals, respectively. The atomic orbitals are combined to produce mathematically the π and π^* orbitals as described in Chapter 2. Since oxygen is more electromagnetic and $a > b$, it becomes clear why it is often stated that an electron is transferred from oxygen to carbon in the $\pi \rightarrow \pi^*$ transition.

Some of the molecular orbitals for benzene are represented mathematically and pictorially in Fig. 6-6. Notice that a difference in sign between adjacent atomic orbitals of the wave function represents a node (point of zero probability) in the molecular orbital. Using the D_{6h} character table, the symmetries of the orbitals can be shown to be a_{1u}, e_{1g}, e_{2u}, and b_{2g}, for ψ_1, $\psi_2 - \psi_3$, $\psi_4 - \psi_5$, and ψ_6, respectively.

In addition to the above description of ground and excited states one more convention, that used for molecules with symmetry $D_{\infty h}$, will be described. With this terminology the electronic arrangement is indicated by summing up the contributions of the separate atoms to obtain the net orbital angular momentum. If all electrons are paired, the sum is zero. Contributions are counted as follows: one unpaired electron in a σ orbital is zero, one in a π orbital one, and one in a δ orbital two. For more than one electron, the total is $|\Sigma m_l|$. If the total is zero, the state is described as Σ, one as π, and two as Δ. The multiplicity is indicated by a superscript, e.g., the ground state of NO is $^2\pi$. A plus or minus sign often follows the symbol to illustrate, respectively, whether the molecular orbitals are symmetric or antisymmetric to a plane through the molecular axis.

ASSIGNMENT OF TRANSITIONS

If the energies of the molecular orbitals in all molecules could be set up unambiguously (as in Fig. 6-4), the assignment of transitions to the observed bands would be simplified. The $n \rightarrow \pi^*$ would be lower in energy than the $\pi \rightarrow \pi^*$ which in turn would be lower in energy than $\sigma \rightarrow \pi^*$. In addition to different electron-electron repulsions in different states, two other effects complicate the picture by affecting the energies and the degeneracy of the various states. These effects are spin-orbit coupling and higher state mixing.

SPIN-ORBIT COUPLING. There is a magnetic interaction between the electron spin magnetic moment (signified by quantum number $m_s = \pm\frac{1}{2}$) and the magnetic moment due to the orbital motion of an electron. To understand the nature of this effect, consider the nucleus as though it were moving about the electron (this is equivalent to being on earth and thinking of the sun moving across the sky). We consider the motion from this reference point because we are interested in effects at the electron. The charged nucleus circles 'the electron and this is equivalent in effect to placing the electron in the middle of a coil of wire carrying currrent. As moving charge in a solenoid creates a magnetic field in the center, the orbital motion described above causes a magnetic field at the electron position. This magnetic field can interact with the spin magnetic moment of the electron giving rise to spin-orbit interaction. The orbital moment may either complement or oppose the spin moment, giving rise to two different energy states. A splitting of the doubly degenerate energy state of the electron (previously designated by the spin quantum numbers $\pm \frac{1}{2}$) has occurred, lowering the energy of one and raising the energy of the other. Whenever an electron can occupy a set of degenerate orbitals which permit circulation about the nucleus, this interaction is possible. For example, if an electron can occupy the d_{yz} and d_{xz} orbitals of a metal ion, it can circle the nucleus around the z axis. This effect is discussed in more detail in Appendix A.

HIGHER STATE MIXING. We have just discussed the symmetry of various excited states in a molecule. If in the orbital energy scheme predicted from simple considerations, a high energy orbital has the same symmetry as a lower energy orbital, accurate wave functions for each of these orbitals may include contributions from both simple model orbitals. In this case we say there is *higher state mixing*. The lower energy orbital will be lower in energy than that predicted by the simple model, and transitions involving this orbital will be at different energies from those predicted by the simple model. This mixing is similar to the interaction of atomic orbitals to form a bond or to the resonance phenomenon. In the section on the valence bond (Chapter 2) it was shown that a linear combination of wave functions produced a lower energy than any of the individual wave functions. Similarly, in the case of higher state mixing:

$$\psi^0 = a\psi_1 \pm b\psi_2$$

where ψ^0 is the more accurate wave function, ψ_1 is the wave function for the simple model ground state, and ψ_2 the simple model excited state. This is a typical quantum mechanical resonance.

An appreciation for some of the difficulties encountered in assigning transitions can be obtained from reading the literature.[5] As mentioned above it is adequate for many purposes to employ the $n \rightarrow \pi^*$ and $\pi \rightarrow \pi^*$ designation for electronic transitions. However, one should appreciate the possible complexity of the excited state. The following phenomena are characteristic[4] of an $n \rightarrow \pi^*$ transition and can be used to aid in making this assignment.

(1) The *molar absorptivity* of the transition is generally less than 2000. An explanation for this is offered in the section on intensity.

(2) A *blue shift* (hypsochromic shift, or shift toward shorter wave lengths) is observed for this transition in high dielectric or hydrogen-bonding solvents. This indicates that the energy difference between the ground and excited state is increased in a high dielectric or hydrogen-bonding solvent. In general, for solvent shifts it is often difficult to ascertain whether the excited state is raised in energy or the ground state lowered. The shift may also result from a greater lowering of the ground state relative to the excited state or a greater elevation of the excited state relative to the ground state. It is thought that the solvent shift in the $n \rightarrow \pi^*$ transition results from a lowering of the energy of the ground state and an elevation of the energy of the excited state. In a high dielectric solvent the molecules arrange themselves about the absorbing solute so that the dipoles are properly oriented for maximum interaction (i.e., solvation which lowers the energy of the ground state). When the excited state is produced, its dipole will have a different orientation from the ground state. Since solvent molecules cannot rearrange to solvate the excited state during the time of a transition, the excited state energy is raised in a high dielectric solvent.[6]

Hydrogen bonding solvents cause pronounced blue shifts. This is reported to be due to hydrogen bonding of the solvent hydrogen with the lone pair of electrons in the n orbital undergoing the transition. In the excited state there is only one electron in the n orbital, the hydrogen bond is weaker and, as a result the solvent does not lower the energy of this state nearly as much as that of the ground state. In these hydrogen-bonding systems an adduct is formed, and this specific solute-solvent interaction is the main cause of the blue shift.[7] If there is more than one lone pair of electrons on the donor, the shift can be accounted for by the inductive effect of hydrogen bonding.

(3) The $n \rightarrow \pi^*$ band often disappears in acidic media due to protonation or upon formation of an adduct that ties up the lone pair, e.g., $BCH_3^+I^-$ (as in $C_5H_5NCH_3^+I^-$ where B is the base molecule containing the n electrons). This behavior is very characteristic if there is only one pair of n electrons on B.

(4) Blue shifts occur upon the attachment of an electron-donating group to the chromophore (i.e., the series $CH_3C \overset{\displaystyle O}{=\!\!\!-} H$, $CH_3C \overset{\displaystyle O}{=\!\!\!-} CH_3$ $CH_3C \overset{\displaystyle O}{=\!\!\!-} OCH_3$ and $CH_3C \overset{\displaystyle O}{=\!\!\!-} N(CH_3)_2$). A molecular orbital treatment[8]

indicates this shift results from a raising of the excited π^* level relative to the n level.

(5) The absorption band corresponding to the $n \rightarrow \pi^*$ transition is absent in the hydrocarbon analogue of the compound.   This would involve, for example, comparison of the spectra of benzene and pyridine or of $H_2C{=}O$ and $H_2C{=}CH_2$.

(6) Usually, but not always, the $n \rightarrow \pi^*$ transition gives rise to the lowest energy singlet-singlet transition.

In contrast to the above behavior, $\pi \rightarrow \pi^*$ transitions have a high intensity. A slight red (bathochromatic) shift is observed in high dielectric solvents and upon introduction of an electron-donating group. It should be emphasized that in the above systems only the difference in energy between the ground and excited states can be measured from the frequency of the transition, so only the relative energies of the two levels can be measured. Other considerations must be invoked to determine the actual change in energy of an individual state.

OSCILLATOR STRENGTHS

A convenient parameter for expressing the intensity of an absorption band is the oscillator strength or f number.

$$f = 4.315 \times 10^{-9} \int \epsilon d\bar{\nu} \qquad (6\text{-}3)$$

where ϵ is the molar absorptivity and $\bar{\nu}$ is the frequency expressed in wave numbers. The concept of oscillator strength is based on a simple classical model for an electronic transition. The derivation* indicates that $f = 1$ for an allowed transition. The quantity f is evaluated graphically from equation (6-3) by plotting ϵ versus the wavenumber $\bar{\nu}$ in cm^{-1} and calculating the area of the band. Values of f from 0.1 to 1 correspond to molar absorptivities in the range 10,000 to 100,000, depending on the width of the peak.

For a single, symmetrical peak, f can be approximated by the expression:

$$f \approx (4.6 \times 10^{-9}) \epsilon_{max} \Delta\nu_{1/2} \qquad (6\text{-}4)$$

where ϵ_{max} is the molar absorptivity of the peak maximum and $\Delta\nu_{1/2}$ is the half intensity band width, i.e., the width at $\frac{1}{2}\epsilon_{max}$.

*For this derivation, see General References, Barrow, pages 80 and 81.

INTENSITY OF ELECTRONIC TRANSITIONS

The following selection rules are pertinent to electronic absorption spectroscopy:

(1) *Transitions between states of different multiplicity are multiplicity forbidden*, i.e., electronic transitions in which the spin of an electron changes are forbidden.

(2) *In a molecule which has a center of symmetry, transitions between two gerade or two ungerade states (i.e., $g \rightarrow g$ or $u \rightarrow u$) are Laporte forbidden. The allowed transitions are $g \rightarrow u$ and $u \rightarrow g$.* As a result of this rule, *d-d* transitions in octahedral complexes are Laporte forbidden. Mechanisms for the breakdown of this selection rule are discussed later. In general, transitions which occur without a change in the *l* value of the orbital are forbidden.

(3) *Simultaneous excitation of more than one electron is forbidden.*

The integrated intensity, *I*, of an absorption band for a transition between states *a* and *b* depends on the following relation:

$$I \propto \left| \int_{-\infty}^{\infty} \psi^*_b M \psi_a dv \right|^2 \tag{6-5}$$

The integral in equation (6-5) is called the *transition-moment integral*; ψ^*_b and ψ_a are the wave functions for the excited state and for the ground state, *M* is the electric dipole-moment operator, and *dv* is a volume element. The operator *M* is related to the difference in the electronic dipole moments of the ground and excited state. This difference in electronic dipole moment arises because of a different electron distribution in the two states and can be thought of as representing charge migration during the transition. When the transition moment integral becomes zero, the transition is forbidden.

It is often possible to tell from the symmetry properties of a system whether or not the transition moment integral will vanish. Such considerations lead to the selection rules stated at the beginning of this section. The quantity *M* can be treated as a vector quantity and can be resolved into *x*, *y*, and *z* components. The integral in equation (6-5) has the components:

$$\int \psi^*_b M_x \psi_a \, dv \tag{6-6}$$

$$\int \psi^*_b M_y \psi_a \, dv \tag{6-7}$$

$$\int \psi^*_b M_z \psi_a \, dv \tag{6-8}$$

In order to have an allowed transition at least one of these integrals must be nonzero. An integral can be nonzero only if the integrand belongs to the symmetry species A_1. The product of $\psi_b^* M_x \psi_a$ or one of the other two integrands must be A_1 for an allowed transition. The mechanics of this operation can best be described by an example. Consider the $\pi \to \pi^*$ transition in formaldehyde. The ground state, like all ground states containing no unpaired electrons, is A_1. The excited state is also A_1 ($b_1 \times b_1 = A_1$). The symmetry of the dipole moment vector components M_x, M_y, and M_z for a C_{2v} molecule is indicated in the C_{2v} character table (Table 6-1) by x, y, and z. These results can be verified by performing the operations E, C_2, σ_v and σ_v' on the x, y, and z dipole moment vectors (i.e., arrows along the x, y, and z axes). The table indicates M_z, the dipole moment vector lying along the z-axis, is A_1. Since $A_1 \times A_1 \times A_1 = A_1$, the integrand $\psi_b^* M_z \psi_a$ is A_1, and the $\pi \to \pi^*$ transition is allowed.

For an $n \to \pi^*$ transition, the ground state is A_1 and the excited state A_2. The character table indicates that no dipole moment component has symmetry A_2. Therefore none of the three integrals (equations 6-6 to 6-8) can be A_1, and the transition is forbidden ($A_2 \times A_2$ is the only product of A_2 that is A_1).

Selection rule (2), stated at the beginning of this section, follows from equation (6-5). It should be emphasized that selection rule (2) and this discussion apply to molecules or ions with a center of symmetry. In order that the value of the integral in equation (6-5) not vanish, the integrand must be gerade. Secondly, the product of two functions is ungerade only if one is gerade and the other ungerade. Thirdly, all components of the vector M are ungerade. Therefore, the integrand $\psi_a M \psi_b^*$ can be gerade only if the ground or excited state wave function is ungerade and the other gerade, i.e., $g \to u$ or $u \to g$ transitions are allowed. The other selection rules can also be derived[1] from equation (6-5).

Equation (6-5) can be expanded to include the vibrational wave function for the ground and excited states:

$$\int \psi_{el}^a M \psi_{el}^b \, dv \int \psi_{vib}^a \psi_{vib}^b \, dv$$

The earlier qualitative discussion of Fig. 6-2 can be more completely stated in terms of these integrals. When the ground state (ψ_{vib}^a) and excited state (ψ_{vib}^b) vibrational wave functions are both appreciable and of the proper symmetry, the total integral will be nonzero and the transition will be allowed.

The discrepancy between the theoretical prediction that a transition is forbidden and the experimental detection of a weak band assignable to this transition is attributable to the approximations of the theory. More refined calculations which include effects from spin-orbit coupling often predict low intensities for otherwise forbidden transitions. For example, a transition between a pure singlet state and a pure triplet state is forbidden. However, if spin-orbit coupling is present, the singlet could have the same total angular momentum as the triplet and the two states could interact. The interaction is indicated by equation (6-9):

$$\psi = a\,{}^1\psi + b\,{}^3\psi \qquad (6\text{-}9)$$

where ${}^1\psi$ and ${}^3\psi$ correspond to pure singlet and triplet states, respectively, ψ to the actual ground state, and a and b are coefficients indicating the relative contribution of the pure states. If $a \gg b$, the ground state is essentially singlet with a slight amount of triplet character and the excited state will be essentially triplet. This slight amount of singlet character in the predominantly triplet excited state leads to an intensity integral for the singlet-triplet transition which is not zero and explains why a weak peak corresponding to a multiplicity-forbidden transition can occur.

POLARIZED ABSORPTION SPECTRA

If the incident radiation employed in an absorption experiment is polarized, only those transitions with similarly oriented dipole moment vectors will occur. In a powder, the molecules or complex ions are randomly oriented. All allowed transitions will be observed, for there will be a statistical distribution of crystals with dipole moment vectors aligned with the polarized radiation. However, suppose, for example, a formaldehyde crystal, with all molecules arranged so that their z axes are parallel, is examined. As indicated in the previous section, the integrand $\psi^* M_z \psi$ has appropriate symmetry for the ${}^1A_{(\pi,\pi*)} \leftarrow {}^1A$ transition, but $\psi^* M_x \psi$ and $\psi^* M_y \psi$ do not. When the z axes of the molecules in the crystal are aligned parallel to light which has its electric vector polarized in the z direction, light will be absorbed for the ${}^1A_{(\pi,\pi*)} \leftarrow {}^1A$ transition. Light of this wavelength polarized in other planes will not be absorbed. If this crystal is rotated so that the z axis is perpendicular to the plane of polarization of the light, no light is absorbed. This behavior supports the assignment of this band to the transition ${}^1A_1 \leftarrow {}^1A_1$.

To determine the expected polarization of any band, the symmetry species of the product $\psi_a \psi_b$ is compared with the components of M, as was done above for formaldehyde.

Charge Transfer Transitions

A transition in which an electron is transferred from one atom or group in the molecule to another is called a *charge-transfer* transition. More accurately stated, the transition occurs between molecular orbitals which are essentially centered on different atoms. Very intense bands result with molar absorptivities of 10^4 or greater. The frequency at maximum absorbancy, ν_{max}, often, but not always, occurs in the ultraviolet region. The anions ClO_4^- and SO_4^{2-} show very intense bands. Since MnO_4^- and CrO_4^{2-} have no d electrons, the intense colors of these ions cannot be explained on the basis of d–d transitions; they are attributed to charge transfer transitions.[9] The transitions in MnO_4^- and CrO_4^{2-} are most simply visualized as an electron transfer from a nonbonding orbital of an oxygen atom to the manganese or chromium ($n \rightarrow \pi^*$), in effect reducing these metals in the excited state.[10] An alternate assignment for this transition involves excitation of an electron in a π bonding molecular orbital, consisting essentially of oxygen atomic orbitals, to a molecular orbital which is essentially the metal atomic orbital.

In the case of a pyridine complex of iridium(III), a charge transfer transition which involves oxidation of the metal has been reported.[11] A metal electron is transferred from an orbital which is essentially an iridium atomic orbital to an empty π^* antibonding orbital in pyridine.

In gaseous sodium chloride, a charge transfer absorption occurs from the ion pair Na^+Cl^- to an excited state described as sodium and chlorine atoms with the same internuclear distance as the ion pair. A charge transfer absorption occurs in the ion pair, N-methylpyridinium iodide[36] (see Fig. 6-9). This transition involves an electron transition from I^- to a ring antibonding orbital. The excited state is represented in Fig. 6-9. A very intense charge transfer absorption is observed in addition compounds formed between iodine and several Lewis bases. This phenomenon will be discussed in more detail in a later section.

APPLICATIONS

Most applications of electronic spectroscopy have been made in the wavelength range from 2100 to 7500 Å, for this is the range accessible with most recording spectrophotometers. Relatively inexpensive commercial instruments can now be obtained to cover the range 1900 to 8000 Å. The near infrared region, from 8000 to 25,000 Å, has also provided much useful information. Spectra can be examined through the 1900 to 25,000 Å region on samples of vapors, pure liquids, or solutions. Solids can be examined as single crystals or as discs formed by mixing the material with KCl or NaCl and pressing with a hydraulic press until a clear disk is formed.[12] Spectra of powdered solids can also be examined over a more limited region (4000 to 25,000 Å) as reflectance spectra or on mulls of the solid compounds.[12]

FINGERPRINTING

Since many different substances have very similar ultraviolet and visible spectra, this is a poor region for product identification by the "fingerprinting" technique. Information obtained from this region should be used in conjunction with other evidence to confirm the identity of the compound. Evidence for the presence of functional groups can be obtained by comparison of the spectra with reported data. For this purpose, v_{max}, ϵ_{max}, and band shapes can be employed. It is also important that the spectra be examined in a variety of solvents to be sure the band shifts are in accord with expectations (see discussion of blue shifts).

Spectral data have been compiled in Lang,[13] Hershenson,[14] "Organic Electronic Spectral Data,"[15] and in data available from ASTM.[16] A review article by Mason[17] and the text by Jaffe and Orchin[1] are excellent for this type of application. If a functional group (chromophore) is involved in conjugation or steric interactions, or is attached to electron-releasing groups, its spectral properties are often different from those of an isolated functional group. These differences can often be predicted semiquantitatively for molecules in which such effects are expected to exist.[17]

The spectra of some representative compounds and examples of the effect of substituents on the wavelength of a transition will be described briefly.

SATURATED MOLECULES. Saturated molecules without lone pair electrons undergo high energy $\sigma \rightarrow \sigma^*$ transitions in the far ultraviolet. For example, methane has a maximum at 1219 Å and ethane at 1350 Å corresponding to this transition. When lone pair electrons are available, a lower energy $n \rightarrow \sigma^*$ transition is often detected in addition to the $\sigma \rightarrow \sigma^*$. For example, in triethylamine two transitions are observed, at 2273 and 1990 Å.

Table 6-2 contains a listing of absorption maxima for some saturated compounds and gives some indication of the variation in the range and intensity of transitions in saturated molecules.

CARBONYL AND THIOCARBONYL COMPOUNDS. There is a considerable amount of literature available on carbonyl compounds.[17] The effects of substituent, conjugation, steric effects, and solvent effects on the various transitions are reported. Absorptions near 4000 Å ($\epsilon_{max}\sim 10^{-3}$) and 2900 Å ($\epsilon_{max} \sim 10$) are assigned to the triplet and singlet $n \rightarrow \pi^*$ transitions, respectively. (Both of these transitions are $n \rightarrow \pi^*$, but the spin of the electron changes in the triplet transition.) An $n \rightarrow \sigma^*$ transition occurs in the region of 1800 Å and the $\pi \rightarrow \pi^*$ occurs at shorter wavelengths. The latter two bands are the most intense, sometimes having molar absorptivities as high as 20,000 to 30,000.

TABLE 6-2. FREQUENCIES OF ELECTRONIC TRANSITIONS
IN SOME SATURATED MOLECULES

Compound	λ_{max}Å	ϵ_{max}	Medium
H_2O	1667	1480	vapor
MeOH	1835	150	vapor
Me_2O	1838	2520	vapor
Me_2S	2290, 2100	140, 1020	ethanol
S_8	2750	8000	ethanol
F_2	2845	6	vapor
Cl_2	3300	66	vapor
Br_2	4200	200	vapor
I_2	5200	950	vapor
ICl	~4600	153	CCl_4
SCl_2	3040	1150	CCL_4
PI_3	3600	8800	Et_2O
AsI_3	3780	1600	pet. ether

Upon conjugation of the carbonyl group with a vinyl group, four π energy levels are formed. The highest occupied π level has a higher energy and one of the lowest empty π^* levels has a lower energy than the corresponding levels in a nonconjugated carbonyl group. The lone pair and σ electrons are relatively unaffected by conjugation. As a result, the $\pi \rightarrow \pi^*$ and $n \rightarrow \pi^*$ transition energies are lowered and the absorption maxima are shifted to longer wavelengths when the carbonyl is conjugated. The difference is greater for the $\pi \rightarrow \pi^*$ than for the $n \rightarrow \pi^*$ transition. The $n \rightarrow \sigma^*$ band is not affected appreciably and often lies beneath the shifted $\pi \rightarrow \pi^*$ absorption band. As stated earlier, electron-donating groups attached to the carbonyl cause a blue shift in the $n \rightarrow \pi^*$ transition and a red shift in $\pi \rightarrow \pi^*$.

It is of interest to compare the spectra of thiocarbonyl compounds with those of carbonyl compounds. In the sulfur compounds, the carbon-sulfur π interaction is weaker and, as a result, the energy difference between the π and π^* orbitals is smaller than in the oxygen compounds. In addition, the ionization potential of the sulfur electrons in the thiocarbonyl group is less than the ionization potential of oxygen electrons in a carbonyl. The n electrons are of higher energy in the thiocarbonyl and the $n \to \pi^*$ transition requires less energy in these compounds than in carbonyls. The absorption maximum in thiocarbonyls occurs at longer wavelengths and in some compounds is shifted into the visible region.

INORGANIC SYSTEMS. The SO_2 molecule has two absorption bands in the near ultraviolet at 3600 Å ($\epsilon = 0.05$) and 2900 Å ($\epsilon = 340$) corresponding to a triplet and singlet $n \to \pi^*$ transition. The gaseous spectrum shows considerable vibrational fine structure, and analysis has produced information concerning the structure of the excited state.[18]

TABLE 6-3. CHARACTERISTIC ABSORP-
TION MAXIMA FOR SOME
INORGANIC ANIONS

	λ	ϵ
Cl^-	1810	10^4
Br^-	1995	11,000
	1900	12,000
I^-	2260	12,600
	1940	12,600
OH^-	1870	5000
SH^-	2300	8000
$S_2O_3^{-2}$	2200	4000
$S_2O_8^{-2}$	2540	22
NO_2^-	3546	23
	2100	5380
	2870	9
NO_3^-	3025	7
	1936	8800
$N_2O_2^{-2}$	2480	4000

In nitroso compounds, an $n \to \pi^*$ transition involving the lone pair electrons on the nitrogen occurs in the visible region. An $n \to \pi^*$ transition involving an oxygen lone pair occurs in the ultraviolet.

The nitrite ion in water has two main absorption bands at 3546 Å ($\epsilon = 23$) and 2100 Å ($\epsilon = 5380$) and a weak band at 2870 Å ($\epsilon = 9$). The assignment of these bands has been reported,[19] and this article is an excellent reference for gaining an appreciation of how the concepts discussed in this chapter are used in band assignments. The band at 3546 Å is an $n \to \pi^*$ transition ($^1B_1 \leftarrow {}^1A_1$) involving the oxygen lone pair. The band at 2100 Å is assigned as $\pi \to \pi^*$ ($^1B_2 \leftarrow {}^1A_1$), and the band at 2870 Å is assigned to an $n \to \pi^*$ transition ($^1A_2 \leftarrow {}^1A_1$) involving the oxygen lone pair.

The absorption peaks obtained for various inorganic anions in water or alcohol solution are listed in Table 6-3. For the simple ions (Br^-, Cl^-, OH^-) the absorption is attributed to charge transfer in which the electron is transferred to the solvent.

MOLECULAR ADDITION COMPOUNDS OF IODINE

The absorption band maximum for iodine (core plus $\sigma^2 \pi^4 \pi^{*4}$) occurs at about 5200 Å in the solvent CCl_4 and is assigned to a $\pi^* \to \sigma^*$ transition. When a donor molecule is added to the above solution, two pronounced changes in the spectrum occur (see Fig. 6-7).

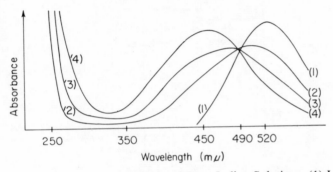

Fig. 6-7. Spectra of Iodine and Base-Iodine Solutions. (1) I_2 in CCl_4; (2, 3, 4) same I_2 concentration but increasing base concentration in the order $2 < 3 < 4$.

A blue shift is detected in the iodine peak and a new peak arises in the ultraviolet region which is due to a charge transfer transition. The existence of an isosbestic point at 490 mμ indicates that there are only two absorbing species in the system; namely, free iodine and the complex $B:\hat{I}\!-\!\hat{I}|$. As indicated in Chapter 5, an equilibrium constant can be calculated from absorbance measurements for this system. The constant value for K obtained over a wide range of donor concentrations is evidence for the existence of an addition compound.

The bonding in iodine addition compounds can be described by the following equation:

$$\psi^0 = a\psi_{cov} + b\psi_{el}$$

where ψ_{el} includes contributions from purely electrostatic forces while

ψ_{cov} includes contributions from covalent interactions (these are often described as charge transfer interactions). The covalent contribution to the bonding, ψ_{cov}, is discussed in Chapter 2. In many of these complexes $b > a$ in the ground state. In these cases, the band around 2500 Å arises from a charge transfer transition in which an electron from this ground state is promoted to an excited state in which $a > b$. In view of these coefficients the charge transfer band assignment can be approximated by a transfer of a base electron, n_b, to the iodine σ^* orbital. These considerations and the blue shift that occurs in the normal $\pi^* \rightarrow \sigma^*$ iodine transition upon complexation can be explained by consideration of the relative energies of the molecular orbitals of iodine and the complex (Fig. 6-8). In Fig. 6-8, n_b refers to the donor orbital on the base, $\sigma_{I_2}^*$ and

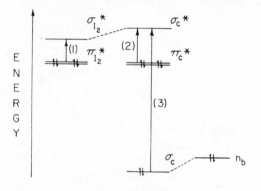

Fig. 6-8. Some of the Molecular Orbitals in a Base-Iodine Addition Compound.

$\pi_{I_2}^*$, to the free iodine antibonding orbitals involved in the transition leading to iodine absorption. The σ_c, π_c^*, and σ_c^* orbitals are molecular orbitals in the complex which are very much like the original base and iodine orbitals because of the weak Lewis acid-base interaction (2 to 10 kcal). The orbitals n_b and $\sigma_{I_2}^*$ combine to form molecular orbitals in the complex, σ_c and σ_c^* in which σ_c, the bonding orbital, is essentially n_b and σ_c^* is essentially $\sigma_{I_2}^*$. Since σ_c^* is slightly higher in energy than the corresponding $\sigma_{I_2}^*$, the transition in complexed iodine [arrow (2) in Fig. 6-8] requires slightly more energy than the corresponding transition in free I_2 [arrow (1)] and a blue shift is observed. The charge-transfer transition occurs at higher energy in the ultraviolet region and is designated in Fig. 6-8 by arrow (3). Some interesting correlations have been made which indicate that the blue shift is related to the magnitude of the base-iodine interaction.[20,21] This would be expected qualitatively from the treatment in Fig. 6-8 as long as the energy of π_c^* differs very little from $\pi_{I_2}^*$ or else its energy changes in a linear manner with the enthalpy, ΔH. A relationship involving the charge transfer band, the ionization potential of the base, I_b, and the electron affinity of the acid, E_a, is also reported:[22,23]

$$\nu = I_b - E_a - \Delta \tag{6-10}$$

where Δ is an empirically determined constant for a related series of bases.

The enthalpies for the formation of these charge transfer complexes are of interest and significance to both inorganic and organic chemists. For many inorganic systems, especially in the areas of coordination chemistry and nonaqueous solvents, information about donor and acceptor interactions is essential to understanding many phenomena. Since the above adducts are soluble in CCl_4 or hexane, the data can be interpreted more readily than results obtained in polar solvents where large solvation heats are encountered. As a result of these solvation effects structural interpretations of the effect of substituents on pK_b and on stability constant data are often highly questionable. Some typical results from donor-I_2 systems which illustrate the wide range of systems that can be studied are contained in Table 6-4.

TABLE 6-4. EQUILIBRIUM CONSTANTS AND ENTHAL-
PIES OF FORMATION FOR SOME DONOR-I_2 ADDUCTS

Donor	K (liter mole^{-1})	$-\Delta H$ (kcal mole^{-1})
C_6H_6	0·15 (25°)	1·4
Toluene	0·16 (25°)	1·8
CH_3OH	0·47 (20°)	1·9
Dioxane	1·14 (17°)	3·5
$(C_2H_5)_2O$	0·97 (20°)	4·3
$(C_2H_5)_2S$	180 (25°)	8·3
$CH_3C(O)N(CH_3)_2$	6·1 (25°)	4·7
Pyridine	270 (20°)	7·8
$(C_2H_5)_3N$	5130 (25°)	12·0

The following are a few examples of the information that can be obtained by studying enthalpies of association of iodine adducts:

(1) The donor properties of the π electron systems of alkyl substituted benzenes have been reported.[24]

(2) A correlation of the heat of formation of iodine adducts of a series of para-substituted benzamides with the Hammett substituent constants[25]

of the benzamides is reported. The high degree of accuracy of this method is indicated by this correlation.

(3) The donor properties of a series of carbonyl compounds $[(CH_3)_2CO,\ CH_3C(O)N(CH_3)_2,\ (CH_3)_2NC(O)N(CH_3)_2,\ CH_3C(O)OCH_3,$ $CH_3C(O)SCH_3]$ have been evaluated and interpreted[26] in terms of conjugative and inductive effects of the group attached to the carbonyl functional group.

(4) The donor properties of sulfoxides, sulfones, and sulfites have been investigated.[27] The results are interpreted to indicate that sulfur-oxygen π bonding is less effective in these systems than carbon-oxygen π bonding is in ketones and acetates.

(5) The effect of ring size on the donor properties of cyclic ethers and sulfides has been investigated.[28] It was found that for saturated cyclic sulfides, of general formula $(CH_2)_nS$, the donor properties of sulfur are in the order, $n = 5 > 6 > 4 > 3$. The order for the analogous ether compounds is: $4 > 5 > 6 > 3$. Explanations of these effects are offered.

(6) The donor properties of a series of primary, secondary, and tertiary amines have been evaluated.[29,30] Reversals in the order of donor strength of amines toward different acids are obtained and an explanation is offered.

In addition to iodine, there are several other Lewis acids that form charge transfer complexes which absorb in the ultraviolet or visible regions. For example, the relative acidities of I_2, ICl, Br_2, SO_2, and phenol toward the donor N,N-dimethylacetamide have been evaluated. Factors affecting the magnitude of the interaction[31] and information regarding the bonding in the adducts are reported. Good general reviews of charge-transfer complexes are available.[32,33,34,35]

EFFECT OF SOLVENT POLARITY ON CHARGE TRANSFER SPECTRA

The ion pair N-methylpyridinium iodide undergoes a charge-transfer transition which can be represented as in Fig. 6-9.[36] It has been found that the position of the charge-transfer band is a function of the solvating ability of the solvent. A shift to lower wavelengths is detected in the better solvating solvents. The positions of the bands are reported as transition energies, E_T. Transition energies (kcal mole^{-1}) are calculated from the frequency as described in Chapter 5. The transition energy is referred to as the Z value. Some typical data are reported in Table 6-5. An explanation for the observed shift has been proposed.[36] The dipole moment of the ion pair, $C_5H_5NCH_3^+I^-$, is reported to be perpendicular

TABLE 6-5. Z- VALUES FOR
SOME COMMON SOLVENTS

Solvent	E_T or Z value[a]
H_2O	94·6
CH_3OH	83·6
C_2H_5OH	79·6
CH_3COCH_3	65·7
$(CH_3)_2NCHO$	68·5
CH_3CN	71·3
Pyridine	64·0
CH_3SOCH_3	71·1
H_2NCHO	83·3
CH_2Cl_2	64·2
Isooctane	60·1

[a]The E_T or Z value is the transition energy in kcal mole^{-1} at 25°C, 1 atm pressure, for the compound 1-ethyl-4-carbomethoxypyridinium iodide.

to the dipole moment of the excited state (Fig. 6-9). Polar solvent molecules will align their dipole moments for maximum interaction with the ground state, lowering the energy of the ground state by solvation. The dipole moment of the solvent molecules will be perpendicular to the dipole moment of the excited state, producing a higher energy for the excited state than would be found in the gas phase. Since solvent molecules cannot rearrange in the time required for a transition, the relative lowering of the ground state and raising of the excited state increases the energy

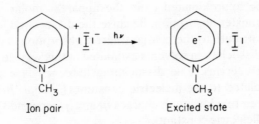

Ion pair   Excited state

Fig. 6–9. Ion Pair and Charge Transfer Excited State of N-methylpyridinium Iodide.

of the transition, E_T, over that in the gas phase (Fig. 6-10), shifting the wavelength of absorption to higher frequencies. Hydrogen-bonding solvents are often found to increase E_T more than would be expected by comparing their dielectric constants with other solvents. This is due to the formation of hydrogen bonds with the solute anion. The use of the dielectric constant to infer solvating ability can lead to difficulty because the local dielectric constant in the vicinity of the ion may be very different from the bulk dielectric constant.

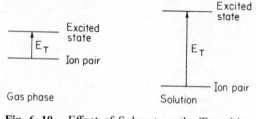

Fig. 6–10. Effect of Solvent on the Transition Energy, E_T.

The data obtained from these spectral shifts are employed as an empirical measure of the ionizing power of the solvent. The results can be correlated with a scale of "solvent polarities" determined from the effect of solvent on the rate of solvolysis of t-butyl chloride.[36] Other applications of these data to kinetic and spectral studies are reported.[36]

Significant differences exist between "solvating power" inferred from the dielectric constant and the results from spectral and kinetic parameters. Although methanol and formamide are found to have similar Z values, the dielectric constants are 32.6 and 109.5, respectively. Solvent effects cannot be understood solely on the basis of the dielectric constant. The extent of ion-pair association of the pyridinium salts in various solvents can be approximated from the apparent molar absorptivities of the charge-transfer absorption, because the dissociated ion pair is not expected to contribute to the charge transfer absorption. The tendencies of ion pairs to dissociate in solvents estimated in this way do not correlate with transition energies. The dissociating tendency is expected to be more closely related to the dielectric constant ($F = q_1 q_2 / D r^2$, where F is the force between two ions with charges q_1 and q_2 separated by a distance r, and D is the dielectric constant).

The band positions for the $n \rightarrow \pi^*$ transitions in certain ketones in various solvents are found to be linearly related to the Z values for the solvents. A constant slope is obtained for a plot of E_T versus Z for many ketones.[37,38] Deviations from linearity by certain ketones in this plot can be employed to provide interesting structural information about the molecular conformation. Cycloheptanone, for example, does not give a linear plot of E_T versus Z. The deviation is attributed[37] to solvent effects on the relative proportion of the conformers present in solution.

SPECTRA OF TRANSITION METAL COMPLEXES

As mentioned in Chapter 3, the spectra of transition metal complexes can be interpreted with the aid of ligand field theory. The treatment here will not be encylcopedic; selected topics will be covered. The aim is to give an appreciation for a very powerful tool in coordination chemistry: the utilization of electronic spectra in the solution of structural problems. More advanced treatments containing references to the spectra of many complexes are available.[39,40,41]

SELECTION RULES AND INTENSITIES OF THE TRANSITIONS

The following selection rules are reviewed for they are pertinent to the problem at hand:

A. Transitions in which the number of unpaired electrons changes in going from the ground to excited state are referred to as *spin* or *multiplicity forbidden*.

B. Transitions within a given set of p or d orbitals (i.e., those which only involve a redistribution of electrons in the given sub-shell) are *Laporte forbidden* if the molecule has a center of symmetry.

As a result of the Laporte rule, d–d transitions in octahedral complexes are forbidden and many complexes would be colorless except for the following:

(1) If the ion does not have perfect O_h symmetry, but is distorted so the center of symmetry is destroyed, the d and p orbitals of the complex are "mixed" (hybridized) and the transition occurs between d levels with different amounts of p character. The intensity is roughly proportional to the extent of mixing and is often in the range, $\epsilon \sim 20$ to 50.

(2) A complex with O_h symmetry can absorb light by the following mechanism. In the course of the normal vibrations of an octahedral complex, some of the molecules are slightly distorted from O_h symmetry at any given time. The d and p orbitals mix in the unsymmetrical configuration and a very low intensity transition is observed ($\epsilon \sim 5$ to 25). These transitions are said to be *vibronically allowed*[42] and the effect is described as *vibronic coupling*. This amounts to mixing the electronic and vibrational wave functions in such a way that the product $\psi_{el}\psi_{vib}$ has symmetry necessary for the integrand of the transition moment integral (equation 6-5) to be A_1.

In complexes of Mn^{II}, a d^5 case, there are no spin-allowed $d-d$ transitions; all are both multplicity and Laporte forbidden. If it were not for vibronic coupling, Mn^{II} complexes would be colorless. Hexaquomanganese(II) ion is very pale pink, all absorption peaks in the visible region being of very low intensity. Since there is no center of symmetry in a tetrahedral molecule, somewhat more intense absorptions ($\epsilon = 100$ to 1000) than those in octahedral complexes are often obtained for $d-d$ transitions in T_d complexes.

An aid in making band assignments results from the fact that multiplicity-allowed transitions are broad while multiplicity-forbidden transitions are usually sharp. Multiplicity-allowed $t_{2g} \rightarrow e_g$ transitions lead to an excited state in which the equilibrium internuclear distance between the metal ion and ligand is larger than in the ground state. In the course of the electronic transition no change in distance can occur (Franck-Condon principle), so the electronically excited molecules are in vibrationally excited states with bond distances corresponding to the configuration of the ground state involved in the transition. The interaction of an excited state with solvent molecules not in the primary coordination sphere is variable because neighboring solvent molecules are various distances away when the excited molecule is produced. Since the solvent cannot rearrange in the transition time, a given excited vibrational state in different molecules will undergo solvent interactions with solvent located at varying distances. Varying solvation energies produce a range of variable energy, vibrationally excited states and a broad band results.

In some spin-forbidden transitions, rearrangement occurs in a given level. For example, in Cr^{III} complexes a transition occurs from a ground state containing three unpaired electrons in t_{2g} to an excited state in which t_{2g} has two paired and one unpaired electron. In these multiplicity-forbidden transitions there is little difference in the equilibrium internuclear distances of the excited and ground states. Sharp lines result from these transitions to a low energy vibrational level of an excited state whose potential energy curve is similar in shape and equilibrium internuclear distance to the ground state.

NATURE OF ELECTRONIC TRANSITIONS IN COMPLEXES

The simplest case to illustrate the phenomena giving rise to the color of most transition metal ion complexes is the d^1 case, e.g., Ti^{III} in an octahedral field. The ground state of the free ion is described by the term symbol ^2D and, as indicated earlier, the degenerate d levels are split in the presence of an octahedral field into a triplet T_{2g} and doublet E_g set. As shown in Chapter 3 the extent of the splitting is a function of Dq.

This is represented graphically in Fig. 6-11. As Dq increases, ΔE, the energy (hence the frequency) of the transition increases. The slope of the T_{2g} line is $-4Dq$ and that of E_g is $+6Dq$. The difference, ΔE, is $10Dq$ or Δ. The value of Δ (in units cm^{-1}) can be obtained directly from the frequency of the absorption peak. For example, $Ti(H_2O)_6^{3+}$ has an absorption maximum at about 5000 Å (20,000 cm^{-1}). The transition is described

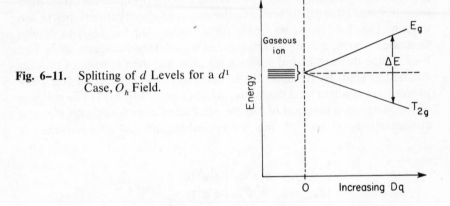

Fig. 6–11. Splitting of d Levels for a d^1 Case, O_h Field.

as $T_{2g} \rightarrow E_g$. The Δ value for water toward Ti^{III} is about 20,000 cm^{-1} (Dq is 2000 cm^{-1}). Since this transition occurs with the absorption of the green component of visible light, the color transmitted is purple (blue + red). As the ligand is changed, Dq varies and the color of the complex changes. The color of the solution is the complement of the color or colors absorbed, the transmitted bands determining the color. Caution should be exercised in inferring absorption bands from visual observation; e.g., violet and purple are often confused.

For a d^9 complex in an *octahedral* field the energy level diagram is obtained by inverting that of the d^1 complex (see Fig. 6-12). The inversion

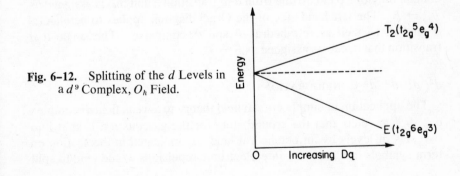

Fig. 6–12. Splitting of the d Levels in a d^9 Complex, O_h Field.

164 ELECTRONIC ABSORPTION SPECTROSCOPY

results because the ground state of a d^9 configuration is doubly degenerate $[t_{2g}{}^6 e_g{}^3$ can be $t_{2g}{}^6(d_{x^2-y^2})^2(d_{z^2})^1$ or $t_{2g}{}^6(d_{x^2-y^2})^1(d_{z^2})^2]$ and the excited state is triply degenerate $[t_{2g}{}^5 e_g{}^4$ can be $(d_{xy})^2(d_{yz})^2(d_{xz})^1(e_g)^4$ or $(d_{xy})^2(d_{yz})^1$ $(d_{xz})^2(e_g)^4$ or $(d_{xy})^1(d_{yz})^2(d_{xz})^2(e_g)^4]$. Therefore, the transition is $E \to T_2$. In effect the electronic transition causes the motion of a positive hole from the e_g level in the ground state to the excited state and the appropriate energy diagram results by inverting that for the electronic transition for a d^1 case. In order to preserve the center of gravity, the slopes of the lines in Fig. 6-12 must be $-6Dq$ for E and $+4Dq$ for T_2. The results described above are often summarized by an Orgel diagram as in Fig. 6-13. Since the tetrahedral splitting for d^1 is just the opposite of that for octahedral splitting (Chapter 3), d^1 tetrahedral and d^9 octahedral complexes have similar Orgel diagrams, as indicated in Fig. 6-13. The splitting of the states as a function of Dq for octahedral complexes with electron configurations d^1 and d^6 and for tetrahedral d^4 and d^9 complexes is

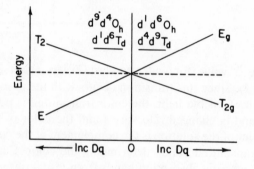

Fig. 6-13. Orgel Diagram for d^1, d^4, d^6, and d^9 Complexes.

described by the right half of Fig. 6-13. The spectra of these complexes contain only one band arising from d–d transitions, and this is assigned as $T_{2g} \to E_g$. The left hand side of the Orgel diagram applies to octahedral d^4 and d^9 as well as tetrahedral d^1 and d^6 complexes. The single d–d transition that occurs is assigned as $E \to T_2$.

d^2, d^7, d^3, d^8 CONFIGURATIONS

The application of simple crystal field theory to a weak field d^2 complex e.g., V^{III}, predicts that the ground state for the gaseous ion is split into two sets of levels by an octahedral field. As indicated in the section on term symbols in Chapter 1, interelectronic repulsions would tend to split the levels of the gaseous ion to a greater extent than if these interactions were neglected. Since this is generally true for all the states in complexes formed by cations with more than one d electron, the nature of this splitting will be considered in detail for d^2 octahedral complexes. In Chapter 1, the two triplet states for a d^2 gaseous ion were found to be ^3F and ^3P. The following degenerate arrangements are possible for the ground state of the octahedral d^2 complex: $d_{xy}{}^1, d_{xz}{}^1, d_{yz}{}^0; d_{xy}{}^0, d_{xz}{}^1, d_{yz}{}^1; d_{xy}{}^1, d_{xz}{}^0, d_{xy}{}^1$. The ground state is orbitally triply degenerate and the symbol $^3T_{1g}(F)$ is used to describe this state. The following information is conveyed: (1) the symbol T indicates it is orbitally triply degenerate; (2) the superscript indicates a spin multiplicity of three, i.e., two unpaired electrons; (3) the g indicates a gerade state; (4) the symbol (F) indicates this state arose from the gaseous ion ^3F state (see Fig. 6-15). In addition to the $^3T_{1g}(F)$ ground state an excited state exists corresponding to the configuration in which the two electrons are paired in the t_{2g} level. Transitions to these states are multiplicity forbidden but sometimes weak absorption bands assigned to these transitions are observed.

The triplet excited state $t_{2g}{}^1 e_g{}^1$ will be considered next. If an electron is excited out of d_{xz} or d_{yz} so that the remaining electron is in d_{xy}, the excited electron will encounter less electron-electron repulsion from the electron in d_{xy} if it is placed in d_{z^2}. The $d_{x^2-y^2}$ orbital is less favorable because of the proximity of an electron in this orbital to the electron remaining in d_{xy}. This gives rise to the arrangement (a) in Fig. 6-14. Similarly, if the electron is excited out of d_{xy} it will be most stable in $d_{x^2-y^2}$. The remaining electron can be in either d_{xz} or d_{yz} giving rise to (b) and (c). This set (Fig. 14a, b, and c) gives rise to the T_{2g} state which is

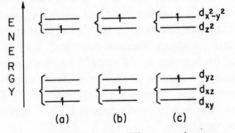

Fig. 6–14. Possible Electron Arrangements for $t_{2g}{}^1 e_g{}^1$.

orbitally triply degenerate and has a multiplicity of three. The arrangements ($d_{xy}{}^1, d_{x^2-y^2}{}^1; d_{xz}{}^1, d_{z^2}{}^1; d_{yz}{}^1, d_{z^2}{}^1$) are higher in energy and also produce an orbitally triply degenerate state, $T_{1g}(P)$. Other possible arrangements corresponding to $t_{2g}{}^1 e_g{}^1$ involve reversing one of the electron spins to produce states with singlet multiplicity. Transitions to these states from the triplet ground state are multiplicity forbidden. Finally a two-electron transition producing the excited state $(e_g)^2$ or $d_{z^2}{}^1$, $d_{x^2-y^2}{}^1$ gives rise to a singly degenerate $^3A_{2g}$ state. It is instructive to indicate how these states relate to the gaseous ion. As illustrated in the section on term symbols, the ground state for the gaseous ion V^{III} (a d^2 ion) is ^3F. The ligand field in the complex removes the sevenfold orbital degeneracy of this state (i.e., $m_L = 3, 2, 1, 0, -1, -2, -3,$) into two three-fold degenerate states, $T_{1g}(F)$ and T_{2g}, and one nondegenerate state, A_{2g}. This is indicated in the Orgel diagram (Fig. 6-15) for a d^2, O_h complex.

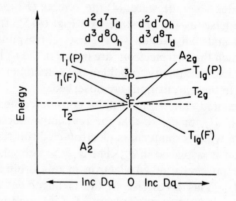

Fig. 6–15. Orgel Diagram for d^2, d^3, d^7, and d^8 Complexes.

For zero Dq i.e., the gaseous ion, only two states, ^3F and ^3P, exist. As Dq increases, ^3F is split into the $T_{1g}(F)$, T_{2g}, and A_{2g} states. The degeneracy of the ^3P state is not removed by the ligand field and this becomes the triplet $T_{1g}(P)$ state in an octahedral complex. The (P) indicates this state arises from the gaseous ion ^3P state. The energies of these states as a function of Dq can be calculated theoretically by evaluating the electrostatic perturbation of the ligands on the d orbitals.[43] The Tanabe and Sugano diagrams (which will be discussed later)[44] contain the results of calculations for strong fields.

Thus we have shown that more states can arise in a d^2 complex than the two predicted by a simple splitting of the d orbitals (Chapter 3). The results obtained for various ligand fields for all first row transition metal ions[43,44] are shown by the diagrams in Appendix C. Use of the Orgel diagrams in predicting spectra and making assignments can be demonstrated by considering V^{III} and Ni^{II} complexes.

Use of Orgel Diagrams

The Orgel diagram for octahedral and tetrahedral complexes of metal ions with d^2, d^7, d^3, and d^8 electron configurations is presented in Fig. 6-15. States with energies intermediate between ^3P and ^3F are not indicated because they have a different multiplicity. Consequently, transitions to these states are multiplicity forbidden and usually not observed. These states are included in the Tanabe and Sugano diagrams (see Appendix C). For V^{III}, three transitions involving the states shown in Fig. 6-15 could occur: $T_{1g}(F) \rightarrow T_{2g}$, $T_{1g}(F) \rightarrow T_{1g}(P)$, and $T_{1g}(F) \rightarrow A_{2g}$ where (F) and (P) indicate the free ion state from which these T_{1g} states arise. The transition to A_{2g} in V^{III} is a two electron transition. Such transitions are relatively improbable, and hence have low intensities. This transition has not been observed experimentally. The spectra obtained for octahedral V^{III} complexes consist of two absorption bands assigned to $^3T_{1g}(F) \rightarrow {}^3T_{2g}(F)$ and $^3T_{1g}(F) \rightarrow {}^3T_{1g}(P)$. In $V(H_2O)_6^{3+}$ these occur at about 17,000 and 24,000 cm^{-1}, respectively.

For octahedral nickel(II) complexes, the Orgel diagram (left-hand side Fig. 6-15, d^8) indicates three expected transitions: $^3A_{2g} \rightarrow {}^3T_{2g}$, $^3A_{2g} \rightarrow {}^3T_{1g}(F)$, $^3A_{2g} \rightarrow {}^3T_{1g}(P)$. (A similar result is obtained from the use of the Tanabe and Sugano diagram in Appendix C.) Experimental absorption maxima corresponding to these transitions are summarized in Table 6-6 for octahedral Ni^{II} complexes. (Numbers in parentheses correspond to shoulders on the main band.) Spectra of the octahedral

TABLE 6-6. ABSORPTION MAXIMA OF OCTAHEDRAL Ni^{II}
COMPLEXES (ν_{max} in cm^{-1})

Ligand	$^3A_{2g} \rightarrow {}^3T_{2g}$	$^3A_{2g} \rightarrow {}^3T_{1g}(F)$	$^3A_{2g} \rightarrow {}^3T_{1g}(P)$
H_2O	8500	15,400	26,000
NH_3	10,750	17,500	28,200
$(CH_3)_2SO$	7728	12,970	24,038
$HC(O)N(CH_3)_2$	8503	13,605 (14,900)	25,000
$CH_3C(O)N(CH_3)_2$	7576	12,738 (14,285)	23,809

NH_3, $HC(O)N(CH_3)_2$, and $CH_3C(O)N(CH_3)_2$ complexes are given in Fig. 6-16. These complexes are colored purple, green, and yellow, respectively.

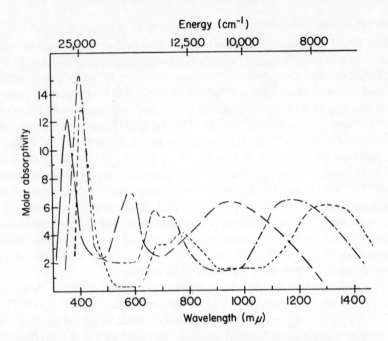

Fig. 6–16. Molar Absorptivity, ϵ, for Some Nickel(II) Complexes in CH_3NO_2 Solution. – – – , $Ni(NH_3)_6(ClO)_2$; ---, $Ni[HC(O)N(CH_3)_2]_6$ $(ClO_4)_2$; — - — , $Ni[CH_3C(O)N(CH_3)_2]_6(ClO_4)_2$.

CALCULATION OF Dq AND β FOR Ni^{II} COMPLEXES

The graphical information contained in the Orgel diagrams is more accurately represented by the series of equations which relates the energies of these various states to the Dq value of the ligand. The derivation of these equations has been reported[44]. For Ni^{II} in an octahedral field, the energies, E, of the states relative to the spherical field are given by equations (6-11) to (6-13).

For $^3T_{2g}$: $\qquad\qquad\qquad E = -2Dq$ $\qquad\qquad\qquad$ (6-11)

For $^3A_{2g}$: $\qquad\qquad\qquad E = -12Dq$ $\qquad\qquad\qquad$ (6-12)

For $^3T_{1g}(F)$ and $^3T_{1g}(P)$:

$$[6Dq\,p - 16(Dq)^2] + [-6Dq - p]E + E^2 = 0 \quad (6\text{-}13)$$

where p is the energy of the ^3P state. There are two roots to the last equation corresponding to the energies of the states $^3T_{1g}(F)$ and $^3T_{1g}(P)$.

From equations (6-11) and (6-12) it is seen that the energies of both $^3T_{2g}$ and $^3A_{2g}$ are linear functions of Dq. For any ligand which produces a spin-free octahedral nickel complex, the difference in energy of these states ($^3T_{2g} - {}^3A_{2g}$) in the complex is $10Dq$. As can be seen from the Orgel or Tanabe and Sugano diagrams, the lowest energy transition is $^3A_{2g} \rightarrow {}^3T_{2g}$. Since this transition is a direct measure of the energy difference of these states, Δ (or $10Dq$) can be equated to the transition energy, i.e., the frequency of this band (cm^{-1}).

Equation (6-13) can be solved for the energies of the other states. However, the above equations have been derived by assuming that the ligands are point charges or point dipoles and that there is no covalence in the metal-ligand bond. If this were true, the value for Dq just determined could be substituted into equation (6-13), the energy of ^3P obtained from the atomic spectrum of the gaseous ion,[45] and the energy of the other two levels in the complex calculated from equation (6-13). The frequencies of the expected spectral transitions are calculated for one band from the difference in the energies of the levels $^3T_{1g}(F) - {}^3A_{2g}$ and for the other band from the energy difference $^3T_{1g}(P) - {}^3A_{2g}$, because the transitions (see Table 6-6) correspond to these differences. The experimental energies obtained from the spectra (Table 6-6) are almost always lower than the values calculated in this way. The deviation may be attributed to covalence in the bonding. The effect of covalence is to delocalize metal ion electron density onto the ligand and thus reduce electron-electron repulsions of the d electrons in the complexed metal ion compared to the repulsions in the gaseous state. This has the effect of decreasing the difference in energy between the ^3P and ^3F states in the complex relative to that in the gaseous ion. As a result, the gas phase value cannot be used for p[in equation (6-13)], but p must be experimentally evaluated for each complex. Equation (6-13) can be employed for this calculation by using the Dq value from the $^3A_{2g} \rightarrow {}^3T_{2g}$ transition and the experimental energy, E, for the $^3A_{2g} \rightarrow {}^3T_{1g}(P)$ transition. The only unknown remaining in equation (6-13) is p. The lowering of ^3P is a measure of covalence, among other effects, and is sometimes expressed as β°, a percentage lowering of the energy of the ^3P state in the complex compared to the energy of ^3P in the free, gaseous ion.[45] It is calculated by using equation (6-14):

$$\beta^\circ = [(B - B')/B] \times 100 \qquad (6\text{-}14)$$

where B equals the energy value of ^3P in the free gaseous ion and B' is the experimental energy value of ^3P in the complex. In the case of nickel(II), the energy of ^3P in the complex can be substituted along with Dq into equation (6-13) and the other root calculated. The difference in the energy of this root and A_{2g} gives the frequency of the middle band $[^3A_{2g} \rightarrow \, ^3T_{1g}(F)]$. The agreement of the calculated and experimental value for this band is good evidence for O_h symmetry. The above discussion will be made clearer by referring to Appendix D where a sample calculation of Dq, $\beta°$, and the frequency of the $^3A_{2g} \rightarrow \, ^3T_{1g}(F)$ transition is presented for $Ni[(CH_3)_2SO]_6(ClO_4)_2$.

Most often the quantity β is used instead of $\beta°$ where β is defined as:

$$\beta = B'/B \qquad (6\text{-}15)$$

The two quantities are easily related if equation (6-14) is rewritten as $\beta° = (1 - \beta) \times 100$.

Equations have been worked out to indicate the relationship between energy and Dq for the various states in other metal ion complexes. However, with many other ions the spectral data cannot be solved easily for Dq and β because of complications introduced by spin-orbit coupling. The consequences of this effect are indicated in Fig. 6-17. The three T_{2g} states are split by spin-orbit (s.o.) coupling as indicated in Fig. 6-17b. Coupling lowers the energy of the ground state and the extent of lowering depends upon the magnitude of the coupling. When the ground state is lowered by spin-orbit coupling, the energies of all the bands in the spectrum have contributions from this lowering, $\Delta_{s.o.}$ (see Fig. 6-17).

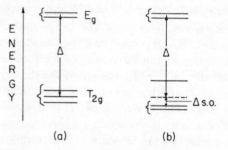

Fig. 6-17. Contribution to Δ from Spin-Orbit Coupling. (a) d level splitting with no s.o. coupling. (b) Split of T_{2g} level by s.o. coupling.

When the contribution to the total energy from $\Delta_{s.o.}$ cannot be determined, the evaluation of Δ and β is not very accurate. Spin-orbit coupling in an excited state is not as serious a problem because transitions to both of the split levels often occur and the energies can be averaged. When the ground state is split, only the lower level is populated. Thus accurate values for D_q and β without corrections for s.o. coupling can only be obtained for ions in which the ground state is A or E (e.g., Ni^{2+}). A further complication is introduced by the effect Jahn-Teller distortions have on the energies of the levels.

Ni^{II}, Mn^{II} (weak field), Co^{III} (strong field), and Cr^{III} form many octahedral complexes whose spectra permit accurate calculation of Dq and β without significant complications from spin-orbit coupling or Jahn-Teller distortions. Ti^{III} has only minor contributions from these complicating effects. In the case of tetrahedral complexes the magnitude of the splitting by spin-orbit interactions more nearly approaches that of crystal field splitting (Dq', the splitting in a tetrahedral field, is about $\frac{4}{9}Dq$). As a result, spin-orbit coupling makes appreciable contributions to the energies of the observed bands. A procedure has been described[46] which permits evaluation of Dq and β for tetrahedral Co^{II}. A sample calculation is contained in Appendix D.

Both σ and π bonding of the ligand with the metal ion contribute to the quantity Dq. When π bonding occurs, the metal ion t_{2g} orbitals will be involved, for they have proper directional and symmetry properties. If π bonding occurs with empty ligand orbitals (e.g., d in Et_2S or p in CN^-), Dq will be larger than in the absence of this effect. If π bonding occurs with filled ligand orbitals and filled t_{2g} orbitals (as in the case with the ligand OH^- and Co^{III}), the net result of this interaction is antibonding and Dq is decreased. These effects are illustrated with the aid of Fig. 6-18. In Fig. 6-18a the d electrons in T_{2g} interact with the empty ligand orbitals, lowering the energy of T_{2g} and raising the energy of the orbitals in the complex. An empty π^* orbital of the ligand could be involved in this type of interaction. Since T_{2g} is lowered in energy and E_g is not affected (the E_g orbitals point toward σ electron pairs on the ligands), Dq will increase. In the second case (Fig. 6-18b), filled ligand π orbitals interact with higher energy filled or empty metal d orbitals, raising the energy of T_{2g} and lowering Dq.

It is informative to relate the energies of the observed $d-d$ transitions to the energy levels associated with the molecular orbital description of octahedral complexes. The scheme illustrated in Fig. 6-19 is obtained by the procedures described in Chapter 3 (neglecting π bonding). The difference between T_{2g} and E_g^* is $10Dq$. As metal-ligand σ bond strength increases, E_g is lowered, E_g^* is raised by the same amount, and Dq increases. If T_{2g} metal electrons form π bonds with empty p or d orbitals of the ligand, the energy of the T_{2g} level in the complex is lowered and Dq is increased. Electron-electron repulsions of the T_{2g} electrons and the metal nonbonding electrons raise the energy of the T_{2g} set and decrease

Dq. The above ideas have been employed in the interpretation of the spectra of some transition metal acetylacetonates.[47,48]

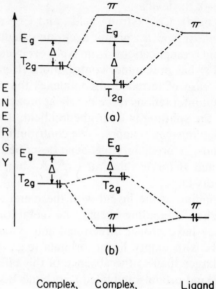

Complex,   Complex,   Ligand
no π including π π orbital
bonding   bonding

Fig. 6–18. Effect of π Bonding on the Energy of the T_{2g} Level and on Dq. (a) Filled metal orbitals, empty ligand orbitals. (b) Filled metal orbitals, filled ligand orbitals.

The magnitude of Dq is determined by many factors: interactions from an electrostatic perturbation, the metal-ligand σ bond, the metal to ligand π bond, the ligand to metal π bond, and metal electron–ligand electron repulsions. Additional references [39,40,42] on the material presented in this section are available.

Much useful information regarding the metal ion–ligand interaction can be obtained from an evaluation of Dq and β. For a series of amides of the type $R_1C(O)N{\Large<}^{R_2}_{R_3}$ it was found that whenever R_1 and R_2 are both alkyl groups, lower values for Dq and β result for the six coordinate nickel complexes than when either R_1 or both R_2 and R_3 are hydrogens. This is not in agreement with the observation that toward phenol and iodine the donor strengths of these amides are found to increase with the number of alkyl groups. It was proposed that a steric effect exists between neighboring coordinated amide molecules[49] in the metal complexes. A study of the nickel(II) complexes of some primary alkyl

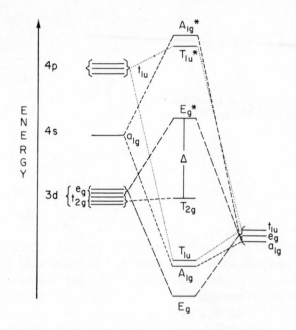

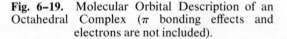

Fig. 6–19. Molecular Orbital Description of an Octahedral Complex (π bonding effects and electrons are not included).

amines indicated that even though water replaces the amines in the complexes, the amines interact more strongly with nickel than does water, and almost as strongly as ammonia.[50] A large Dq is also reported for the nickel complex of ethyleneimine.[51] These results are interpreted and an explanation involving solvation energies is proposed for the instability of the alkylamine complexes in water.[50] There have been many other studies of this type, and there will be further applications of the information from this kind of study in inorganic chemistry.

For certain types of complexes, McClure[52] has proposed a scheme which permits resolution of the various contributions to Dq which were mentioned above. Complexes of Co^{III} will be discussed to illustrate the approach, but the treatment is not limited to this ion. As indicated by the Tanabe and Sugano diagram (Appendix C), for a strong field d^6 complex the spin-allowed transitions are $^1A_{1g} \rightarrow {}^1T_{1g}$ and $^1A_{1g} \rightarrow {}^1T_{2g}$. The spectrum illustrated in Fig. 6-20a is that for $Co(NH_3)_6{}^{3+}$, and the bands are assigned as indicated. When one of the ammonia molecules in the complex is

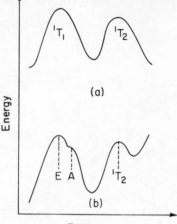

Fig. 6–20. Spectra of (a) $Co(NH_3)_6{}^{3+}$ and (b) $Co(NH_3)_5Cl^{2+}$.

replaced by a different group, which we arbitrarily locate on d_{z^2}, that group interacts differently with cobalt than does ammonia. If this group were chlorine, the σ interaction would be weaker and the π interaction greater. The relative energies of d_{z^2}, d_{xz} and d_{yz} will be affected differently in $Co(NH_3)_5Cl^{2+}$ than in $Co(NH_3)_6{}^{3+}$, for the stronger π interaction of Cl^- raises the energy of d_{xz} and d_{yz} and a weaker σ interaction from Cl^- lowers that of d_{z^2}. The degeneracy of the triplet states is removed and $^1T_1$ is split into E and A states producing the spectrum indicated in Figure 6-20b. Equations have been derived[39] to relate the extent of the splitting to the change in the σ and π bonding interaction. Splitting of the $^1T_2$ band is not observed and the equations indicate that, for chloride, the splitting of the ^1T band will be less than that of $^1T_1$. The splitting of $^1T_2$ is so small that it is not resolved for this complex. Various groups other than Cl^- can be substituted on the pentammines. The following order[39] of σ bond interaction with the metal ion results from spectral studies on these complexes:

$$NH_3 > H_2O > F^- > Cl^- > Br^- > I^-$$

The order of π repulsion is:

$$I^- > Br^- > Cl^- > F^- > NH_3$$

STRUCTURAL EVIDENCE FROM ELECTRONIC SPECTRA

In the simple ligand field description of metal ion complexes we were concerned with the effect the ligands had on the energies of the d levels of the metal ions. Since octahedral, square planar, and tetrahedral fields cause different splittings of the five d orbitals, geometry will have a pronounced effect upon the $d \rightarrow d$ transitions in a metal ion complex. Spectral data for these transitions should provide information about the structure of complexes. Our initial concern will be with how structure affects the energies of the various states in a metal ion.

The structures of six-coordinate complexes can be classified as cubic, tetragonal, or rhombic, if the equivalences of the ligands along the x, y, and z axes are represented by $x = y = z$, $x = y \neq z$, and $x \neq y \neq z$, respectively. The splitting of the states for a d^1 case is represented in Fig. 6-21. Since d–d electron repulsions are not present in the d^1 case, the states can be correlated with the d orbitals as indicated. The reason for the splitting in a tetragonal complex $trans$-$TiA_4B_2^{3+}$, can be understood for the case indicated in Fig. 6-21 where A occupies a higher position in the spectrochemical series than B. Metal electron–ligand electron

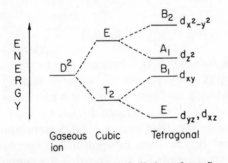

Fig. 6–21. Orbital Splitting for d^1 Complexes in Cubic and Tetragonal Fields.

repulsions are less for states consisting of orbitals directed toward the ligands, B, located on the z axis. As a result, d_{z^2} is lower in energy than $d_{x^2-y^2}$, and d_{xz} and d_{yz} are lower than d_{xy}. More bands will be observed in the spectrum of the tetragonal complex than the octahedral complex.

The energies and splittings of the various states for a spin-paired Co^{III} complex are indicated in Fig. 6-22. Since this is an ion with more than one d electron, we must concern ourselves with states and not orbitals. The $^1T_{1g}$ state of the octahedral complex splits into $^1A_{2g}$ and ^1E_g states in a tetragonal field, while T_{2g} splits into ^1E_g and $^1B_{2g}$. The splitting that occurs in a rhombic field is also indicated. Hydrated trisglycinatocobalt(III) exists as a violet α isomer and a red β isomer. One isomer must be cubic (1,2,3 isomer where $x = y = z$), and the other isomer must be rhombic (1,2,6). The spectrum[53] of the β isomer consists of two bands. The α isomer also gives rise to two bands, one of which is asymmetric and must consist of two or more absorption bands which are not resolved. Therefore, the α isomer must be the 1,2,6 isomer and the β isomer the 1,2,3 isomer.

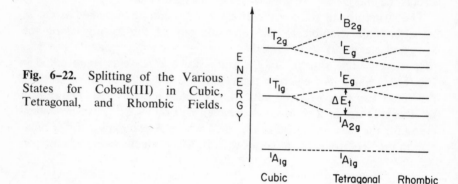

Fig. 6–22. Splitting of the Various States for Cobalt(III) in Cubic, Tetragonal, and Rhombic Fields.

Both *cis*- and *trans*-$CoA_4B_2^+$ isomers are tetragonal. However, the difference in energy between the $^1A_{2g}$ and ^1E_g states (ΔE_t in Fig. 6-22) is usually about twice as large in *trans* complexes as it is in *cis* complexes[52,53] [$\Delta E_t(cis) = -C(\Delta_A - \Delta_B)$ and $\Delta E_t(trans) = 2C(\Delta_A - \Delta_B)$, where C is a constant usually less than one, Δ_A and Δ_B represent the crystal field splitting of A and B (i.e., their position in the spectrochemical series), and the minus sign accounts for the fact that the energies of ^1E_g and $^1A_{2g}$ are interchanged in *cis* and *trans* complexes]. Usually, when Δ_A and Δ_B differ appreciably, the $^1A_{2g}$ and ^1E_g splitting gives rise to a doublet for the low energy peak in the *trans* compound, while this band is simply broadened in the *cis* compound.[54] When Δ_A and Δ_B are similar, this criterion cannot be employed. It is also found that *cis* isomers often have larger molar absorptivity values for $d \rightarrow d$ transitions than *trans* isomers. The ultraviolet charge transfer band can also be used to distinguish between *cis*- and *trans*-cobalt(III) complexes[55] when both isomers are available. The frequency of the band is usually higher in the *cis* than the *trans* compound. The benzoylacetonates of Co^{III} and Cr^{III} are examples in which Δ_A and Δ_B are nearly equal and the *trans* complex has a larger ϵ value than the *cis* complex.[56]

The energies of the states for Ni^{II} in octahedral and tetragonal fields are indicated by the diagram in Fig. 6-23. If certain assumptions are made concerning the metal-ligand distance, the dipole moment of the ligand, and the effective charge of the nickel nucleus, is is possible to calculate[57] the change in energy that occurs for the various states as the ligand arrangement is varied from O_h to D_{4h}.*This corresponds to lengthening the metal-ligand distance along d_{z^2} to infinity. The change in energy for the various levels as a function of the distortion is indicated in Fig. 6-23. The percentages on the abscissa indicate progressive weakening of two *trans* ligands (e.g., 100 percent weakening represents a square planar complex). It is thus easy to see why the spectrum of a square planar or tetragonally distorted nickel complex should differ from that of a regular octahedral complex. Similar diagrams are reported by Furlani and Sartori[57] for distortions from O_h to C_{2v} symmetry (where C_{2v} corresponds to a *cis* six-coordinate complex of type $MB_4A_2^{2+}$) and also for changes from D_{4h} to D_{2d} to T_d geometry. The point to be made here is that pronounced differences are expected between the spectra of complexes of a given metal ion with different ligand arrangements.

As indicated by the variation in color and similarity in spectra of the complexes whose spectra are reproduced in Fig. 6-16, color is a very poor criterion of structure. Octahedral nickel(II) complexes will usually have three absorption bands in the regions: 8000 to 13,000, 15,000 to 19,000, and 25,000 to 29,000 cm^{-1}. The exact position will depend upon the quantities Δ and β. The molar absorptivities of these bands will generally be below 20. As indicated in the section on Dq calculations, the fit of the calculated and experimental frequences of the middle peak has been proposed as confirmatory evidence for the existence of an O_h complex.

Spin-free tetragonal nickel(II) complexes, in which the two ligands occupying either *cis* or *trans* positions are different from the other four but have Dq values which are similar, will give spectra which will be very much like those of the O_h complexes. For example, the distortion in *trans* complexes will be very close to 0 per cent (see Fig. 6-23) and a spectrum typical of octahedral complexes is expected. In general, molar absorptivities will be higher for tetragonal complexes than for octahedral ones. A rule of *average environment* relates the band maxima in these slightly distorted tetragonal complexes to the Dq values of the ligands. The band position is determined by a Dq value which is an average of those of all the surrounding ligands.[39,58]

---

*We shall not be concerned with the details of this calculation here but only with the results.

As indicated in Fig. 6-23, there will be a continuous change in spectral properties as the amount of tetragonal distortion increases. Eventually, for highly distorted tetragonal complexes, the spectra will resemble those of square planar complexes. With large distortion, the multiplicity of the lowest energy state becomes singlet and a diamagnetic complex results. The diamagnetic tetragonal or square planar complexes have high intensity absorption bands ($\epsilon = 100$ to 350) with maxima in the 14,000 to 18,000 cm^{-1} region. The spectra may contain one, two, or three peaks,[59,60]

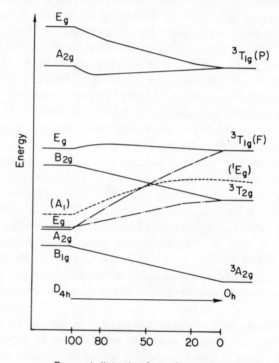

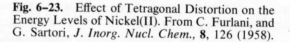

Per cent distortion from O_h symmetry

Fig. 6–23. Effect of Tetragonal Distortion on the Energy Levels of Nickel(II). From C. Furlani, and G. Sartori, *J. Inorg. Nucl. Chem.*, **8**, 126 (1958).

and band assignments are often difficult. However, by using spectral and magnetic data, square planar or highly distorted tetragonal nickel(II) complexes can be easily distinguished from nearly octahedral or tetrahedral complexes.

Just as distortion from O_h to D_{4h} changes the energies and properties of the various levels, so does distortion from D_{4h} (planar) to D_{2d} to T_d.

Fig. 6-24 contains spectra for O_h, D_{4h}, D_{2d}, and T_d complexes.[61,62,63] Because of the large ϵ values for the T_d nickel complex ($NiCl_4^{2-}$), $\epsilon/5$ is plotted. As can be seen, different spectra are obtained for different structures. The spectrum for a T_d complex is expected (see Fig. 6-25) to contain three bands ν_1, ν_2, and ν_3 corresponding to the three spin-allowed transitions: $^3T_1(F) \rightarrow {}^3T_2$, ν_1; $^3T_1(F) \rightarrow {}^3A_2$, ν_2; and $^3T_1(F) \rightarrow {}^3T_1(P)$, ν_3

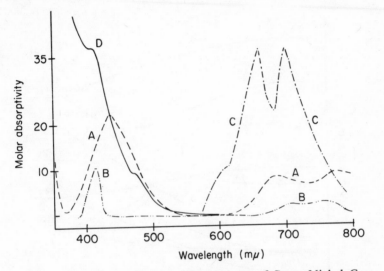

Fig. 6–24. Electronic Absorption Spectra of Some Nickel Complexes. A, Ni $(\phi_3PO)_4(ClO_4)_2$ in $CH_3No_2(D_{2d})$; B, Ni[$(CH_3)_2SO]_6$ ($Clo_4)_2$ in $(CH_3)_2SO(O_h)$; C, $NiCl_4^{2-}$ in $CH_3NO_2(T_d)$; D, Ni(II) (dimethylglyoxinate)$_2$ in $CHCl_3(D_{4h})$. Curve C is a plot of $\epsilon/5$.

(see Fig. 6-25). The ν_1 band occurs in the range 3000 to 5000 cm^{-1} and is often masked by absorption of either the organic part of the molecule or the solvent. It has been observed for Ni^{2+} in silicate glasses and in $NiCl_4^{2-}$. The ν_2 band occurs in the 6500 to 10,000 cm^{-1} region and has an appreciable molar absorptivity ($\epsilon = 15$ to 50). The ν_3 band is found in the visible region (12,000 to 17,000 cm^{-1}) and shows an intense absorption ($\epsilon = 100$ to 200).

It is proposed[61] that the complex [Ni(O—P$\phi_3)_4$](ClO$_4)_2$ has a D_{2d} configuration. Absorption peaks occur in the spectrum at 24,300, 14,800, and 13,100 cm^{-1} with ϵ values of approximately 24, 8, and 9, respectively (Fig. 6-24). The first cationic tetrahedral nickel(II) complex was prepared[63] with the ligand hexamethylphosphoramide, (O—P—[N(CH$_3)_2]_3$, abbreviated HMPA. The similarity of the spectrum of this complex to that of $NiCl_4^{2-}$ was employed to establish tetrahedral structure. In another complex, $Ni(NO_3)_4{}^{2-}$, it was shown[64] that the nickel is six co-ordinate and the anion must contain bidentate nitrate groups.

The above examples are only a few of the very many cases which indicate the utility of near infrared, visible, and ultraviolet spectroscopy in providing information about the structure of complexes. The number of bands, their frequencies, and molar absorptivities should all be considered. The spectra in solution should be checked against spectra of

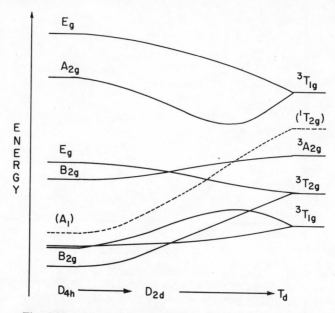

Fig. 6-25. Energy Levels for T_d, D_{4h}, and D_{2d} Complexes. From C. Furlani and G. Sartori, *J. Inorg. Nucl. Chem.,* **8,** 126 (1958).

solids (reflectance or mulls) to be sure that drastic changes in structure do not occur in solution either through ligand replacement by solvent or through expansion of the coordination number by solvation.

Spectral data are available to enable similar conclusions to be drawn concerning the structure of transition metal ions other than nickel. The salient differences between spectra for various structures have been summarized.[40] Magnetic data should be used in conjunction with spectral data to aid in assigning structures to complexes.[65] One may also employ x-ray powder diffraction to investigate possible structural similarities. For example, assignment of a T_d structure for the nickel complex $Ni[O{-}P{-}(NR_2)_3]_4(ClO_4)_2$ received support from its x-ray powder diffraction pattern.[63] The powder pattern of the nickel complex is identical to the analogous zinc complex which is expected to be tetrahedral.

Other kinds of structural applications of visible spectroscopy have been reported. The Dq values for the nitrite ion are different for the nitro ($-NO_2$) and nitrito ($-ONO$) isomers. As a result of the difference in average Dq, $[(Co(NH_3)_5ONO]^{2+}$ is red, while $[Co(NH_3)_5NO_2]^{2+}$ is yellow. Limitations of this kind of application have been reported.[66]

The use of electronic spectra to provide structural information is nicely illustrated in a study of the electronic structure of the vanadyl ion.[67] Spectra of the vanadyl ion, VO^{2+}, are interpreted to indicate that there is considerable oxygen-to-metal π bonding in the V—O bond. The similarity in the charge transfer spectra of solids known by x-ray analysis to contain the VO^{2+} group and of solutions is presented as evidence that aqueous solutions contain the species $VO(H_2O)_5^{2+}$ and not $V(OH)_2^{2+}$. Protonation of VO^{2+} would have a pronounced effect on the charge transfer spectrum. It is proposed that the oxygen is not protonated because its basicity is weakened by π bonding with vanadium. A complete molecular orbital scheme for $VO(H_2O)_5^{2+}$ is presented,[67] and assignments are made for the spectrum of $VOSO_4 \cdot 5H_2O$ in aqueous solution. Similar studies on other oxy-cations provide evidence for considerable metal-oxygen π bonding[68] and aid in elucidating the electronic structures of these species.

In summary, it is worthwhile mentioning that electronic spectroscopy is most useful in the study of transition metal ion complexes, is least useful in the study of compounds containing only σ bonds, and is of intermediate utility in the area of charge transfer spectra and solvation effects. It is interesting that the utility is directly proportional to our understanding of the theory in the particular area. The inorganic chemist must keep abreast of forthcoming theoretical developments with an eye toward possible applications.

MISCELLANEOUS APPLICATIONS OF THE PRINCIPLES RELATED TO ELECTRONIC TRANSITIONS

The principles discussed in this chapter are of importance to inorganic chemists for applications other than structure determination. Florescence, phosphorescence, and photochemistry all have to do with electronic transitions. In photochemical reactions, the reactant is a molecule in a reactive excited state. Understanding of the photochemical reaction requires an understanding of the structure and reactivity of the excited state. In some cases, molecules which are singlets in the ground state become reactive radicals by being excited to a triplet state containing unpaired electrons.

The final application that will be mentioned involves measuring the ionization potential of molecules. It is found[69] that photons may cause ionization rather than dissociation of molecules, even though the ionization potential is greater than the dissociation energy. The onset of ion current is measured[69] as the wavelength of the light impinging on the molecule is decreased. The ionization potential is calculated from the wavelength necessary to cause photoionization.

EXERCISES

1. The compound ϕ_3 as is reported [*J. Mol. Spectry.*, **5.** 118–132 (1960)] to have two absorption bands, one near 2700 Å and a second around 2300 Å. One band is due to the $\pi \rightarrow \pi^*$ transition of the phenyl ring and the other is a charge transfer transition from the lone pair electrons on arsenic to the ring. The 2300 band is solvent dependent, and the 2700 band is not.
   a. Which band do you suspect is $\pi \rightarrow \pi^*$?
   b. What effect would substitution of one of the phenyl groups by CF_3 have on the frequency of the charge transfer transition?
   c. In which of the following compounds would the charge transfer band occur at highest frequency, $\phi_3 P$, $\phi_3 Sb$, or $\phi_3 Bi$?

2. What effect would changing the solvent from a nonpolar to polar one have on the frequency for the following:
   a. Both ground and excited states are neutral (i.e., there is no charge separation)?
   b. The ground state is neutral and the excited state polar?
   c. The ground state is polar, the excited state has greater charge separation and the dipole moment vector in the excited state is perpendicular to the ground state moment?
   d. The ground state is polar and the excited state neutral?

3. Would you have a better chance of detecting vibrational fine structure in an electronic transition in liquid CCl_4 or CH_3CN? Why?

4. Do the excited states that result from $n \rightarrow \pi^*$ and $\pi \rightarrow \pi^*$ transitions in pyridine belong to the same species? To which species do they belong?

5. Under what conditions can electronic transitions occur in the infrared spectrum? Which compounds would you examine to find an example of this?

6. Refer to equation (6-5) and explain why the transition that occurs in the ion pair N-methylpyridinium iodide does not occur in the solvent separated ion pair.

7. Recall the center of gravity rule and explain why the blue shift in the iodine transition should be related to the heat of interaction of iodine with a donor (see Fig. 6-8).

8. Refer to the Tanabe and Sugano diagrams in Appendix C. For Cr^{III} and a ligand with D_q/B of 1, how many bands should occur in the spectrum? Assign these transitions and list them in order of increasing wavelength.

9. In complexes with weak field ligands ($Dq/B = 0.7$), octahedral Co^{2+} exhibits a spectrum with three well separated bands, Make a tentative assignment using the Tanabe and Sugano diagrams and list the assignments in order of decreasing frequency. Would the spectrum of a strong field complex be any different? Describe the spectrum you would expect for a strong field complex.

10. A nickel complex NiR_4Cl_2 has an absorption spectrum with peaks that have ϵ values of around 150. R and Cl occupy similar positions in the spectrochemical series. Are the chlorines coordinated?

11. Two different isomers of $Co(NH_3)_4(SCN)_2{}^+$ were separated. How could you determine whether the SCN group in both were bonded through the sulfur? If both isomers were coordinated through sulfur, how would you determine which is *cis* and which is *trans*? (HINT; — SCN is near Cl^- in the spectrochemical series, while —NCS⁻ creates a stronger field; $Co(NH_3)_4Cl_2{}^+$ is easily prepared.)

REFERENCES CITED

1. H. H. Jaffe and M. Orchin, "Theory and Applications of Ultraviolet Spectroscopy," Wiley, New York, 1962.
2. M. Kasha, *Discussions Faraday Soc.*, **9**, 14 (1950).
3. M. Kasha, *Chem. Revs.*, **41**, 401 (1947); J. R. Platt, *J. Opt. Soc. Am.*, **43**, 252 (1953): A. Terenin, *Acta Physics Chim. USSR*, **18**, 210 (1943) (in English).
4. M. Kasha, "The Nature and Significance of $n \rightarrow \pi^*$ Transitions," in *Light and Life*, ed. by W. D. McElroy and B. Glass, Johns Hopkins, Baltimore, 1961.
5. J. Sidman, *Chem. Revs.*, **58**, 689 (1958).
6. H. McConnell, *J. Chem. Phys.*, **20**, 700 (1952).
7. G. J. Brealey and M. Kasha, *J. Am. Chem. Soc.*, **77**, 4462, 1955.
8. S. Nagakura, *Bull. Chem. Soc. Japan*, **25**, 164 (1952). In English.
9. L. E. Orgel, *Quart. Revs.*, **8**, 422 (1954).
10. S. P. McGlynn, and M. Kasha, *J. Chem. Phys.*, **24**, 481 (1956).
11. C. K. Jørgenson, *Acta Chem. Scand.*, **11**, 166 (1957); R. J. P. Williams, *J. Chem. Soc.*, **1955**, 137.
12. R. P. Bauman, "Absorption Spectroscopy," Wiley, New York, 1962.
13. L. Lang, "Absorption Spectra in the Ultraviolet and Visible Region," Vols. 1, 2, Academic, New York, 1961. Vol. 3 in preparation.
14. H. M. Hershenson, "Ultraviolet and Visible Absorption Spectra–Index for 1930-54," Academic, New York, 1956.
15. "Organic Electronic Spectral Data," Vols. 1–5, Interscience, New York, 1963. Compilation of spectral data from 1946 to 1961.
16. "ASTM (American Society for Testing Materials) Coded IBM Cards for Ultraviolet and Visible Spectra" ASTM, Philadelphia, 1961.
17. S. F. Mason, *Quart. Revs.*, **15**, 287 (1961).
18. N. Metropolis, *Phys. Rev.*, **60**, 283, 295 (1941).
19. S. J. Strickler and M. Kasha, *J. Am. Chem. Soc.*, **85**, 2899 (1963).
20. T. Kubota, *J. Chem. Soc. Japan*, **78**, 196 (1957).
21. M. Tamres, et al., *J. Am. Chem. Soc.*, **75**, 4358 (1953).
22. H. McConnell, J. S. Ham and J. R. Platt, *J. Chem. Phys.*, **21**, 66 (1953).

23. G. Briegleb and J. Czekalla. *Z. Phys. Chem. (Frankfurt)*, **24**, 37 (1960).
24. R. M. Keefer and L. J. Andrews, *J. Am. Chem. Soc.*, **77**, 2164 (1955).
25. R. L. Carlson and R. S. Drago, *J. Am. Chem. Soc.*, **85**, 505 (1963).
26. R. L. Middaugh, R. S. Drago, and R. J. Niedzielski, *J. Am. Chem. Soc.*, **86**, 388 (1964).
27. R. S. Drago, B. Wayland, and R. L. Carlson, *J. Am. Chem. Soc.*, **85**, 3125 (1963).
28. Sister M. Brandon, O.P., M. Tamres, and S. Searles, Jr., *J. Am. Chem. Soc.*, **82**, 2129 (1960); M. Tamres and S. Searles, Jr., *J. Phys. Chem.*, **66**, 1099 (1962).
29. H. Yada, J. Tanaka, and S. Nagakura, *Bull. Chem. Soc. Japan*, **33**, 1660 (1960).
30. R. S. Drago, D. W. Meek, R. Longhi, and M. Joesten, *Inorg. Chem.*, **2**, 1056 (1963).
31. R. S. Drago and D. A. Wenz, *J. Am. Chem. Soc.*, **84**, 526 (1962). Other donors studied toward these acids are summarized here.
32. L. E. Orgel, *Quart. Revs.*, **8**, 422 (1954); L. J. Andrews and R. M. Keefer, "Advances in Inorganic Chemistry and Radiochemistry, Vol. 3, eds. H. J. Emeleus and A. G. Sharpe, pp. 91-128, Academic, New York, 1961.
33. O. Hassel and Chr. Rømming, *Quart. Revs.*, **16**, 1 (1962).
34. S. P. McGlynn, *Chem. Revs.*, **58**, 1113 (1958).
35. G. Briegleb, "Elektronen Donator-Acceptor-Komplexes." Springer Verlag. Berlin, 1963.
36. E. M. Kosower, et al., *J. Am. Chem. Soc.*, **78**, 5700, 5838 (1956); E. M. Kosower, *J. Am. Chem. Soc.*, **80**, 3253, 3261, 3267 (1958); E. M. Kosower, "Charge Transfer Complexes," in "The Enzymes," Vol. 3, eds. Boyer, Lardy, and Myrbach, p. 171, Academic Press, New York, 1960. The Spectrum of N-methylpyridinium iodide in many solvents is treated exhaustively in these references.
37. E. M. Kosower and G. Wu, *J. Am. Chem. Soc.*, **83**, 3142 (1961).
38. E. M. Kosower, G. Wu, and T. S. Sorenson. *J. Am. Chem. Soc.*, **83**, 3147 (1961).
39. C. K. Jørgensen, "Absorption Spectra and Chemical Bonding in Complexes," Addison-Wesley, Reading, Mass., 1962.
40. T. M. Dunn, "Modern Coordination Chemistry," eds. J. Lewis and R. G. Wilkins, Interscience, New York, 1960.
41. C. J. Ballhausen, "Introduction to Ligand Field Theory," McGraw-Hill, New York, 1962.
42. A. D. Liehr and C. J. Ballhausen, *Phys. Rev.*, **106**, 1161-63 (1957).
43. L. E. Orgel, *J. Chem. Soc.*, **1952**, 4756.
44. Y. Tanabe and S. Sugano, *J. Phys. Soc. Japan*, **9**, 753, 766 (1954).
45. C. E. Moore, "Atomic Energy Levels Circular 467," Vol. 2, National Bureau of Standards, 1952. Volumes 1 and 3 contain similar data for other gaseous ions.
46. F. A. Cotton and M. Goodgame, *J. Am. Chem. Soc.*, **83**, 1777 (1961).
47. D. W. Barnum, *J. Inorg. Nucl. Chem.*, **21**, 221 (1961).
48. T. S. Piper and R. L. Carlin, *J. Chem. Phys.*, **36**, 3330 (1962).
49. R. S. Drago, D. W. Meek, M. D. Joesten, and L. LaRoche, *Inorg. Chem.*, **2**, 124 (1963).

50. R. S. Drago, D. W. Meek, R. L. Longhi, and M. D. Joesten, *Inorg. Chem.*, **2**, 1056 (1963).
51. R. W. Kiser and T. W. Lapp, *Inorg. Chem.*, **1**, 401 (1962).
52. D. S. McClure, "Advances in the Chemistry of Coordination Compounds," ed. S. Kirshner, p. 498, Macmillan, New York, 1961. And the references contained therein.
53. F. Basolo, C. J. Ballhausen, and J. Bjerrum, *Acta Chem. Scand.*, **9**, 810 (1955).
54. Y. Shimura, *Bull. Chem. Soc. Japan*, **25**, 49 (1952); L. E. Orgel. *J. Chem. Phys.*, **23**, 1004 (1955).
55. F. Basolo, *J. Am. Chem. Soc*, **72**, 4393 (1950); Y. J. Shimura, *J. Am. Chem. Soc.*, **73**, 5079 (1951); K. Nakamoto, J. Fujita, M. Kobayashi, and R. Tsuchida, *J. Chem. Phys.*, **27**, 439 (1957). And references contained therein.
56. R. C. Fay and T. S. Piper. *J. Am. Chem. Soc.*, **84**, 2303 (1962).
57. C. Furlani and G. Sartori, *J. Inorg. Nuc. Chem.*, **8**, 126 (1958).
58. C. K. Jørgensen, "Energy Levels of Complexes and Gaseous Ions," Gjellerups, Copenhagen, 1957.
59. W. Manch and W. Fernelius, *J. Chem. Educ.*, **38**, 192 (1961).
60. G. Maki, *J. Chem. Phys.*, **29**, 162 (1958); ibid. **29**, 1129 (1958).
61. F. A. Cotton and E. Bannister, *J. Chem. Soc.*, **1960**, 1873.
62. N. S. Gill and R. S. Nyholm, *J. Chem. Soc.*, **1959**, 3997.
63. J. T. Donoghue and R. S. Drago, *Inorg. Chem.*, **1**, 866 (1962).
64. D. K. Straub, R. S. Drago, and J. T. Donoghue, *Inorg. Chem.*, **1**, 848 (1962).
65. B. N. Figgis and J. Lewis, "Modern Coordination Chemistry," eds. J. Lewis and R. G. Wilkins, Interscience, New York, 1960.
66. M. Linhard, H. Siebert, and M. Weigel, *Z. anorg. U. Allgem. Chem.*, **278**, 287 (1955).
67. C. J. Ballhausen and H. B. Gray, *Inorg. Chem.*, **1**, 111 (1962).
68. H. B. Gray and C. R. Hare, *Inorg. Chem.*, **1**, 363 (1962); C. R. Hare, I. Bernal, and H. B. Gray, *Inorg. Chem.*, **1**, 831 (1962).
69. K. Watanabe, *J. Chem. Phys.*, **22**, 1564 (1954). And other references by this author.

GENERAL REFERENCES

A. The following references may be consulted for further study:
C. J. Ballhausen, "Introduction to Ligand Field Theory," McGraw-Hill, New York, 1962.
G. M. Barrow, "Introduction to Molecular Spectroscopy," McGraw-Hill, New York, 1962.
R. P. Bauman, "Absorption Spectroscopy," Wiley, New York, 1962.
E. A. Braude and F. C. Nachod, "Determination of Organic Structures by Physical Methods," pp. 131–195, Academic, New York, 1955.
G. L. Clark, "The Encyclopedia of Spectroscopy," Reinhold, New York, 1960.
A. B. F. Duncan and F. A. Matsen in "Chemical Applications of Spectroscopy," ed. A. Weissberger, pp. 12–21, 581–706, Interscience, New York, 1956.

A. E. Gillam and E. S. Stern, "Electronic Absorption Spectroscopy," 2nd ed., Arnold, London, 1957.

M. Kasha, "Molecular Excitation, Modern Concepts of Chemistry Series," Ronald, New York, in prep.

G. W. King, "Spectroscopy and Molecular Structure," Holt, Rinehart, and Winston, New York, 1964.

W. D. Phillips and F. Nachod, "Determination of Organic Structures by Physical Methods," pp. 131–195, Academic, New York, 1955.

C. N. R. Rao, "Ultraviolet and Visible Spectroscopy," Butterworths, London, 1961.

A. Streitwieser, Jr., "Molecular Orbital Theory for Organic Chemists," pp. 249–283, Wiley, New York, 1962.

A. Walsh, *J. Chem. Soc.*, **1953**, 2260.

B. Spectral curves, wavelengths of the absorption peaks, and molar absorptivities for many compounds are tabulated in the following references:

ASTM (American Society for Testing Materials), "Coded IBM Cards for Ultraviolet and Visible Spectra," ASTM, 1916 Race Street, Philadelphia.

H. M. Hershenson, "Ultraviolet and Visible Absorption Spectra—Index for 1930–54," Academic, New York, 1956.

L. Lang, "Absorption Spectra in the Ultraviolet and Visible Region," vols 1–3 (vol 3 in prep.), Academic, New York, 1961.

Organic Electronic Spectral Data," vols. 1–5, Interscience, New York, 1963. Compilation of spectral data from 1946 to 1961.

7 Vibration and Rotation Spectroscopy: Infrared, Raman, and Microwave

INTRODUCTION

HARMONIC AND ANHARMONIC VIBRATIONS

As discussed earlier (Chapter 5), quanta of radiation in the infrared region have energies comparable to those required for vibrational transitions in molecules. Let us begin this discussion by considering the classical description of the vibrational motion of a diatomic molecule. For this purpose it is convenient to consider the diatomic molecule as two masses, A and B, connected by a spring. In Fig. 7-1a the equilibrium position is indicated. If a displacement of A and B is carried out moving them to A' and B' (as in Fig. 7-1b), there will be a force acting to return the system to that in Fig. 7-1a. If this restoring force, f, is proportional the the displacement Δr, i.e.,

$$f = k\Delta r \qquad (7-1)$$

the resultant motion that develops when A' and B' are released and allowed to oscillate is described as *simple harmonic motion*. In equation (7-1), k, the Hooke's law constant for the spring, is called the *force*

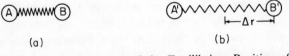

(a)   (b)

Fig. 7-1. Displacement of the Equilibrium Position of Two Masses Connected by a Spring.

constant for a molecular system held together by a chemical bond.

For harmonic oscillation of two masses connected by a spring, a plot of the potential energy of the system as a function of the distance r between the masses is a parabola which is symmetrical about the equilibrium internuclear distance, r_e, as the minimum (see Fig. 7-2). The force constant is a measure of the curvature of the potential well. This classical model does not hold for a molecule because a molecular system cannot

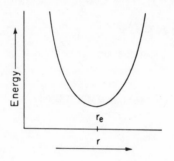

Fig. 7–2. Potential Energy Versus Distance, r, for a Harmonic Oscillator.

occupy a continuum of energy states but can only occupy discrete, quantized energy levels. A quantum mechanical treatment of the molecular system yields the following equation for the permitted energy states of a molecule which is a simple harmonic oscillator:

$$E_v = \mathbf{h}\nu(\mathrm{v} + \tfrac{1}{2}) \qquad (7\text{-}2)$$

where v is an integer 0, 1, 2, . . ., representing the vibrational quantum number of the various states, E_v is the energy of the vth state, **h** is Planck's constant, and ν is the *fundamental vibration frequency* ($\sec^{-1}$) (i.e., the frequency for the transition from state, v = 0 to v = 1). These states are indicated in the Morse potential energy curve of a real molecule (see Fig. 6-1). Note that this curve (Fig. 6-1) is not a perfect parabola. The vibrational energy levels are not equally spaced, as equation (7-2) requires, but actually converge. The levels converge by virtue of the molecule undergoing anharmonic rather than harmonic oscillation, i.e., equation (7-1) is not obeyed. This deviation from harmonic oscillation occurs in all molecules and becomes greater as the vibrational quantum number increases. As will be seen later, the assumption of harmonic oscillation will be sufficiently accurate for certain purposes (e.g., the description of fundamental vibrations) and is introduced here for this reason.

ABSORPTION OF RADIATION BY MOLECULAR VIBRATIONS— SELECTION RULES

In order for molecules to absorb infrared radiation as vibrational excitation energy, there must be a change in the dipole moment of the molecule as it vibrates. Consequently the stretching of homonuclear diatomic molecules will not give rise to infrared absorptions. According to this selection rule, any change in direction or magnitude of the dipole during a vibration gives rise to an oscillating dipole which can interact with the oscillating electric field component of infrared radiation giving rise to absorption of radiation. A vibration which results in a change in direction of the dipole is illustrated by the N—C—H bending mode of HCN. There is little change in the magnitude of the dipole but an appreciable change in direction when the molecule vibrates.

The following second selection rule can be derived from the harmonic oscillator approximation. This selection rule, which is rigorous for a harmonic oscillator, states that in the absorption of radiation only transitions for which $\Delta v = +1$ can occur. Since most molecules are in the v_0 vibrational level at room temperature, most transitions will occur from the state v_0 to v_1. This transition is indicated by arrow *1* of Fig. 7-3. The frequency corresponding to this energy is called the *fundamental frequency*. According to this selection rule, radiation with energy corresponding to transitions indicated by arrows *2* and *3* in Fig. 7-3 will not

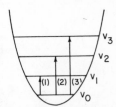

Fig. 7–3. Vibrational States Corresponding to a Normal Vibrational Mode in a Harmonic Oscillator.

induce transitions in the molecule. Since most molecules are not perfect harmonic oscillators, this selection rule breaks down and transitions corresponding to 2 and 3 do occur. The transition designated as 2 occurs at a frequency about twice that of the fundamental (*1*) while *3* occurs at about three times that of the fundamental. These transitions (*2* and *3*) are referred to as that *first* and *second overtones*, respectively. The intensity of the first overtone is often an order of magnitude less than that of the fundamental and that of the second overtone an order of magnitude less than the first overtone.

Force Constant

The difference in energy, ΔE, between two adjacent levels, E_v and E_{v+1}, is given by the equation (7-3) for a harmonic oscillator:

$$\Delta E = (\mathbf{h}/2\pi)(k/\mu)^{1/2} \qquad (7\text{-}3)$$

where k is the stretching force constant and μ the reduced mass [$\mu = m_A m_B/(m_A + m_B)$ for the diatomic molecule A—B]. The relationship between energy and frequency, $\Delta E = \mathbf{h}\nu = \mathbf{h}c\bar{\nu}$, was presented in Chapter 5. The symbol ν will be used interchangeably for frequency (sec^{-1}) or wavenumber (cm^{-1}) but the units will be indicated when necessary. In the HCl molecule, the absorption of infrared radiation with $\nu = 2890$ cm^{-1} corresponds to a transition from the ground state to the first excited vibrational state. This excited state corresponds to a greater amplitude and frequency for the stretching of the H—Cl bond. Converting ν to energy produces ΔE of equation (7-3). Since all other quantities are known, this equation can be solved to produce: $k = 4.84 \times 10^5$ dynes/cm. Stretching force constants for various diatomic molecules are summarized in Table 7-1.

TABLE 7-1. STRETCHING FORCE
CONSTANTS FOR VARIOUS DIATOMIC
MOLECULES (CALCULATED BY THE
HARMONIC OSCILLATOR
APPROXIMATION)

Molecule	ν (cm^{-1})	$k(dynes/cm^{-1})$
HF	3958	8.8×10^5
HCl	2885	4.8×10^5
HBr	2559	3.8×10^5
HI	2230	2.9×10^5
F_2[a]	892	4.5×10^5
Cl_2[a]	557	3.2×10^5
Br_2[a]	321	2.4×10^5
I_2[a]	213	1.7×10^5
CO	2143	18.7×10^5
NO	1876	15.5×10^5

[a]Observed by Raman spectroscopy

The force constants in Table 7-1 are calculated by using equation (7-3) which was derived from the harmonic oscillator approximation. When an anharmonic oscillator model is employed, somewhat different values are obtained. For example, a force constant of 5.157×10^5 dynes cm^{-1}

results for HCl. The latter value is obtained by measuring the first, second, and third overtones and evaluating the anharmonicity from the deviation of these frequencies from 2, 3, and 4 times the fundamental, respectively. Since these overtones are often not detected in the larger molecules more commonly encountered, we shall not be concerned with the details of the anharmonicity calculation.

The force constant for some other stretching vibrations of interest are listed in Table 7-2. A larger force constant is often interpreted as being indicative of a stronger bond, but there is no simple correlation between bond dissociation energy and force constant.

TABLE 7-2. STRETCHING
FORCE CONSTANTS, k, FOR
VARIOUS STRETCHING VIBRA-
TIONS (HARMONIC OSCILLATOR
APPROXIMATION)

Bond	k(dynes cm^{-1})
$\geqslant$C—C$\leqslant$	4.5×10^5
$\geqslant$C—C$\leqslant$	5.2×10^5
$\geqslant$C$=$C$<$	9.6×10^5
—C—C—	15.6×10^5
$>$C$=$O	12.1×10^5
—C—N	17.73×10^5
$\equiv$C—H	5.9×10^5
$\geqslant$C—H	4.8×10^5

Triple bonds have stretching force constants of the order of magnitude of 13 to 18×10^5, double bonds about 8 to 12×10^5 and single bonds below 8×10^5 dynes cm^{-1}. In general force constants for bending modes are much less than those for stretching modes.

As indicated by equation (7-3), the reduced mass is important in determining the frequency of a vibration. If for example a hydrogen bonded to carbon is replaced by deuterium, there will be a negligible change in the force constant but an appreciable change in the reduced mass. As indicated by equation (7-3), the frequency should be lower by a factor of about $1/\sqrt{2}$. Normally a vibration involving hydrogen will occur at 1.3 to 1.4 times the frequency of the corresponding vibration in the deuterated molecule.

VIBRATIONS IN A POLYATOMIC MOLECULE

If a system containing n atoms is described by a set of Cartesian coordinates, the general motion of each atom in the system can be described by utilizing three positional coordinates. The molecule is said, therefore, to have $3n$ degrees of freedom. Certain combinations of these individual degrees of freedom correspond to translational motion of the molecule as a whole without any change in interatomic dimensions. There are three such combinations which represent the x, y, and z components of the translational motion, respectively. For a nonlinear molecule there are three combinations which correspond to rotation about the three principal axes of the molecule. Therefore, *for a nonlinear molecule there are $3n - 6$ normal modes of vibration* which result in a change in bond lengths or angles in the molecule. *Normal modes are so defined as to represent independent self-repeating motions in a molecule which is a harmonic oscillator.* The center of mass of the molecule does not change in the vibrations associated with the normal mode nor is angular momentum involved in these vibrations. *All general vibrational motion which a molecule may undergo can be resolved into either one or a combination of these normal modes.*

For a linear molecule all the vibrations can be resolved into $3n-5$ normal modes. The additional mode obtained for a linear molecule is indicated in Fig. 7-4b where plus signs indicate motion of the atoms into the paper and minus signs represent motion out of the paper. For the nonlinear molecule (Fig. 7-4a) the motion indicated corresponds to a rotation. For a linear molecule a similar motion corresponds to a bending of the bonds, and hence this molecule has an additional normal vibrational mode ($3n - 5$ for a linear molecule vs. $3n - 6$ for a nonlinear one).

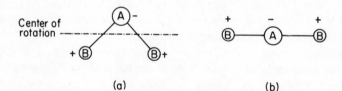

(a)   (b)

Fig. 7–4. Rotational and Bending Modes for (a) Nonlinear and (b) Linear Molecules.

As will be seen later there are many applications for which we need to know which bands correspond to the fundamentals.

Effects Giving Rise to Absorption Bands

Sulfur dioxide is predicted to have three normal modes from the $3n - 6$ rule. The spectral data (Table 7-3) show the presence of more than three bands. The three bands at 1361, 1151, and 519 cm^{-1} are the fundamentals and are referred to as the ν_3, ν_1, and ν_2 bands, respectively

TABLE 7-3. INFRARED
SPECTRUM OF SO_2

$\nu(cm^{-1})$	Assignment
519	ν_2
606	$\nu_1 - \nu_2$
1151	ν_1
1361	ν_3
1871	$\nu_2 + \nu_3$
2305	$2\nu_1$
2499	$\nu_1 + \nu_3$

(see Fig. 7-5). The ν_n symbolism is used to label the various frequencies of fundamental vibrations and should not be confused with the symbols v_0, v_1, v_2, etc., used to designate various vibrational levels of one mode in a molecule. By convention the highest frequency, totally symmetric vibration is called ν_1, the second highest totally symmetric

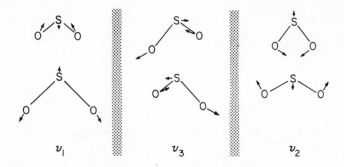

Fig. 7-5. The Three Fundamental Vibrations for Sulfur Dioxide.

vibration ν_2, etc. When the symmetric vibrations have all been assigned, the highest frequency asymmetric vibration is counted next followed by the remaining asymmetric vibrations in order of decreasing frequency. An exception is made to this rule for the bending vibration of a linear molecule, which is labeled ν_2. Another common convention involves labeling stretching vibrations ν, bending vibrations δ, and out of plane bending vibrations π. Subscripts, *as* for asymmetric, *s* for symmetric, and *d* for degenerate are employed with these symbols.

The ν_1 mode in SO_2 is described as the *symmetric stretch*, ν_3 as the *asymmetric stretch*, and ν_2 as *the bending mode*. In general, the asymmetric stretch will occur at higher frequency than the symmetric stretch, and stretching modes occur at much higher frequencies than bending modes. There is a slight angle change in the stretching vibrations in order for the molecule to retain its center of mass. The other absorption frequencies in Table 7-3 are assigned as indicated. The overtone of ν_1 occurs at about $2\nu_1$ or 2305 cm^{-1}. The bands at 1871 and 2499 cm^{-1} are each referred to as *combination bands*. Absorption of radiation of these energies occurs with the simultaneous excitation of both vibrational modes of the combination. The 606 cm^{-1} band is a *difference band* which involves a transition from the state in which the ν_2 mode is excited to that in which the ν_1 mode is excited. Note that all the bands in the spectrum are accounted for by these assignments. Making the assignments is seldom this simple and, as will be shown later, much other information is employed to substantiate these assignments.

A more complicated case is the CO_2 molecule where four fundamentals are predicted by the $3n - 5$ rule. A single band results from the two degenerate vibrations, ν_2 of Fig. 7-6 which correspond to bending modes

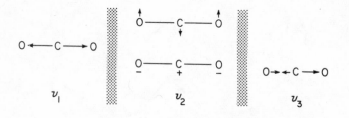

Fig. 7-6. Carbon Dioxide Fundamental Vibration Modes.

at right angles to each other. Later we shall see how symmetry considerations aid in predicting the number of degenerate bands to be expected. In more complex molecules some of the fundamentals may be accidentally degenerate because two vibration frequencies just happen to be equal. This is not easily predicted and the occurrence of this phenomenon introduces a serious complication. The assignment of the CO_2 fundamentals is more difficult than SO_2 because many more bands appear in the infrared and Raman spectra. Bands at 2349, 1340 and 667 cm^{-1} have been assigned to ν_3, ν_1 and ν_2, respectively. The tests of these assignments have been described in detail by Herzberg[1] and will not be repeated here. In this example the fundamentals are the three most intense bands in the spectrum. In some cases, there is only a small dipole moment change in a vibration, and the fundamental is weak (see the first selection rule).

The above discussion of the band at 1340 cm^{-1} has been simplified. Actually, it is an intense doublet with band maxima at 1286 and 1388 cm^{-1}. This splitting is due to a phenomenon known as *Fermi resonance*. The overtone $2\nu_2(2 \times 667 = 1334$ cm^{-1}) and the fundamental ν_1 should occur at almost the same frequency. The two vibrations interact by a typical quantum mechanical resonance, and the frequency of one is raised and the other lowered. The wave function describing these states corresponds to a mixing of the wave functions of the two initial states (ν_1 and $2\nu_2$) which arise from the harmonic oscillator approximation. We cannot say that one line corresponds to ν_1 and the other to $2\nu_2$, for both are mixtures of ν_1 and $2\nu_2$. This interaction also accounts for the high intensity of what in the absence of interaction would have been a weak overtone ($2\nu_2$). The intensity of the fundamental is distributed between the two bands, for both bands consist partly of the fundamental vibration.

The presence of Fermi resonance can sometimes be detected in more complex molecules by examining deuterated molecules or by determining the spectrum in various solvents. Since the Fermi resonance interaction requires that the vibrations involved have nearly the same frequency, the interaction will be affected if one mode undergoes a frequency shift from deuteration or a solvent effect while the other mode does not. The two frequencies will no longer be equivalent and the weak overtone will revert to a weak band or not be observed in the spectrum. Other requirements for the Fermi resonance interaction will be discussed in the section on symmetry considerations.

Normal Coordinate Analyses and Band Assignments

Degeneracy, vibration frequencies outside the range of the instruments, low intensity fundamentals, overtones, combination bands, difference bands, and Fermi resonance all complicate the assignment of fundamentals. The problem can be resolved for simple molecules by a technique known as a *normal coordinate analysis*. A normal coordinate analysis involves solving the classical mechanical problem of the vibrating molecule assuming a particular form of the potential energy (usually the valence force field). The details of this calculation are beyond the scope of this text but are described elsewhere.[1-3] The results of this involved calculation produce the force constants and indicate exactly the form of each vibration in terms of the normal coordinates. There is one normal coordinate corresponding to the atomic displacements in each normal mode. Only after this analysis can the absorption spectra be completely interpreted in terms of molecular vibrations.

GROUP VIBRATIONS

In complex molecules a complete normal coordinate analysis is often not possible. Assignments are frequently made by taking advantage of the experimental observation that many functional groups absorb in a narrow region of the spectrum regardless of the molecule that contains the group. In the acetone molecule,* for example, one of the normal modes of vibration consists of a C—O stretching motion with negligible motion of the other atoms in the molecule. Similarly the methyl groups can be considered to undergo vibrations which are independent of the motions of the carbonyl group. In various molecules it is found that carbonyl absorptions due to the stretching vibration occur in roughly the same spectral region (~ 1700 cm^{-1}). As will be seen in the section on applications, the position of the band does vary slightly (± 150 cm^{-1}) because of the mass, inductive, and conjugative effects of the groups attached. The methyl group has five characteristic absorption bands; two bands in the region 3000 to 2860 (from the asymmetric and symmetric stretch), one around 1470 to 1400 (the asymmetric bend), one around 1380 to 1200 (the symmetric bend), and one in the region 1200 to 800 cm^{-1} (rocking mode). This dissecting of the molecule into groups is a valuable approximation referred to as the *concept of group vibrations*. Many functional groups in unknown compounds have been identified by using this assumption. Unfortunately, in many complicated molecules there are many group vibrations that overlap and assignment of the bands in a spectrum becomes difficult. It is possible to perform experiments which help resolve this problem: deuteration will cause a shift in vibrations involving hydrogen (e.g., C—H , O—H , or N—H stretches and bends) by a factor of 1.3 to 1.4; characteristic shifts, which aid in assignments, occur with certain donor functional groups (e.g., C=O) when the spectrum is examined in hydrogen-bonding solvents or in the presence of acidic solutes.

LIMITATIONS OF THE GROUP VIBRATION CONCEPT

The limitations of the group vibration concept should be emphasized so that incorrect interpretations of infrared spectral data can be recog-

---

*This molecule has been analyzed by a normal coordinate treatment.

nized. The group vibration concept implies that the vibrations of a particular group are relatively independent of the rest of the molecule. If the center of mass is to be retained, this is impossible. All of the nuclei in a molecule must undergo their harmonic oscillations in a synchronous manner in normal vibrations. When a vibration involves motion of a functional group containing light atoms in a molecule consisting otherwise of heavy atoms, very little motion of the heavy atoms is required to maintain the center of gravity, and the group vibration concept is applicable. When the atoms in a molecule are of similar mass and are connected by bonds with similar force constants, the entire molecule will participate in the vibration. This simultaneous vibration of more than one group is referred to as coupling (or mixing) of the group vibrational modes. Coupling can be understood by considering this interaction in a manner somewhat similar to the formation of molecular orbitals from atomic orbitals. In Fig. 7-7, the hypothetical linear molecule A—B—C is

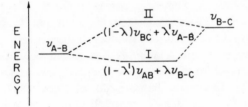

Fig. 7-7.   Energetics for Coupling of Vibrational Modes.

considered. The two group vibrations of similar energies $\nu_{A—B}$ and $\nu_{B—C}$ are indicated on the extreme right and left. The coupled vibrations, I and II, indicated in the center are essentially $\nu_{A—B}$ and $\nu_{B—C}$, respectively. They occur at different energies than the group vibrations because of contributions to each coupled vibration from the vibration of the third atom. For example, the vibration I, which is essentially $\nu_{A—B}$, actually involves some motion of the B—C bond. When the B—C vibration occurs there will be some A—B motion. An important requirement for extensive coupling is that the frequencies of the two group vibrations be close together. Coupling is necessary because of the assumption of group vibrations, and should be distinguished from a combination band where the radiation excites two distinct fundamentals.

The C—H and C—N group stretching vibrations in the H—C—N molecule are coupled. The absorption band attributed to the C—H stretch actually involves C—N motion to some extent and vice versa, i.e., the observed frequencies cannot be described as being a pure C—H and a pure C—N stretch. Evidence to support this comes from deuteration studies where it is found that deuteration affects the frequency of the band assigned to the C—N stretch. The C—N absorption occurs at 2089 and 1906 cm^{-1} in the molecules H—C—N and D—C—N, respectively. As indicated by equation (7-3), deuteration should have very little effect on the C—N frequency, for it has little effect on the C—N reduced mass. The only way the frequency can be affected is to have a coupling of the C—D stretch with the C—N stretch. Since the C—N and C—D frequencies are closer than C—N and C—H, there is more extensive coupling in the deuterated compound. Upon deuteration the C—H stretch decreases from 3312 to 2629 cm^{-1}. In the absence of coupling a decrease of about 1/1.3 would result in an expected absorption band around 2540 instead of 2629 cm^{-1}. It would be improper to draw conclusions concerning the C—H bond strength or the acidity of the proton from comparison of the frequency for the C—H stretch in H—CN with data for other C—H vibrations. The force constants for the C—H bonds can be calculated for the various compounds by a normal coordinate analysis. These values should be employed for such comparisons.

As an example of the difficulties that could be encountered let us consider the stretching vibration for the carbonyl group in a series of compounds. The absorption bands occur at 1928, 1827, and 1828 cm^{-1} in F_2CO, Cl_2CO, and Br_2CO, respectively.[4] One might be tempted to conclude from the frequencies that the high electronegativity of fluorine causes a pronounced increase in the C—O force constant. However, a normal coordinate analysis[4] shows that the C—O and C—F vibrations are coupled and the C—O stretch also involves considerable C—F motion. The frequency of this normal mode is higher than would be expected for an isolated C—O stretching vibration with an equivalent force constant. There is a corresponding lowering of the C—F stretching frequency. Since chlorine and bromine are heavier, they make little contribution to the carbonyl stretch. The normal coordinate analysis indicates that the C—O stretching force constants are 12.85, 12.61, and 12.83 millidynes/Å in F_2CO, Cl_2CO, and Br_2CO, respectively. This example should be kept in mind whenever conclusions are drawn from the frequencies of infrared bands. For an accurate treatment, force constants obtained from normal coordinate analyses should be compared and not frequencies read directly from spectra.

A normal coordinate analysis and infrared studies of C^{12}-, C^{13}-, O^{16}-, O^{18}-, H- and D-substituted ketones containing an ethyl group attached to the carbonyl group indicate[5] that the band near 1750 cm^{-1} assigned to

C—O stretch in these ketones corresponds to a normal mode which consists of about 75 per cent C—O and 25 per cent C—C stretching motions.

RAMAN SPECTROSCOPY

Raman spectroscopy is concerned with vibrational and rotational transitions, and in this respect it is similar to infrared spectroscopy. Since the selection rules are different, the information obtained some-times complements that obtained from an infrared study and provides valuable structural information.

In a Raman experiment, a monochromatic beam of light illuminates the sample, and observations are made on the scattered light at right angles to the incident beam (Fig. 7-8). Monochromatic light of different

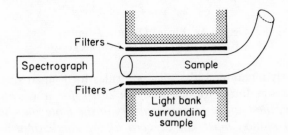

Fig. 7–8. The Raman Experiment (Schematic).

frequencies can be employed as sources. A quantum of the incident light of frequency $v°$ and energy $\mathbf{H}v°$ can collide with a molecule and be scattered with unchanged frequency. This is referred to as *Rayleigh scattering*. It is also possible for the incident quantum to induce a transition in the molecule. For simplicity, consider a change from the ground to the first vibrational state ($v = 0$ to $v = 1$) in a diatomic molecule. Let the frequency difference from $0 \rightarrow 1$ be represented by v_v. The energy difference between these two states would be $\mathbf{h}v_v$. The light quantum which is scattered now has a frequency $v° - v_v$ and the *Stokes line* in the spectrum indicated in Fig. 7-9 results. The measured value of v_v is identical to the infrared frequency that would excite this vibra-tional mode if it were infrared active. A molecule in the vibrationally excited state $v = 1$ can collide with an incident light quantum of frequency $v°$. The molecule can return to the ground state by giving its additional energy $\mathbf{h}v_v$ to the photon. This photon when scattered will have a fre-quency $v° + v_v$. The spectral line with this frequency is referred to as an anti-Stokes line (see Fig. 7-9). Because there are other mechanisms for returning to the ground state, there are fewer molecules in the $v = 1$ state than in $v = 0$ and the intensity of the anti-Stokes line is much lower than that of the Stokes line.

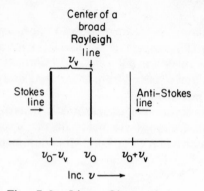

Fig. 7-9. Lines Observed in a Raman Spectrum (Schematic).

As previously mentioned, the selection rules for Raman spectroscopy are different from those for infrared. *In order for a vibration to be Raman active, the change in polarizability of the molecule with respect to vibrational motion must not be zero at the equilibrium position of the normal vibration,* i.e.,

$$(\partial \alpha / \partial r)_{r_e} \neq 0 \qquad (7\text{-}4)$$

where α is the polarizability and r represents the distance along the normal coordinate. If the plot of polarizability, α, vs. distance from the equilibrium distance, r_e, along the normal coordinate is that represented by Fig. 7-10a, the vibration will be Raman active. If the plot is represented by the curves *1* or *2* of Fig. 7-10b, $\partial \alpha / \partial r$ will be zero at or near the equilibrium distance, r_e, and the vibration will be Raman inactive.

Small amplitudes of vibration (as are normally encountered in a vibration mode) are indicated by the region on the distance axis on each side of zero and between the dotted lines. As can be seen from Fig. 7-10, the vibration in (a) corresponds to an appreciable change in polarizability occurring in this region, while that in (b) corresponds to practically no change. Hence, the Raman selection rule (7-4) is often stated: *In order for a vibration to be Raman active, there must be a change in polarizability during the vibration.*

The completely symmetric stretch for CO_2 is represented in Fig. 7-11. The two extremes, *A* and *C*, correspond to the points so labeled in Fig. 7-10a. *A* and *C* represent, respectively, more and less polarizable structures than the equilibrium structure, *B*. A plot of α vs. *r* for the symmetric stretch is represented by Fig. 7-10a. The change in polarizability for the asymmetric stretch is represented by one of the curves in Fig. 7-10b. As a result, this vibration is Raman inactive. Infrared activity is just the opposite of Raman activity in this case. *In general, for any molecule that possesses a center of symmetry, there will be no fundamental lines in common in the infrared and Raman spectra.* This is a very valuable generalization for structure determination. If the same absorption band is found in both the infrared and Raman spectra, it is reasonably certain that the molecule lacks a center of symmetry. It is also possible that in a molecule lacking a center of symmetry no identical lines appear because of the low intensity of one of the corresponding lines in one of the spectra.

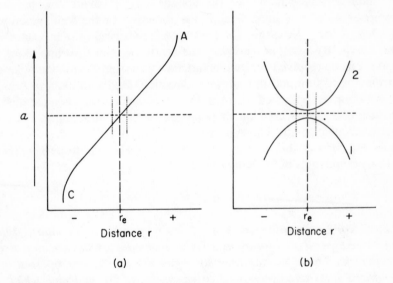

Fig. 7–10. Polarizability as a Function of Distance for Some Hypothetical Molecules.

This discussion serves to illustrate qualitatively the selection rules for Raman spectroscopy. It is often difficult to tell by inspection the form of the polarizability curve for a given vibration. As a result, this concept is more difficult to utilize qualitatively than the dipole moment selection rule in infrared. In a later section it will be shown how character tables and symmetry arguments can provide information concerning the infrared and Raman activity of vibrations.

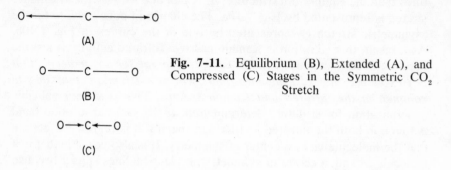

Fig. 7–11. Equilibrium (B), Extended (A), and Compressed (C) Stages in the Symmetric CO_2 Stretch

Polarized and Depolarized Raman Lines

Valuable information can be obtained by studying the polarized components of a Raman line. If the direction of incident radiation is labeled as the y axis, the scattered light is observed at right angles, say the x axis. By using an analyzer, the scattered light traveling along the x axis can be resolved into two polarized components: radiation polarized in the y direction and that in the z direction. Radiation polarized in the y direction is polarized parallel to the direction the incident light is traveling, and that component polarized in the z direction is polarized perpendicular to the incident radiation. The degree of depolarization, ρ, is the ratio of the intensity, I, of the parallel, y ($\parallel$), to perpendicular, z ($\perp$), components of the Stokes line:

$$\rho = \frac{I_{z(\parallel)}}{I_{z(\perp)}}$$

Those Raman lines for which $\rho = \frac{6}{7}$ are referred to as depolarized lines and correspond to vibrations of the molecule which are not totally symmetric. Those Raman lines for which $0 < \rho < \frac{6}{7}$ are referred to as polarized lines and correspond to vibrations of the molecule which are totally symmetric. The use of this information in making band assignments will also be made clearer after a discussion of symmetry considerations.

Significance of the Nomenclature Used to Describe Various Species

In this section the conventions used to label the species A_1, A_2, etc., will be reviewed to refresh the reader's memory. If the vibration is symmetric with respect to the highest-fold rotation axis, the vibration is designated by the letter A. If it is antisymmetric, the letter B is employed. E stands for a doubly degenerate vibration and T for a triply degenerate mode (F is very commonly used instead of T in vibrational spectroscopy). The subscripts g and u refer to symmetry with respect to an inversion through a center of symmetry and are used only for molecules with a center of symmetry. If a vibration is symmetric with respect to the horizontal plane of symmetry, this is designated by ', while '' indicates asymmetry· with respect to this plane. Subscripts 1 and 2 (as in A_1 and A_2) indicate symmetry and asymmetry, respectively, toward a twofold axis which is perpendicular to the principal axis.

Use of Symmetry Considerations to Determine the Number of Active Infrared and Raman Lines

In this section we shall be concerned with classifying the $3n - 6$ (or $3n - 5$ for a linear molecule) vibrations in a molecule to the various species in the point group of the molecule. This information will then be used to indicate the degeneracy and number of infrared and Raman active vibrations. Our approach will be strictly mechanical and no attempt will be made to cover the theory necessary to understand why these mechanical manipulations work. The results of these manipulations have very great practical importance to inorganic chemists, but the derivation of these procedures is beyond the scope of this text. The procedure is best illustrated by considering the possible structures for SF_4 (C_{2v}, C_{3v}, and T_d) represented in Fig. 7-12.

We first consider the C_{2v} structure. (1) The C_{2v} character table (Table 7-4) is consulted and the operations listed (in this case E, C_2, σ_{xy}, σ_{yz}') are carried out on the C_{2v} structure. (2) Count the number of atoms in the molecule which are *not* shifted by these symmetry operations. All five of the atoms are not moved by the identity, E. The sulfur is the only

TABLE 7-4. C_{2v} CHARACTER TABLE

	E	C_2	$\sigma_{v(xz)}$	$\sigma_{v(yz)}'$	
A_1	1	1	1	1	$T_z, \alpha_{x2}, \alpha_{y2}, \alpha_{z2}$
A_2	1	1	-1	-1	R_z, α_{xy}
B_1	1	-1	1	-1	T_x, R_y, α_{zx}
B_2	1	-1	-1	1	T_y, R_x, α_{yz}

atom not moved by the C_2 operation. The sulfur and two fluorine atoms are not moved by reflection in the σ_{xz} plane, but the other two fluorines

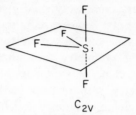

C_{2v}

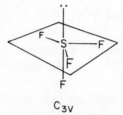

C_{3v}

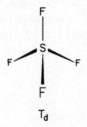

T_d

Fig. 7–12. Some Possible Structures for SF_4.

are. Similarly it is seen that the σ'_{yz} operation results in three atoms being unchanged. In summary:

Symmetry Operation	E	C_2	$\sigma_{v(xz)}$	$\sigma_{v(yz)}$
No. of Unshifted Atoms	5	1	3	3

(3) The next step is to find the "characters," χ (see Chapter 4) for each of the above operations. Table 7-5 contains a listing of the contribution to the total character of each symmetry operation by each unshifted atom in the molecule. This table applies for all point groups. Each of

the number of unshifted atoms determined in (2) is multiplied by the number in Table 7-5 corresponding to the particular symmetry operation,

TABLE 7-5 CONTRIBUTION TO THE TOTAL
CHARACTER PER UNSHIFTED ATOM

Operation	Contribution	Operation	Contribution
E	3	σ	1
C_2	-1	i	-3
C_3^1, C_3^2	0	S_3^1, S_3^5	-2
C_4^1, C_4^3	1	S_4^1, S_4^3	-1
C_6^1, C_6^5	2	S_6^1, S_6^5	0

to give the total character for that operation. The total characters of the operation give the *total representation*. This procedure is shown in Table 7-6. (4) The total representation $(15, -1, 3, 3)$ is some combination

TABLE 7-6 CALCULATION OF THE TOTAL
REPRESENTATION FOR THE C_{2v}
STRUCTURE OF SF_4

	E	C_2	$\sigma_{v(xz)}$	$\sigma_{v(yz)}$
No. of unshifted atoms [from (2)]	5	1	3	3
Character per atom from Table 7-5	3	-1	1	1
Total representation	15	-1	3	3

of the characters listed for the species A_1, A_2, B_1, and B_2 in the character table. These species are referred to as irreducible representations (e.g., $+1, +1, -1, -1$ is the irreducible representation for the symmetry species A_2). The next task is to figure out what combination of the irreducible representations should be taken to give $15, -1, 3, 3$. Equation (7-5) can be employed to factor the total representation:

$$n^{(\gamma)} = (1/g)\Sigma g_j \chi_j^{\gamma} \chi_g \qquad (7\text{-}5)$$

where (γ) refers to a particular species $(A_1, A_2,$ etc.); n refers to the total number of times this species contributes to the total representation; g is the total number of symmetry operations listed in the character table (in the case of a C_{2v} molecule $g = 4$: E, C_2, σ_{xz}, σ'_{yz}); the summation, Σ, is made for each symmetry operation class and g_j is the number of operations in the class j in the character table (in the C_{2v} table these are all one but in the C_{3v} table, for example, one observes the symbol $3\sigma_v$ so $g_j = 3$ when the σ_v operations are considered for a C_{3v} molecule); $\chi_j{}^\gamma$ is the character (number in the character table) of the symmetry operation j on the irreducible representation γ (in the C_{2v} table this is $+1$ for the symmetry operation $J = C_2$ on species A_2 while it is -1 for the $\sigma_{v(xz)}$ operation on the species B_2); χ_g is the total character of the class of the symmetry operation on the total representation χ_r (for example, this corresponds to the last line in Table 7-6 for a C_{2v} structure for SF_4). This is made clearer by calculating the number of contributions to the total representation made by species A_1. For the identity operation E, $g_E = 1$, $\chi_E{}^{A_1} = 1$, and χ_E (from Table 7-6 for E) $= 15$. For the C_2 operation, $g_{C_2} = 1$, $\chi_{C_2}{}^{A_1} = 1$, and $\chi_{C_2} = -1$. The results obtained by applying these operations to the other symmetry operations and to all the species in the character table are as follows:

$$n^{A_1} = \tfrac{1}{4}[1 \cdot 1 \cdot 15 + 1 \cdot 1 \cdot (-1) + 1 \cdot 1 \cdot 3 + 1 \cdot 1 \cdot 3] = 5$$

$$\text{for } E \qquad\qquad \text{for } C_2 \qquad\quad \text{for } \sigma_{v(xz)} \qquad \text{for } \sigma_{v(yz)}$$

$$n^{A_2} = \tfrac{1}{4}[1 \cdot 1 \cdot 15 + \quad\ 1 \cdot 1 \cdot (-1) + 1 \cdot (-1) \cdot 3 + 1 \cdot (-1) \cdot 3] = 2$$
$$n^{B_1} = \tfrac{1}{4}[1 \cdot 1 \cdot 15 + 1 \cdot (-1) \cdot (-1) + 1 \cdot (-1) \cdot 3 + 1 \cdot 1 \cdot 3] \quad\ = 4$$
$$n^{B_2} = \tfrac{1}{4}[1 \cdot 1 \cdot 15 + 1 \cdot (-1) \cdot (-1) + 1 \cdot 1 \cdot 3 \quad\ + 1 \cdot (-1) \cdot 3] = 4$$

The results, $n^{A_1} = 5$, $n^{A_2} = 2$, $n^{B_1} = 4$, and $n^{B_2} = 4$ represent the $3n$ degrees of freedom for a pentatomic C_{2v} structure. Another way to state this result is that if the characters for the irreducible representation A_1 in the character table were multiplied by 5, A_2 times 2, B_1 times 4, and B_2 times 4, the sum would produce the total representation $15, -1, 3, 3$.

To get the total number of vibrations, the three degrees of translational freedom and three of rotational freedom must be subtracted (giving $3n-6$ for a nonlinear molecule). Translation along the x axis can be represented by an arrow lying along this axis. If one performs the symmetry operations at the top of the character table for a C_{2v} structure on this arrow, it is seen that translation along the x axis belongs to the species B_1. This is indicated in the character table by the symbols T_x opposite (to the far right of) B_1. Similarly, translation along the z and y axes transform according to species A_1 and B_2 (indicated by the symbols

T_z and T_y in the table). Rotations along the x, y, and z axes are represented by the symbols R_x, R_y, and R_z and belong to species A_2, B_1, and B_2, respectively. These six degrees of freedom ($1A_1$, $1A_2$, $2B_1$, and $2B_2$) are subtracted from the representation of the total degrees of freedom producing: $n^{A_1} = 4$, $n^{A_2} = 1$, $n^{B_1} = 2$, $n^{B_2} = 2$ corresponding to the nine vibrations predicted from the $3n - 6$ rule.

(5) We have now calculated the species to which the $3n - 6$ vibrations of SF_4 belong if it has a C_{2v} structure. Four are of species A_1, one of A_2, two of B_1, and two of B_2. There are no degenerate vibrations of species E. The next job is to determine which vibrations are infrared active and which are Raman active. Since all ground states (except those for radicals) are A_1, this amounts to finding a component of the transition moment operator M which has the same symmetry as ψ_{vib}^* so that the integrand of $\int \psi_{vib}^* M \psi_{vib}$ is A_1. This can be done in the following way. The dipole moment vectors can be represented by arrows along the x, y, and z axes and as indicated for the transitions these belong to the species B_1, B_2, and A_1. The symbols T_x, T_y, and T_z in the character table can be used to tell which modes involve a change in dipole and hence which modes are infrared active. For the C_{2v} structure of SF_4, A_1, B_2, and B_1 are infrared active while A_2 is infrared inactive. As a result, eight infrared active vibrations are expected: $4A_1$, $2B_1$, and $2B_2$. Similarly, if there is a polarizability term (any α term) opposite one of the species in the table, a mode of that symmetry species will be Raman active. All fundamental vibrations of A_1 symmetry will be polarized while all other fundamental vibrations will be depolarized. With this information it can be shown that for the C_{2v} structure of SF_4, all nine modes are Raman active and the four modes of species A_1 produce polarized Raman lines.

Let us next examine the T_d structure for SF_4 (see Appendix B for the character table). The first step is summarized below:

	E	$8C_3$	$6\sigma_d$	$6S_4$	$3S_4 = 3C_2$
Number of unshifted atoms	5	2	3	1	1
Character per atom	3	0	1	-1	-1
Total representation	15	0	3	-1	-1

Note that *only one* of the C_3 operations (and also one σ_d, S_4, and C_2) is used to calculate the number of unshifted atoms. Next, the total representation must be broken down into the irreducible representations of A_1, A_2, E, T_1, and T_2 by employing the character table and equation

(7–5). The character tables indicate the three translations are of species T_2 and the three rotations of species T_1. Since T_1 and T_2 are triply degenerate, we need subtract only one of each from the total degrees of freedom

$$n^{A_1} = \tfrac{1}{24}[1 \cdot 1 \cdot 15 + 8 \cdot 1 \cdot 0 \quad + 6 \cdot 1 \cdot 3 \quad + 6 \cdot 1 \cdot (-1) \quad + 3 \cdot 1 \cdot (-1)] \quad = 1$$
$$n^{A_2} = \tfrac{1}{24}[1 \cdot 1 \cdot 15 + 8 \cdot 1 \cdot 0 \quad + 6 \cdot (-1) \cdot 3 + 6 \cdot (-1) \cdot (-1) + 3 \cdot 1 \cdot (-1)] \quad = 0$$
$$n^{E} = \tfrac{1}{24}[1 \cdot 2 \cdot 15 + 8 \cdot (-1) \cdot 0 + 6 \cdot 0 \cdot 3 \quad + 6 \cdot 0 \cdot (-1) \quad + 3 \cdot 2 \cdot (-1)] \quad = 1$$
$$n^{T_1} = \tfrac{1}{24}[1 \cdot 3 \cdot 15 + 8 \cdot 0 \cdot 0 \quad + 6 \cdot (-1) \cdot 3 + 6 \cdot 1 \cdot (-1) \quad + 3 \cdot (-1) \cdot (-1)] = 1$$
$$n^{T_2} = \tfrac{1}{24}[1 \cdot 3 \cdot 15 + 8 \cdot 0 \cdot 0 \quad + 6 \cdot 1 \cdot 3 \quad + 6 \cdot (-1) \cdot (-1) + 3 \cdot (-1) \cdot (-1)] = 3$$

to remove three degrees of translation and three of rotation. The total number of vibrations belong to species A_1, E, and $2T_2$ giving rise to the nine modes predicted from the $3n - 6$ rule. The six T_2 vibrations (two triply degenerate sets) are infrared active and give rise to two fundamental bands in the infrared spectrum. All modes are Raman active giving rise to four spectral bands corresponding to fundamentals. Of these, A_1 is polarized. It can be shown similarly that the C_{3v} structure for SF_4 leads to six infrared lines (three A_1 and three E) and six Raman lines (three A_1 and three E), three of which are polarized (A_1).

The actual spectrum is found to contain five infrared fundamentals, and five Raman lines, one of which is polarized. These results, summarized in Table 7-7, eliminate the T_d structure, leaving either C_{2v} or C_{3v} as possible structures. This example demonstrates the point that although there cannot be more fundamental vibrations than allowed by a symmetry type, often not all vibrations are detected. The problems in application of these concepts involve separating overtones and combinations from the fundamentals and, as is often the case, not finding some fundamental vibrations because they have low intensities.

TABLE 7-7. SUMMARY OF ACTIVE MODES EXPECTED FOR VARIOUS CONFIGURATIONS OF SF_4

	C_{2v}	T_d	C_{3v}	Found[a]
Infrared active modes	$8(4A_1, 2B_1, 2B_2)$	$2(2T_2)$	$6(3A_1, 3E)$	5(or 7)
Raman modes	$9(4A_1, A_2, 2B_1, 2B_2)$	$4(A_1, E, 2T_2)$	$6(3A_1, 3E)$	5(or 8)
Polarized modes	$4(4A_1)$	$1(A_1)$	$3(3A_1)$	1

[a]R. E. Dodd, L. A. Woodward, and H. L. Roberts, *Trans. Faraday Soc.*, **52**, 1052 (1956).

Table 7-7 should be verified by the reader by using the character table contained in Appendix B and the procedure described above. By a detailed analysis of the band contours and an assignment of the frequencies, it was concluded that the C_{2v} structure best fits the observed spectrum.

The data available on $CHCl_3$ and $CDCl_3$ are summarized in Table 7-8 and will be discussed briefly because this example serves to review many of the principles discussed. The $3n$ - 6 rule predicts nine normal vibrations. Just as with the C_{3v} structure of SF_4, the total representation shows that these nine vibrations consist of three A_1 and three E species or a total of six fundamental frequencies. All six fundamentals will be IR and Raman active, and the three A_1 fundamentals will give polarized Raman lines. The observed bands which have been assigned to fundamental frequencies are summarized in Table 7-8. These data indicate that the 3033, 667, and 364 bands belong to the totally symmetric vibrations (species A_1), for these bands are Raman polarized. They are labeled ν_1, ν_2, and ν_3, respectively. The other three bands are of species E, and the 1205, 760, and 260 bands are ν_4, ν_5, and ν_6, respectively Note that since the molecule does not have a center of symmetry the IR and Raman spectra have lines in common. The exact form of these fundamental vibrations is illustrated in Appendix E. The bands ν_1 and ν_4 are the C—H stretching and bending vibrations, respectively. Note how deuteration has a pronounced effect on these frequencies but almost no effect on the others. The vibrations at 3033 and 1205 are almost pure C—H modes. Since the very light hydrogen or deuterium atom is moving, very little C—Cl motion is necessary to retain the center of mass (so that there will be no net translation of the molecule, Chapter 5).

TABLE 7-8. INFRARED AND RAMAN FUNDAMENTALS FOR $CHCl_3$

IR Active Vibrations for $CHCl_3$ (cm^{-1})	Raman Active Vibrations for $CHCl_3$ (cm^{-1})	Raman Spectra of $CDCl_3$ (cm^{-1})	Designation
260	262	262	ν_6
364	366 (polarized)	367	ν_3
667	668 (polarized)	651	ν_2
760	761	738	ν_5
1205	1216	908	ν_4
3033	3019 (polarized)	2256	ν_1

The above manipulations are quite simple and yet yield valuable information about the structures of simple molecules. There are many applications of the above concepts. It is strongly recommended that the reader carry out the exercises at the end of this chapter and read Herzberg,[1] pages 271 to 369.

Spectroscopists often use the ν_n symbolism in assigning vibrations.

This can be translated into the language of stretches, bends, and twists by referring to the diagrams in Appendix E or in Herzberg for an example of a molecule with similar symmetry and the same number of atoms. The species of various vibrations can be determined from the diagrams by the procedure outlined in Chapter 4.

SYMMETRY REQUIREMENTS FOR COUPLING, COMBINATION BANDS AND FERMI RESONANCE

There are some important symmetry requirements regarding selection rules for overtone and combination bands. These can be demonstrated by considering BF_3, a D_{3h} molecule, as an example. The D_{3h} character table indicates that the symmetric stretch, ν_1, of species A_1 is infrared inactive (there is no dipole moment change). The species of the combination band $\nu_1 + \nu_3$ (where ν_3 is of species E') is given by the product of $A_1' \times E' = E'$. The combination band is infrared active. The ν_2 vibration is of symmetry A_2'' and is infrared active. The overtone $2\nu_2$ is of species $A_2'' \times A_2'' = A_1'$ which is infrared inactive; $3\nu_2$ is of species A_2'' and is observed in the infrared spectrum. This behavior is strong support for the initial structural assignment, that of a planar molecule, and serves here as a nice example to demonstrate the symmetry requirements for overtones and combination bands.

In the case of Fermi resonance it is necessary that the states which are participating have the same symmetry. For example if $2\nu_2$ is to undergo Fermi resonance with ν_1, the species for $2\nu_2$ must be the same as for ν_1.

Coupling of group vibrations was mentioned earlier in this chapter. In order for coupling to occur the vibrations must be of the same symmetry type. For example, in acetylene the symmetric C—H stretching vibration and the C—C stretching vibrations are of the same symmetry type and are highly coupled. The observed decrease in the frequency of the symmetric C—H stretch upon deuteration is smaller than expected, because of coupling. Since the asymmetric C—H stretch and the "C—C" stretch are of different symmetry, they do not couple, and deuteration has the normal effect on the asymmetric C—D stretch (a decrease from 3287 to 2427 cm^{-1} is observed).

MICROWAVE SPECTROSCOPY

Pure rotational transitions in a molecule can be induced by radiation in the far infrared and microwave regions of the spectrum. Extremely good precision for frequency determination is possible in the microwave region. Compared to the infrared region of the spectrum, where measurements can be made to about 1 cm⁻¹, one can get resolution of about 10^{-8} cm⁻¹ in the microwave region. A wide spectral range plus resolution and accuracy to 10^{-8} cm⁻¹ makes this a very valuable region for fingerprint applications. A list of frequencies has been tabulated[6,7] consisting of 1800 lines for about 90 different substances covering a span of 200,000 mc.* Only in 10 of the cases reported were two of the 1800 lines closer than 0.25 mc.

There are two requirements which impose limitations on microwave studies. (1) The spectrum must be obtained on the material in the gaseous state. A vapor pressure of at least 10^{-3} mm of Hg is required. (2) The molecule must have a permanent dipole moment in the ground state in order to absorb microwave radiation since rotation alone cannot create a dipole moment in a molecule.

DETERMINATION OF BOND ANGLES AND BOND DISTANCES

In addition to the fingerprint application, other useful data can be obtained from the microwave spectrum of a compound. Some of the most accurate bond distance and bond angle data available have been obtained from these studies. Let us first consider a diatomic molecule. The rotational energy, E, for a diatomic molecule is given by the equation:

$$E = \mathbf{h}BJ(J + 1) \tag{7-6}$$

where J is an integer, the rotational quantum number; $\mathbf{h}$ is Planck's constant (6.62×10^{-27} erg sec); and $B = \mathbf{h}/8\pi^2 I$ where I is the moment of inertia. Since $E = \mathbf{h}\nu$, we obtain the relationship for the frequency, ν, corresponding to this energy:

$$\nu = BJ(J + 1) \tag{7-7}$$

There is another selection rule (in addition to the dipole moment requirement) for microwave absorption which states that $\Delta J = \pm 1$. Therefore, the longest wavelength (lowest energy) absorption band in the spectrum will correspond to the transition $J = 0$ to $J = 1$ for which:

$$\Delta \nu = 2B = 2\mathbf{h}/8\pi^2 I \tag{7-8}$$

$\Delta \nu$ is measured and all other quantities are known except I which can than be calculated from equation (7-8).

*1mm equals 299,800 mc or 299.8 kc.

All other lines in the spectrum will occur at shorter wavelengths and will be separated from each other by $2B$(i.e., $v = B[J'(J' + 1) - J(J + 1)]$) see Fig. 7-13) where J' is the quantum number for the higher rotational

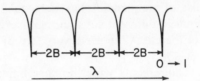

Fig. 7–13.   Illustration of the $0 \rightarrow 1$ and Other Rotational Transitions.

state and J that for the lower. Once the moment of inertia is determined, the equilibrium internuclear separation, r_0, in the diatomic molecule can be calculated with equation (7-9):

$$I = \mu r_0^2 \tag{7-9}$$

where μ is the reduced mass.

In the above discussions we have assumed a rigid rotator as a model. This means that the atoms in the molecule do not vibrate *at all* during the rotation. Because of the influence of centrifugal force on the molecule during the rotation, there will be a small amount of vibration. As a result the bond distance (and I) will be larger for high values of J, and the spacings between the peaks will decrease slightly as J increases.

In a more complex molecule the moment of inertia is related to the bond lengths and angles by a more complex relationship than (7-9). A whole series of simultaneous equations has to be solved to determine all the structural parameters. In order to get enough experimental observations to solve all these equations, isotopic substitution is employed. For pyridine, the microwave spectra of six isotopes (pyridine, 2-deuteropyridine, 3-deuteropyridine, 4-deuteropyridine, pyridine-2-C^{13}, and pyridine-3-C^{13}) were employed. For a more complete discussion of this problem see Gordy, Smith, and Trambarulo.[6]

MEASUREMENT OF THE DIPOLE MOMENT OF A MOLECULE

Accurate dipole moment measurements can be made from microwave experiments. When an electric field is applied to the sample being studied, the rotational ine is split (the Stark effect). The magnitude of the splitting depends upon the product of the dipole moment (to be evaluated) and the electric field strength (which is known).

ROTATIONAL RAMAN SPECTRA

Information equivalent to that obtained in the microwave region can be obtained from the rotational Raman spectrum, where the permanent dipole selection rule does not hold. As a result, very accurate data on homonuclear diatomic molecules can be obtained from the rotational Raman spectrum. Experimentally, the bands are detected as Stokes lines with frequencies corresponding to rotational transitions.

In order for a molecule to exhibit a rotational Raman spectrum, the polarizability perpendicular to the axis of rotation must be anisotropic; i.e., the polarizability must be different in different directions in the plane perpendicular to the axis. If the molecule has a threefold or higher axis of symmetry, the polarizability will be the same in all directions and rotational modes about this axis will be Raman inactive. Other rotations in the molecule may be Raman active.

For diatomic molecules the selection rule $\Delta J = \pm 2$ now, applies so

$$\Delta E = Bh(4J' - 2) \tag{7-10}$$

and the frequency separation between the lines is $4B$. If this separation is not at least ~ 0.1 cm^{-1} the lines cannot be resolved in the Raman spectrum. The rest of the calculation is identical to that described previously. There has been only limited application of this technique to more complex molecules.

APPLICATIONS OF INFRARED AND RAMAN SPECTROSCOPY

Only a limited number of examples will be treated here, for there are excellent texts by Cotton[47] and Nakamoto[20] which are quite comprehensive.

PROCEDURES

The most common infrared equipment covers the wavelength region from 5000 to 650 cm^{-1}. The limiting factor is the material used to construct the prism in the instrument. The prism resolves polychromatic radiation into monochromatic so that variations in absorption of a sample with change in wavelength can be studied. The resulting spectrum is a plot of sample absorbance or percent transmission versus wavelength (see Fig. 7-14). Sodium chloride prisms are employed for the 5000 to 600 cm^{-1} region while a cesium bromide prism is often employed for the region from 600 to 250 cm^{-1}. In some instruments the prism is

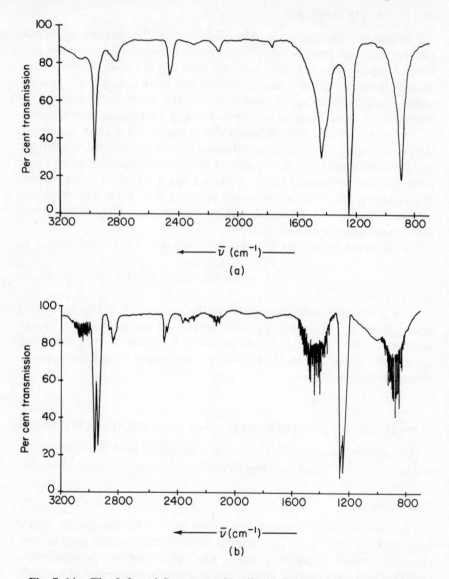

Fig. 7–14. The Infrared Spectrum of (a) liquid CH_3I and (b) gaseous CH_3I. Reproduced from *Introduction to Molecular Spectroscopy* by G. M. Barrow. Copyright 1962. McGraw-Hill Book Company. Used by permission.

replaced by a grating. The cell which holds the sample is often (but not necessarily) constructed of the prism material. Cells constructed of AgCl, CaF$_2$, BaF$_2$, or a special optical material "Ir tran-2" (available from the Connecticut Instrument Corp.) can be employed to construct cells for solvents (such as water) which dissolve the common sodium chloride cells. The silver chloride cells have the disadvantage of darkening on exposure to light.

The wavelength scale usually changes with use, so frequent calibration is necessary. In the 5000 to 650 cm^{-1} region, polystyrene, ammonia, and water vapor are commonly used as standards to calibrate the instrument.

Samples can be examined as gases, liquids, or solids, or in solution. Special cells with long path length, are needed for most gaseous samples. Solid samples are often examined as mulls in either Nujol (paraffin oil) or hexachlorobutadiene. The mull is prepared by first grinding the sample to a fine particle size and then adding enough oil or mulling agent to make a paste. The paste is examined as a thin layer between sodium chloride (or other optical material) plates. The quality of the spectrum obtained is very much dependent on the mulling technique. When the spectrum is examined, peaks from the mulling material will appear in the spectrum and possibly mask sample peaks. If two spectra are obtained, one in Nujol and one in hexachlorobutadiene, all wavelengths in the 5000 to 650 cm^{-1} region can be examined. Solid samples are sometimes examined as KBr discs. The sample and KBr are intimately mixed, ground, and pressed into a clear disc which is mounted and examined directly. Care should be exercised in this procedure, for anion exchange and other reactions may occur with the bromide ion during grinding or pressing. Reflectance spectra of solids can be obtained with commercially available attachments.

Solutions are most easily examined by use of the double beam technique which in effect subtracts out solvent absorption. A solution of the sample is placed in a cell in the sample beam. A cell of the same path length containing pure solvent is placed in the reference beam. The difference in absorption is measured, in effect canceling absorption bands due to the solvent. In regions where the solvent absorption is very large, almost all of the radiation is absorbed by the two solutions, insufficient energy passes through the sample to activate the instrument, and the pen is "dead." No sample absorptions can be detected in these blank regions. As a matter of fact, if one were to interrupt the sample beam in these regions of the spectrum with his hand, the pen would not move. The open regions for several common liquids used for solution work are tabulated in Table 7-9.

Most pure liquids can be examined in standard sodium chloride cells. If the liquid attacks the sample cells slightly or else has a very high absorption, the sample can be examined as a smear between two sodium chloride plates. Plates of NaCl can be purchased for a very reasonable price.

The spectrum obtained for a given sample depends upon the physical state of the sample. Gaseous samples usually exhibit rotational fine structure. This fine structure is dampened in solution spectra because

TABLE 7-9. REGIONS IN WHICH VARIOUS SOLVENTS TRANSMIT AT LEAST 25 PER CENT OF THE INCIDENT RADIATION (i.e., OPEN REGIONS)[a]

(A) For Cells of 1 mm Thickness		(B) For Cells of 0.1 mm Thickness			
Solvent	Open Region	Solvent	Open Region (cm^{-1})	Solvent	Open Region (cm^{-1})
CCl_4	4000–1610	CS_2	4000–2200	CH_3CN	4000–3700
	1500–1270		2140–1595		3500–2350
	1200–1020		1460– 650		2250–1500
	960– 860				1350–1060
		C_6H_6	4000–3100		1030– 930
$CHCl_3$	4000–3100		3000–1820		910– 650
	2980–2450		1800–1490		
	2380–1520		1450–1050	CH_3NO_2	4000–3100
	1410–1290		1020– 680		2800–1770
	1155– 940	CCl_4	4000– 820		1070– 925
	910– 860		720– 650		910– 690
CH_2Cl_2	4000–3180	$CHCl_3$	4000–3020		
	2900–2340		3000–1240		4000–3500
	2290–1500		1200– 805	C_5H_5N	3000–1620
	1130– 935				1400–1230
		CH_2Cl_2	4000–1285		980– 780
CS_2	4000–2350		1245– 900		
	2100–1640		890– 780	$HC(O)N(CH_3)_2$	4000–3000
	1385– 875		750– 650		2700–1780
	845– 650				1020– 870
		$Cl_2C{=}CCl_2$	4000– 935		860– 680
$Cl_2C{=}CCl_2$	4000–1375		875– 820		
	1340–1180		745– 650	CH_3OH[b]	2800–1500
	1090–1015				1370–1150
					970– 700

[a]The infrared spectra of some solvents in the 600 to 450 cm⁻¹ region are contained in reference 37 and F. F. Bentley et al., *Spectrochim. Acta,* **13**, 1 (1958).

[b]Not to be used in NaCl cells.

collisions of molecules in the condensed phase occur before a rotation is completed. This difference between gaseous and liquid spectra is illustrated by the spectra in Fig. 7-14.

In addition to the difference in resolved fine structure, the number of absorption bands and the frequencies of the vibrations vary in the different states. As an illustration, the fundamentals of SO_2 are reported in Table 7-10 for the different physical states.

TABLE 7-10. FREQUENCIES (IN cm^{-1}) FOR SO_2 FUNDAMENTALS IN DIFFERENT PHYSICAL STATES

	Gas	Liquid[a]	Solid
$\nu_2(a_1)$	518	525	528
$\nu_1(a_1)$	1151	1144	1144
$\nu_3(b_1)$	1362	1336	1322
			1310

[a]Raman spectrum.

Other effects not illustrated by the data in Table 7-10 are often encountered. Often there are more bands in the liquid state than in the gaseous state of a substance. Frequently, new bands below 300 cm^{-1} appear in the solid state spectrum. The causes of these frequency shifts, band splittings, and new bands in the condensed states are well understood[8] and will be discussed briefly here.

The stronger intermolecular forces that exist in the solid and liquid state compared to the gaseous state are the cause of slight shifts (assuming that there are no pronounced structural changes with change of phase) in the frequencies. The bands below 300 cm^{-1} are often caused by *lattice vibrations,* i.e., translational and torsional motions of the molecules in the lattice. These vibrations can form combination bands with the intramolecular vibrations and cause pronounced frequency shifts in the higher frequency regions of the spectrum. An additional complication arises if the unit cell of the crystal contains more than one chemically equivalent molecule. When this is the case, the vibrations in the individual molecules can couple with each other. This intermolecular coupling can give rise to frequency shifts and band splitting.

As mentioned earlier, molecular symmetry is very important in determining the infrared activity and degeneracy of a molecular vibration. When a molecule is present in a crystal, the symmetry of the surroundings of the molecule in the unit cell, the so-called *site symmetry,* determines the selection rules. Often bands forbidden in the gaseous state appear in the solid, and degenerate vibrations in gaseous state are split in the solid. The general problem of the effect of site symmetry on the selection rules has been treated theoretically.[9,10] As a simple illustration of this effect, the infrared spectra of materials containing carbonate ion will be considered. The infrared and Raman spectra of $CaCO_3$ in calcite, where the carbonate ion is in a site of D_3 symmetry, contain the following bands (in cm^{-1}): ν_1, 1087 (R); ν_2, 879 (I); ν_3, 1432 (I, R); ν_4, 710 (I, R). The (I) indicates infrared activity and the (R) Raman activity. The infrared spectra of $CaCO_3$ in arognoite, where the site symmetry for carbonate is C_s, differs in that ν_1 becomes infrared active and ν_3 and ν_4 each split into two bands. By using the symmetry considerations previously discussed on the CO_3^{2-} ion, the following results can be obtained:

	ν_1	ν_2	ν_3	ν_4
D_{3h}	$A_1'(R)$	$A_2''(I)$	$E'(I,R)$	$E'(I,R)$
D_3	$A_1(R)$	$A_2(I)$	$E(I,R)$	$E(I,R)$
C_s	$A'(I,R)$	$A''(I,R)$	$A'(I,R) + A'(I,R)$	$A'(I,R) + A'(I,R)$

As a result of all these possible complications, the interpretation of spectra obtained on solids is difficult.

The spectrum of a given solute often varies in different solvents. In hydrogen-bonding solvents the shifts are in part due to specific solute-solvent interactions which cause changes in the electron distribution in the solute. The frequency of the band is also dependent upon the refractive index of the solvent[11] and other effects.[12]

FINGERPRINTING

If an unknown is suspected to be a known compound, its spectrum can be compared directly with that of the known. The more bands the sample contains the more reliable the comparison.

The presence of water in a sample can be detected by its two characteristic absorption bands in the 3600 to 3200 cm^{-1} region and in the 1650 cm^{-1} region. If the water is present as lattice water, these two bands and one in the 600 to 300 cm^{-1} region are observed. If the water is coordinated to a metal ion an additional band in the 880 to 650 cm^{-1} region is often observed.[20] In the clathrate compound $Ni(CN)_2NH_3 \cdot C_6H_6 \cdot xH_2O$, infrared[13] clearly showed the presence of water, although it was not detected in a single crystal x-ray study. In connection with the earlier discussion on the effect of physical state on the spectrum of various substances it is of interest to mention in passing that the benzene is so located in the crystal lattice of this clathrate that the frequencies of the out-of-plane vibrations are increased over those in the free molecule while the in plane vibrations are not affected.

If the product of a reaction is suspected of being contaminated by starting material, this can be confirmed by the presence of a band in the product due to the starting material which is known to be absent in the pure product. Even if spectra are not known, procedures aimed at purification may be attempted. Changes in relative band intensities may then indicate that partial purification has been achieved and may be used as a check on completeness of purification.

A more common analysis employs the group vibration concept to ascertain the presence or absence of various functional groups in the molecule. The following generalizations aid in this application:

(1) Above 2500 cm^{-1} nearly all fundamental vibrations involve a hydrogen stretching mode. The O—H stretching vibration occurs around 3600 cm^{-1}. Hydrogen bonding lowers the frequency and broadens the band. The N—H stretch occurs in the 3300 to 3400 cm^{-1} region. These bands often overlap the hydrogen bonded O—H bands but the N—H peaks are usually sharper. The N—H stretch in ammonium and alkylammonium ions occurs at lower frequencies (2900 to 3200 cm^{-1}). The C—H stretch occurs in the region 2850 to 3000 cm^{-1} for an aliphatic compound and in the region 3000 to 3100 cm^{-1} for an aromatic compound. Absorptions corresponding to S—H, P—H, and Si—H occur around 2500, 2400, and 2300 cm^{-1}, respectively.

(2) The 2500 to 2000 cm^{-1} region involves the stretching vibration for triply-bonded molecules. The group C≡N gives rise to a strong, sharp absorption that occurs in the 2200 to 2300 cm^{-1} region.

(3) The 2000 to 1600 cm^{-1} region contains stretching vibrations for doubly-bonded molecules and bending vibrations for the O—H, C—H, and N—H groups. The carbonyl group in a ketone absorbs around 1700 cm^{-1}. Conjugation in an amide (R—C$\overset{\diagup \text{O}}{-}$N(CH$_3$)$_2$ ↔ RC$\overset{\diagup \text{O}}{=}$N(CH$_3$)$_2$ decreases the C—O force constant and lowers the highly coupled (with C—N) carbonyl absorption to the 1650 cm^{-1} region. Hydrogen bonding lowers the carbonyl vibration frequency. Stretching vibrations from C=C and C=N occur in this region.

(4) The region below 1600 cm^{-1} is referred to as the fingerprint region for many organic compounds. In this region significant differences occur

in the spectra of substances which are very much alike. This is the single bond region and, as mentioned in the section on coupling, it is very common to get coupling of individual single bonds which have similar force constants and connect similar masses (e.g., C—O, C—C, and C—N stretches often couple). The absorption bands in this region for a given functional group occur at different frequencies depending

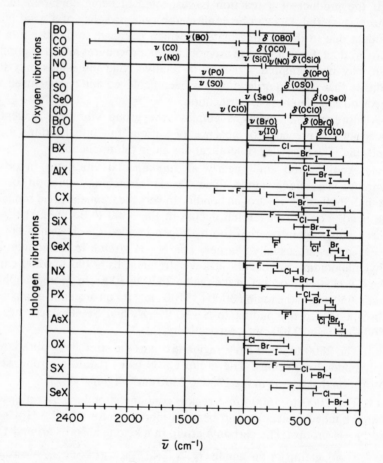

Fig. 7–15. Range of Infrared Group Frequencies for Some Inorganic Materials. The symbol ν_{M-X}, where M and X are general symbols for the atoms involved, corresponds to a stretching vibration. The symbols, ν_1, ν_2, etc., were previously defined. δ corresponds to an in-plane bending vibration (δ_s the symmetric bend, δ_d the asymmetric bend), π to an out-of-plane bend, ρ to rocking and wagging vibrations.

Absorptions of common ions

Ion	Modes (high → low wavenumber)
NCO^-	ν_1; ν_3 H; ν_2
N_3^-	ν_1; ν_3 ⊢-----⊣; ν_2
NCS^-	ν_1; ν_3; ν_2
NO_2^-	ν_1 ν_3; ν_2 H
UO_2^{2+}	$\nu_3 \nu_1$ HH; ν_2 H
ClO_2^-	$\nu_3 \nu_1$ HH; ν_2 H
CO_3^{2-}	ν_3; ν_1; ν_2 ν_4 HH
NO_3^-	ν_3; ν_1; ν_2 ν_4 H H
BO_3^{3-}	ν_3 H; ν_1 ; ν_2 ν_4 ⊢⊣ ⊢⊣
SO_3^{2-}	ν_1 HH; ν_3; ν_2 H; ν_4 ⊢⊣
ClO_3^-	$\nu_3 \nu_1$ HH; ν_2 H; ν_4
BrO_3^-	$\nu_3 \nu_1$ H; $\nu_2 \nu_4$ HH
IO_3^-	ν_3 ν_1 ⊢—⊣; $\nu_2 \nu_4$ ⊢—⊣

Dotted lines for Raman active modes

SO_4^{2-}	ν_3; ν_1 ⋮; ν_4; ν_2
ClO_4^-	ν_3; ν_1 ⋮; ν_4 H; ν_2 ⋮
PO_4^{3-}	ν_3; ν_1; ν_4; ν_2
MnO_4^-	$\nu_3 \nu_1$ H⋮; ν_4 H
CrO_4^{2-}	ν_3 ν_1 ⊢—⊣; $\nu_4 \nu_2$ H⋮
SeO_4^{2-}	$\nu_3 \nu_1$ ⊢—⊣; ν_4 H; ν_2 ⋮
MoO_4^{2-}	$\nu_1 \nu_3$ ⋮H; ν_4 H; ν_2 ⋮
AsO_4^{3-}	$\nu_3 \nu_1$ ⊢—⊣; ν_4 ⋮; ν_2 ⋮
WO_4^{2-}	ν_1 ν_3 ⋮H; $\nu_4 \nu_2$ ⋮ ⋮

(* Indicates bridged or bidentates) metal complexes

M–CN	$\nu(CN)$; $\nu(MC)$; $\delta(CMC)$
M–NCS*	$\nu(CN)$; $\nu(CS)$; $\delta(NCS)$
M–CO*	$\nu(CO)$; $\nu(MC)$
M–NH₃	$\delta_d(NH_3)$; $\delta_s(NH_3)$; $\rho_r(NH_3)$; $\nu(MN)$ $\delta(NMN)$
M–NH₂	(For Hg $^{2+}$ complex) $\delta(NH_2)$ $\rho_w(NH_2),\rho_t(NH_2)$ $\rho_r(NH_2)$ $\nu(MN)$
M–NO₂*	$\nu(NO_2)$ H; $\delta(NO_2)$ $\rho_w(NO_2)$ $\nu(MN)$
M–ONO	$\nu(ONO)$ H; $\nu(ONO)$ H; $\delta(ONO)$ H
M–OCO₂*	$\nu(CO)$ H; $\nu(CO)$ H; $\nu(CO)$ H; π $\delta(OCO)$ HH; $\nu(MO)$
M–ONO₂	$\nu(NO)$ HH; $\nu(NO)$ HH; $\nu(NO)$ H; π H
M–OSO₃*	$\nu(SO)$ H; $\delta_d(OSO)$; $\delta_d(OSO)$
M–OH₂	$\delta(HOH)$ H; $\rho_w(OH_2), \rho_r(OH_2), \rho_t(OH_2)$

$$\overline{\nu}\,(cm^{-1})$$

2000   1500   1000   500   0

upon the skeleton of the molecule, because each vibration often involves oscillation of a considerable number of atoms of the molecular skeleton.

An extensive compilation of characteristic infrared group frequencies has been compiled to aid in this application. Figures 7-15 and 7-16 are

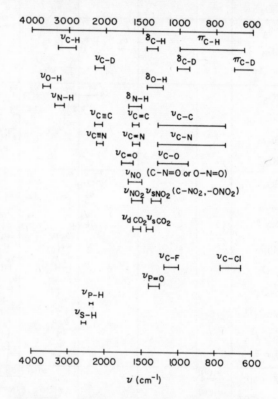

Fig. 7–16. Range of Infrared Group Frequencies for Some Organic Compounds (See reference 11, pp. 563 to 580, for a very extensive compilation.)

constructed from data compiled by Colthup[14] and Nakamoto.[20] There are references that also list or discuss regions and trends for many group vibrations in the infrared[14-20] and Raman[21-23] spectra.

SPECTRA OF GASES

The spectra of gases are often very much different from the spectra of materials in the condensed phase or in solution. As can be seen in

Fig. 7-14, a significant difference is the presence of considerable fine structure in the gaseous spectrum. The fine structure is due to a combination of vibrational and rotational transitions. For example, in a diatomic molecule, not only do transitions corresponding to the pure vibrational mode, ν_0, occur but also absorption corresponding to $\nu_0 \pm \nu_r$ where ν_r represents the rotational frequency is detected. Since any finite sample contains many molecules, many different rotational states will be present and there will be a whole series of lines corresponding to different ν_r values (i.e., transitions between many different rotational states). This phenomenon is illustrated in Fig. 7-17. The Q branch

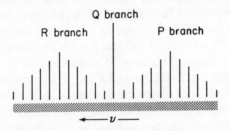

Fig. 7–17. Illustration of the Transitions Giving Rise to P, Q, and R Branches in a Spectrum of a Gas.

corresponds to the transition in which ν_r is zero (i.e., a transition with no change in rotational quantum number), the R branch to $\nu_0 + \nu_r$, and the P branch to $\nu_0 - \nu_r$.

The frequencies of all the bands in Fig. 7-17 can be expressed by the following equation:

$$\nu = \nu_0 + 2\mathbf{h}m/8\pi^2 I$$

where m has all integral values, including zero, from $+J$ to $-J$ (where J is the rotational quantum number) depending on the selection rules. When $m = 0$, the vibrational transition is one that occurs with no change in rotational quantum number. A Q branch results. When m is less than zero ($J_{n+1} \rightarrow J_n$ transitions), lines in the P branch result, while lines in the R branch correspond to m greater than zero.

A series of selection rules for the combination of vibration and rotation transitions in various molecules is helpful in deducing structure:

(1) *Diatomic molecules.* Most diatomic molecules do not possess a Q branch. Nitric oxide (NO) is the only known example for stable mole-

cules. The diatomic molecule must possess angular momentum about the molecular axis to have a Q branch. (Σ states, $L = 0$, have no Q branch.)

(2) *Linear polyatomic molecules.* If the changing dipole moment for a given vibrational mode is parallel to the principal rotation axis in the molecule, a so-called *parallel band* results which *has no Q branch.* The selection rule for this case is $\Delta J = \pm 1$; ΔJ cannot be zero. If the dipole moment change for the vibration has any vector component perpendicular to the principal axis, a *perpendicular band* will result *with a Q branch,* and ΔJ can be $0, \pm 1$. The asymmetric C—O stretch in CO_2 is a parallel band, while the C—O bending vibration is a perpendicular band. The utilization of these criteria in making and substantiating assignments of vibrations is apparent. If in the spectrum of a triatomic molecule, any of the infrared bands (ν_1, ν_2, or ν_3) consists of a single P and R branch without any Q branch (i.e., a zero gap separation), the molecule must be linear. This type of evidence can be used to support linear structures for N_2O, HCN, and CO_2. The rotational spacings can be employed, as discussed under the section on microwave spectroscopy, to evaluate the moment of inertia. Note that even though CO_2 does not have a permanent dipole (and hence is microwave inactive) the rotational spacings can be obtained from the fine structure in the infrared spectrum.

(3) *Nonlinear polyatomic molecules.* For our discussion of vibration-rotation coupling in nonlinear polyatomic molecules it is necessary to define the terms *spherical, symmetric,* and *asymmetric top.* Every nonlinear molecule has three finite moments of inertia. In a spherical top, e.g., CCl_4, all three moments are equal. In a symmetric top, two of the three moments are equal. For example, if one selects the C_3 axis of CH_3Br as the z axis, then the moment of inertia along the x axis is equal to that along the y axis. Any molecule with a three or higher fold rotation axis is a symmetric top molecule (unless it is a spherical top). In an asymmetric top none of the three moments are equal. Molecules with no symmetry or those with only a twofold rotation axis (H_2O, for example) are asymmetric top molecules.

For symmetric top molecules, those vibrations which have oscillating dipole moments that are parallel to the principle axis produce *a parallel absorption band with P, Q, and R branches.* The symmetric C—H stretching and bending frequencies in CH_3Br are examples of parallel bands. The type of spectrum obtained for a parallel band is illustrated in Fig. 7-18. In this example the rotational fine structure in the R branch is not resolved. The parallel band for a symmetric top molecule is similar to the perpendicular band for a linear molecule. For a perpendicular absorption band in a symmetric top molecule, several Q bands are detected often with overlapping unresolved P and R branches. The C—Cl bending vibration in CH_3Cl is an example of a perpendicular band in a

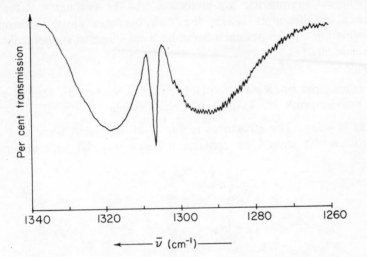

Fig. 7-18. A Parallel Band for CH_3Br (Symmetric Top). From *Introduction to Molecular Spectroscopy* by G. M. Barrow. Copyright 1962. McGraw-Hill Book Company. Used by permission.

symmetric top molecule. A typical spectrum for this case is illustrated in Fig. 7-19. In a spherical top the selection rule for a perpendicular

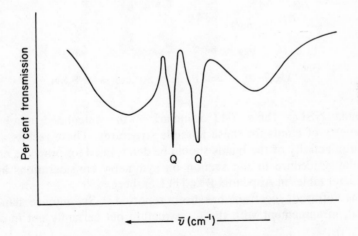

Fig. 7-19. Perpendicular Band Containing Two Q Branches.

band is $\Delta J = 0, \pm 1$. This information can be employed to support band assignments.

It becomes very difficult in some cases to distinguish between symmetric and asymmetric top molecules. As the symmetry of the asymmetric top becomes lower, the task becomes easier. Considerable information can be obtained from the band shape to support vibrational assignments.*

APPLICATION OF RAMAN AND INFRARED SELECTION RULES TO THE DETERMINATION OF INORGANIC STRUCTURES

(1) $N-SF_3$. The structures in Fig. 7-20 represent some of the possibilities that should be considered for a material with an empirical

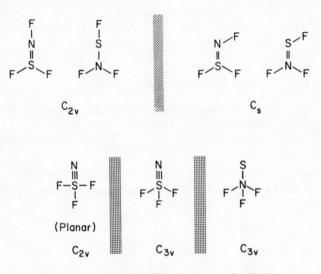

Fig. 7-20. Some Possible Structures for F_3SN.

formula NSF_3. Table 7-11 summarizes the calculated number and symmetry of bands for these possible structures. These results and the infrared activity of the bands should be determined for practice, employing the procedure in the section on symmetry considerations and the character tables in Appendix B and in Herzberg.[1]

The infrared spectrum has been reported.[24] Six intense bands are found, in agreement with the C_{3v} structure but certainly not in conflict

---

*See Herzberg[1] for an explanation of the phenomena discussed above (pp. 380–390). Many applications of these principles are discussed in this reference.

with other possible structures. Some of the fundamentals may be of such low intensity that they are not seen. However, it was found that

TABLE 7-11. CALCULATED NUMBER OF BANDS
FOR VARIOUS STRUCTURES OF NSF_3

C_{3v}	C_{2v} (C_2 axis is the z axis)	C_s
$3A_1$ (IR active)	$4A_1$ (IR active)	$7A'$ (IR active)
	$3B_1$ (IR active)	$2A''$ (IR active)
$3E$ (IR active)	$2B_2$ (IR active)	

five of the bands (ν_1, ν_2, ν_3, ν_5) had P, Q, and R branches. This is good evidence that the molecule being investigated is a symmetric top molecule* and supports a C_{3v} structure. The spectral data are contained in Table 7-12 where they are compared with data reported for POF_3.[25] The forms of the vibrations are diagrammed in Appendix E (see ZXY_3 molecule). These data, combined with an NMR study, have been employed to support the C_{3v} structure F_3S—N. The F_3N—S structure has not been eliminated by these data. Polarized Raman studies were not carried out. These would not add a great deal of structural information but would help confirm the assignments. The A_1 bands should be polarized and the E bands depolarized.

TABLE 7-12. FUNDAMENTAL
VIBRATION FREQUENCIES FOR
NSF_3 AND OPF_3

	NSF_3	OPF_3
ν_1	1515	1415
ν_2	775	873
ν_3	521	473
ν_4	811	990
ν_5	429	485
ν_6	342	345

The frequencies of the observed bands provide information to favor the F_3SN structure. The S—N stretch is the only fundamental vibration that could be expected at a frequency of 1515 cm^{-1}. (A very rough approximation for this frequency can be obtained by employing the $C^{\times}C$

*Reference 1, page 419.

force constant and the S and N masses in equation 7-3.) The NF stretching vibrations in NF_3 occur at 1031 cm^{-1} and would not be expected to be as high as 1515 cm^{-1} in F_3N—S. The F_3SN structure receives further support from a microwave and mass spectroscopic study.[26] The low moment of inertia calculated from the microwave studies cannot be explained unless the sulfur atom is at the center of mass.

(2) The same approach as that outlined above was employed to prove that perchlorylfluoride, ClO_3F, has a C_{3v} structure instead of O_2ClOF.[27]

(3) An appreciation for some of the difficulties encountered in making spectral assignments can be obtained from an article by Wilson and Hunt[28] on the reassignment of the spectrum of SO_2F_2. Often a set of band assignments may appear self-consistent but these assignments may not be a unique set. The effect of isotopic substitution on spectral shifts can be employed to provide additional support for the assignments made.

(4) The infrared and Raman spectra have been interpreted to indicate a planar structure for N_2O_4.[29] Structures corresponding to the planar D_{2h} model and the staggered D_{2d} configuration were considered. Since the infrared and Raman spectra have no lines in common, it is proposed that the molecule has a center of symmetry. A rigorous assignment of the bands could not be made with the available data.

(5) The spectral data for B_2H_6 support the bridged hydrogen structure.[30] The entire spectrum is analyzed, assignments are made, and conclusions regarding the structure are drawn from the rotational fine structure of some of the perpendicular bands.

(6) An infrared and Raman study[31] supports a C_{2v} planar T-shaped structure for ClF_3. Too many fundamentals were observed for either a D_{3h} or C_{3v} structure. Some of the bands had P, Q, and R branches, while others had only P and R branches. Since all fundamentals for a tetraatomic C_{3v} molecule (e.g., PF_3) have P, Q, and R branches, this structure is eliminated.

(7) The infrared and Raman spectra of $B_2(OCH_3)_4$ have been interpreted to indicate[32] a planar arrangement for the boron and oxygen atoms. Many bands were found in the spectrum. Assignments were made which are consistent with a planar C_{2h} molecule. More fundamentals were found than would be predicted from a D_{2d} model. The infrared and Raman spectra do not have a coincidence of any of the vibrations assigned[32] to B—B or B—O modes but as would be expected for the proposed structure, the CH_3 and O—C vibrations are found in the infrared and Raman. Good agreement is found for the bands assigned to the O—C and —CH_3 modes in this molecule and in the $B(OCH_3)_3$ molecule illustrating the applicability of the group frequency concept. The above

assignments indicate a planar structure, but since the interpretation is very much dependent on the correctness of the assignments, they should be confirmed by isotopic substitution. The band assignments made are consistent with those calculated from a normal coordinate analysis assuming a C_{2h} model.

HYDROGEN BONDING SYSTEMS

In general, hydrogen bonding to an X—H molecule results in a decrease in the frequency of and a broadening of the absorption band due to the X—H stretching vibration. The spectrum of free phenol (where X = C_6H_5O—) and hydrogen-bonded phenol are indicated in Fig. 7-21. For a large number of electron-pair donor molecules, a relation-

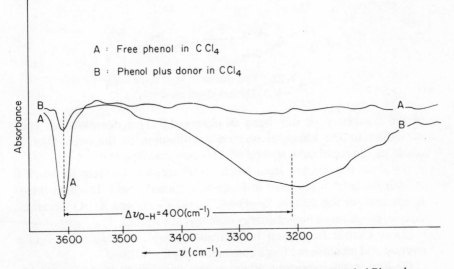

Fig. 7–21.   Infrared Spectrum of Phenol and a Hydrogen Bonded Phenol.

ship has been reported between the frequency shift upon complexation, $\Delta\nu_{0-H}$ cm^{-1}, and the enthalpy of adduct formation[33] (i.e., the enthalpy for the reaction B + H—O—C_6H_5 $\xrightarrow{CCl_4}$ B : H—O—C_6H_5). A linear equation:

$$-\Delta H \text{ (kcal mole}^{-1}) = 0.016\Delta\nu_{0-H} + 0.63 \qquad (7\text{-}11)$$

was found empirically. In view of the considerable effort involved in an enthalpy measurement (often a week's work), this relationship is a welcome one. There are only a few established exceptions[34] to this generalization for the acid phenol, but the correlation should not be applied to a different class of donors from those reported, without first verifying the relationship by measuring the enthalpy for a sample compound.

CHANGES IN THE SPECTRA OF DONOR MOLECULES UPON COORDINATION

The infrared spectrum of N,N-dimethylacetamide in the solvent CCl_4 has an absorption band at 1662 cm^{-1} due to a highly coupled carbonyl absorption. The low frequency compared to acetone (1715 cm^{-1}) is attributed to a resonance interaction with the lone pair on the nitrogen (see Fig. 7-22). Upon complexation with several Lewis acids a decrease

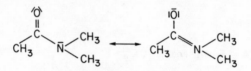

Fig. 7–22. Resonance Structures for N,N-Dimethylacetamide.

in the frequency of this band is observed.[35] This decrease has been attributed to the effect of oxygen coordination to the acid. Oxygen coordination could have several effects upon the vibration:

(1) Since the oxygen atom has to move against the atom to which it is coordinated, an increase in frequency should result. In effect this is to say that for the system X—O=C⟨, the C—O and X—O vibrations couple, producing a higher energy carbonyl absorption.

(2) A change in oxygen hybridization could increase the C—O σ overlap and increase the force constant of the C—O bond.

(3) The most important effect in this case involves decreasing the carbonyl force constant by draining π electron density out of the carbonyl group. This causes the observed decrease in the carbonyl frequency and indicates oxygen coordination. The absence of any absorption in the carbonyl region on the high frequency side of the uncomplexed carbonyl band is further support for oxygen coordination. If there were nitrogen coordination in the complexes, the nitrogen lone pair would be involved, resulting in a decreased C—N vibration frequency and a higher energy carbonyl absorption.

The decrease in the carbonyl stretching frequency of urea upon complexation to Fe^{3+}, Cr^{3+}, Zn^{2+} or Cu^{2+} is interpreted as indicating oxygen coordination in these complexes.[36] The explanation is similar to that described for the amides. This conclusion is supported by x-ray studies on the structure of the iron and chromium complexes.[37] Nitrogen coordination is observed in the compounds $Pd(NH_2CONH_2)_2Cl_2$ and $Pt(NH_2CONH_2)_2Cl_2$, and the spectra show the expected increase in the C—O stretching frequency as well as a decrease in the C—N frequency.

Decreases in the P—O stretching frequencies indicative of oxygen coordination are observed when triphenylphosphine oxide[38] and hexamethylphosphoramide, $OP—[N(CH_3)_2]_3$,[39] are coordinated to metal ions, phenol or iodine. A decrease in the S—O stretching frequency indicative of oxygen coordination, is observed when dimethyl sulfoxide or tetramethylene sulfoxide is complexed to many metal ions, iodine and phenol.[40] The S—O stretching frequency increases in the palladium complex of dimethyl sulfoxide compared to free sulfoxide. This is an indication of sulfur coordination in this complex. The N—O stretching frequency of pyridine N-oxide is decreased upon complexation.[41]

The infrared spectra of some ethylenediaminetetraacetic acid complexes indicate that this ligand behaves as a tetradentate, pentadentate, or hexadentate ligand in various complexes. The interpretation is based upon absorption bands in the carbonyl region corresponding to free and complexed carbonyl groups. The procedure is outlined in detail in the literature.[42]

It has been reported[34] that the C≡N stretching frequencies of some substituted benzonitriles increase upon coordination to the Lewis acid stannic chloride. It is proposed[43] that there is little drain of π electron density from the C≡N group and consequently little decrease in this force constant. The coupling effect described above (1) is more important, and the vibration frequency increases.

There have been many papers[44] on the assignment of the absorption bands in simple ammine complexes. The spectra have been analyzed in terms of a single M—NH_3 group, i.e., a local C_{3v} structure. In the sodium chloride range, absorption is usually found in four regions near 3300, 1600, 1300, and 825 cm^{-1}. These have been assigned to N—H stretching, NH_3 degenerate deformation; NH_3 symmetric deformation, and —NH_3 rocking, respectively. Deuteration studies[45] support these assignments. It was concluded that no metal-nitrogen vibrations in these transition metal ion complexes occur in the sodium chloride region. The frequencies of the bands are dependent upon the metal ion, the type of crystal lattice, and the anion.[46] The anion effect is attributed to hydrogen bonding. References by Chatt et al,[46] are highly recommended readings for a discussion of this subject.

It should be pointed out that solid materials can be obtained which contain noncoordinated donor molecules trapped in the crystal lattice. By virtue of the lattice environment, changes in the spectrum of the donor can occur in these instances without coordination. It is thus not possible to prove coordination by a frequency shift in the infrared spectrum of the donor taken on a mull of a solid. This problem can be resolved if the solid can be put in solution and the spectrum compared with the donor in this solvent.

Caution should also be exercised in drawing conclusions regarding the strength of the interaction between a donor and a Lewis acid (including metal ions) from the magnitude of the frequency shift of the donor. This relationship has not been adequately demonstrated with reliable, easily interpreted enthalpy data. There will very probably be cases where good correlations are obtained but no general statements can be made at present.

Excellent discussions of the important role infrared spectroscopy has played in elucidating the structure of many transition metal complexes are available.[20,47] The spectra of metal carbonyls, metal acetylacetonates, cyanide, thiocyanate, and several other types of complexes are discussed.

Change in Spectra Accompanying Change in Symmetry upon Coordination

Evidence to support coordination of the nitrate ion to metal ions can be obtained from infrared studies.[48] Free nitrate ion has D_{3h} symmetry but upon coordination of one of the oxygens, the symmetry is lowered to C_{2v}. The asymmetric stretch in the nitrate ion is split into a high frequency N—O asymmetric stretch and a lower frequency symmetric stretch (see Appendix E for planar XY_3 and ZXY_2 molecules). These occur at 1460 and 1280 cm^{-1} (± 20 cm^{-1}), respectively. An additional NO stretching frequency corresponding roughly to the inactive symmetric stretch in nitrate ion also appears. For complete details see the references.[48]

The infrared spectrum of coordinated nitrite is very much different for —NO$_2$ and —O—N—O isomers.[49] The symmetry of the ions are very different in the two cases.

The sulfate ion is another good example to demonstrate the effect of change in symmetry on spectra. The sulfate ion (T_d symmetry) has two infrared bands in the sodium chloride region: one assigned to ν_3 at 1104 cm^{-1} and one to ν_4 at 613 cm^{-1}. (See Appendix E for the forms of these vibrations.) In the complex [Co(NH$_3$)$_5$OSO$_3$]Br the coordinated sulfate group has lower symmetry, C_{3v}. Six bands now appear at 970

(ν_1), 438 (ν_2), 1032 to 1044 and 1117 to 1143 (from ν_3), 645 and 604 (from ν_4). In a bridged sulfate group the symmetry is lowered to C_{2v} and even more bands appear. For a bridged group the ν_3 band of $SO_4{}^{2-}$ is split into three peaks and the ν_4 band into three peaks.[50] Infrared spectroscopy is thus a very effective tool for determining the nature of the bonding of sulfate ion in complexes.

The infrared spectra of various materials containing perchlorate ion have been interpreted[51] to indicate the existence of coordinated perchlorate. As above, the change in symmetry brought about by coordination increases the number of bands in the spectrum. References to similar studies on other anions are contained in the text by Nakamoto.[20]

In another application of this general idea, it was proposed that the five-coordinate addition compound, $(CH_3)_3SnCl \cdot (CH_3)_2SO$, had a structure in which the three methyl groups were in the equatorial positions because the symmetric Sn—C stretch present in $(CH_3)_3SnCl$ disappeared in the addition compound.[52] In $(CH_3)_3SnCl$ the asymmetric and symmetric stretches occur at 545 cm^{-1} and 514 cm^{-1}, respectively.[53] In the adduct a single Sn—C vibration due to the asymmetric Sn—C stretch, is detected at 551 cm^{-1}. This is expected for the isomer with three methyl groups in the equatorial position because a small dipole moment change is associated with the symmetric stretch in this isomer. For all other possible structures that can be written, at least two Sn—C vibrations should be observed. There is also a pronounced decrease in the frequency of the Sn—Cl stretching mode in the addition compound.

EXERCISES

1. Consider the C_{2v} structure of N—SF$_3$. (a) Show that the total representation is $E = 15$; $2C_3 = 0$; $3\sigma_v = 3$. (b) Indicate the procedure that shows the irreducible representations $4A_1$, $1A_2$ and $5E$ result from this total representation. (c) Show that $4A_1 + 1A_2 + 5E$ equals $E = 15$; $2C_3 = 0$; $3\sigma_v = 3$. (d) Indicate the species for the allowed: (e) infrared, (f) Raman, and (g) Raman polarized bands. (h) How many bands would be seen for (e), (f), and (g), assuming all allowed fundamentals are observed?

2. Consider XeF$_4$ as having D_{4h} symmetry. Using the procedure in Exercise 1, show that the total number of vibrations is indicated by $A_{1g} + B_{1g} + B_{2g} + A_{2u} + B_{1u} + 2E_u$. Also indicate the species for the allowed (a) infrared, (b) Raman, and (c) Raman polarized bands. (d) How many bands would be seen for (a), (b), and (c) assuming all allowed fundamentals are observed?

3. Consider the molecule trans-N$_2$F$_2$.
   a. To which point group does it belong?   Answer: C_{2h}.
   b. How many fundamentals are expected?   Answer: $3n-6 = 6$.
   c. To what species do these belong?   Answer: $3A_g$, $1A_u$, and $2B_u$.
   d. What is the difference between the A_u and B_u vibrations?

e. Which vibrations are infrared and which are Raman active? (B_u and A_u are IR active; the three A_g modes are Raman active.)

f. How many polarized lines are expected?

g. How many lines are coincident in the infrared and Raman? Does this agree with the center of symmetry rule.

h. To which species do the following vibrations belong: N—N stretch, symmetric N—F stretch, and asymmetric N—F stretch.

i. Can the N—N stretch and N—F stretch couple?

4. Indicate to which species the vibrations belong and indicate how many active IR, active Raman, and polarized Raman lines are expected for:

   a. cis-$N_2F_2[(C_{2v})$ 5 IR active, $(3A_1, 2B_2)$; 6Raman $(A_1, A_2, B_1)]$

   b. A linear N_2F_2 molecule $(D_{\infty h})$

5. a. Why is cis-N_2F_2 in the point group C_{2v} instead of D_{2h}?

   b. What symmetry element is missing from the pyramidal structure of SF_4 that is required for D_{4h} (i.e., which one element would give rise to all missing operations)?

6. The far infrared spectrum of gaseous HCl consists of a series of lines spaced 20.68 cm^{-1} apart. (Recall that wavenumbers must be converted to frequency to employ the equations given in this text.)

   a. Calculate the moment of inertia of HCl.

   b. Calculate the equilibrium internuclear separation.

7. Suppose valence considerations enabled one to conclude that the following structures were possible for the hypothetical molecule X_2Y_2:

$$Y-X-X-Y \qquad X-X\underset{Y}{\overset{Y}{\diagdown}} \quad X-X^{Y} \qquad \qquad X-X^{Y}$$

The infrared spectrum of the gas has several bands with P, Q, and R branches. Which structures are eliminated?

8. An X—H fundamental vibration in the linear molecule A—X—H is found to occur at 3025 cm^{-1}. At what frequency is the X—D vibration expected? It is found that the X—D vibration is lowered only about half the expected value and the A—X stretching frequency is affected by deuteration. Explain. Would you expect the A—X—H bending frequency to be affected by deuteration? Why?

9. How many normal modes of vibration does a planar BCl_3 molecule have? Refer to Appendix E and illustrate these modes. Indicate which are infrared inactive. Confirm these conclusions by employing the procedures in the section, Use of Symmetry Considerations to Determine the Number of Active Infrared and Raman Lines. Indicate the Raman polarized and depolarized lines and the parallel and perpendicular vibrations.

10. The following assignments are reported for the spectrum of GeH_4: 2114, T_2; 2106, A_1; 931, E; 819, T_2. Label these using the ν_u symbolism. (E modes are numbered after singly degenerate symmetric and asymmetric vibrations, and T modes are numbered after E modes.) Refer to Appendix E to illustrate the form for each of these vibrations and label them as bends or stetches.

11. Refer to the normal modes for a planar ZXY_2 molecule (Appendix E). Verify the assignment of ν_5 as B_2 and ν_6 as B_1 by use of the character tables. Explain the procedure.

12. a. Indicate the infrared and Raman activities for the modes of the trigonal bipyramidal XY_5 molecule. (Appendix E)

    b. Does this molecule possess a center of symmetry?

13. The spectrum of $Co(NH_3)_6(ClO_4)_3$ has absorption bands at 3320, 3240, 1630, 1352, and 803 cm^{-1}. For purposes of assignment the molecule can be treated as a C_{3v} molecule, $\left[Co—N\begin{smallmatrix} H \\ \\ H \end{smallmatrix}—H \right]^{3+}$. Refer to Appendix E for a diagram of these modes and utilizing the material in this chapter and Chapter 5 assign these modes. Use the ν_n symbolism to label the bands and also describe them as bends, stretches, etc.

14. What changes would you expect to see in the infrared spectrum of CH_3COSCH_3 if

    a. Coordination occurred on oxygen?

    b. Coordination occurred on sulfur?

15. In which case would the spectrum of coordinated $[(CH_3)_2N]_3PO$ be most likely to resemble the spectrum of the free ligand:

    a. Oxygen coordination?

    b. Nitrogen coordination?

    Why?

16. Using a value of $k = 4.5 \times 10^5$ dynes cm^{-1} for the C—C bond stretching force constant, calculate the wave number (cm^{-1}) for the C—C stretching vibration.

17. The compound $HgCl_2 \cdot O\begin{smallmatrix} CH_2—CH_2 \\ \\ CH_2—CH_2 \end{smallmatrix}O$, could be a linear polymer with dioxane in the chair form or a monomer with bidentate dioxane in the boat form. How could infrared and Raman be used to distinguish between these possibilities?

18. Which complex would have more N—O vibrations: $(NH_3)_5CoNO_2^{2+}$ or $(NH_3)_5CoONO^{2+}$?

19. What differences (number of bands and frequencies) are expected between the C—O absorptions of the following:

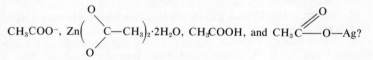

CH_3COO^-, $Zn\left(\begin{smallmatrix} O \\ \\ C—CH_3 \\ \\ O \end{smallmatrix} \right)_2 \cdot 2H_2O$, CH_3COOH, and $CH_3C\begin{smallmatrix} O \\ \\ O—Ag \end{smallmatrix}$?

REFERENCES CITED

1. G. Herzberg, "Infrared and Raman Spectra," pp. 272-276, D. van Nostrand, New York, 1945.

2. G. Barrow, "Introduction to Molecular Spectroscopy," pp. 116–130. McGraw-Hill, New York, 1962.

3. E. B. Wilson, J. C. Decius, and P. C. Cross, "Molecular Vibrations," McGraw-Hill, New York, 1955.

4. J. Overend and J. R. Scherer, *J. Chem. Phys.*, **32**, 1296 (1960).

5. J. O. Halford, *J. Chem. Phys.*, **24**, 830 (1956); S. A. Francis, *J. Chem. Phys.*, **19**, 942 (1951); G. Karabatsos, *J. Org. Chem.*, **25**, 315 (1960).
6. National Bureau of Standards, Circular 518; W. Gordy, W. V. Smith, and R. Trambarulo, "Microwave Spectroscopy," pp. 371–373, Wiley, 1953.
7. C. H. Townes and A. L. Schalou, "Microwave Spectroscopy," pp. 56–59. 110–114, McGraw-Hill, New York, 1955; *Ann. Revs. Phys. Chem.*—see the indices for all volumes.
8. S. Krimm, "Infrared Spectra of Solids" in "Infrared Spectroscopy and Molecular Structure," chapter 8, ed. M. Davies, Elsevier, 1963.
9. H. Winston and R. S. Halford, *J. Chem. Phys.*, **17**, 607 (1949).
10. D. F. Hornig, *J. Chem. Phys.*, **16**, 1063 (1948).
11. M.-L. Josien and N. Fuson, *J. Chem. Phys.*, **22**, 1264 (1954).
12. A. Allerhand and P. R. Schleyer, *J. Am. Chem. Soc.*, **85**, 371 (1963).
13. R. S. Drago, J. T. Kwon, and R. D. Archer, *J. Am. Chem. Soc.*, **80**, 2667. (1958).
14. R. N. Jones and C. Sandorfy, "Chemical Applications of Spectroscopy," pp. 247–580, ed. W. West (vol. IX, "Technique of Organic Chemistry, ed. A. Weissberger), Interscience, New York–London, 1956.
15. L. J. Bellamy, "The Infrared Spectra of Complex Molecules," 2nd ed., Wiley, New York, 1958.
16. Miller and Wilkins, *Anal. Chem.*, **24**, 1253 (1952), for spectra of inorganics in the NaCl region; Miller, Carlson, Bentley, and Jones, *Spectrochim Acta*, **16**, 135 (1960), for spectra of inorganics in the CsBr region.
17. H. M. Hershenson, "Infrared Absorption Spectra," Academic, New York, 1959.
18. K. E. Lawson, "Infrared Absorption of Inorganic Substances," Reinhold, New York, 1961.
19. "And Index of Published Infrared Spectra," British Government publication, available from Her Majesty's Stationery Office. The first two volumes include 10,000 IR spectra published up to 1957.
20. K. Nakamoto, "Infrared Spectra of Inorganic and Coordination Compounds," Wiley, New York, 1963. An excellent reference for inorganic compounds.
21. H. Landolt and R. Bornstein, "Zahlenwerte und Functionen," ex. A. Eucken and K. H. Hellwege, Springer, Berlin, 1951.
22. J. H. Hibben, "The Raman Effect and Its Chemical Applications, Reinhold, New York, 1939.
23. K. W. J. Kohlrausch, "Raman spectren, Hand- und Jahrbuch der Chemischen Physik." vol. 9, ed. A. Euchen and Wolf, Edwards Brothers, Ann Arbor, Michigan 1945.
24. H. Richert and O. Glemser, *Z. anorg. allgem. chem.*, **307**, 328–344 (1961).
25. N. J. Hawkins, V. W. Coher, and W. S. Koski, *J. Chem. Phys.*, **20**, 528 (1952).
26. W. H. Kirchhoff and E. B. Wilson, Jr., *J. Am. Chem. Soc.*, **84**, 334 (1962).
27. D. R. Lide and D. E. Mann, *J. Chem. Phys.*, **25**, 595, 1128 (1956); E. X. Powell and E. R. Lippincott, *J. Chem. Phys.*, **32**, 1883 (1960).
28. M. K. Wilson and G. R. Hunt, *Spectrochim. Acta*, **16**, 570 (1960).
29. R. G. Snyder and J. C. Hisatsune, *J. Mol. Spectry.*, **1**, 139 (1957).
30. W. C. Price, *J. Chem. Phys.*, **16**, 894 (1948).

31. H. H. Claassen, B. Weinstock, and J. G. Malm, *J. Chem. Phys.,* **28**, 285 (1958).
32. H. Becher, W. Sawodny, H. Noth, and W. Meister, *Z. anorg. allgem. chem.,* **314**, 226 (1962).
33. M. D. Joesten and R. S. Drago, *J. Am. Chem. Soc.,* **84**, 3817 (1962).
34. R. S. Drago, B. Wayland, and R. L. Carlson, *J. Am. Chem. Soc.,* **85**, 3125 (1963).
35. C. D. Schmulbach and R. S. Drago, *J. Am. Chem. Soc.,* **82**, 4484 (1960); R. S. Drago and D. A. Wenz, *J. Am. Chem. Soc.,* **84**, 526 (1962).
36. R. B. Penland, S. Mizushima, C. Curran, and J. V. Quagliano, *J. Am. Chem. Soc.,* **79**, 1575 (1957).
37. Y. Okaya, et al., "Abstracts of Papers of 4th International Congress of the International Union of Crystallography," p. 69, Montreal, 1957.
38. F. A. Cotton, et al., *J. Chem. Soc.,* **1961**, 2298, 3735. And references contained therein.
39. J. T. Donoghue and R. S. Drago, *Inorg. Chem.,* **1**, 866 (1962).
40. R. S. Drago and D. W. Meek, *J. Phys. Chem.,* **65**, 1446 (1961). And papers cited therein.
41. J. V. Quagliano, et al., *J. Am. Chem. Soc.,* **83**, 3770 (1961).
42. M. L. Morris and D. H. Busch, *J. Am. Soc.* **78**, 5178 (1956).
43. T. L. Brown and M. Kubota, *J. Am. Chem. Soc.,* **83**, 4175 (1961).
44. G. Svatos, D. Sweeny, S. Mizushima, C. Curran, J. V. Quagliano, *J. Am. Chem. Soc.,* **79**, 3313 (1957). And papers cited therein.
45. S. Mizushima, I. Nakagawa, and J. V. Quagliano, *J. Chem. Phys.,* **23**, 1367 (1955); G. Barrow, R. Krueger, and F. Basolo, *J. Inorg. Nucl. Chem.,* **2**, 340 (1956).
46. J. Chatt, L. A. Duncanson, and L. M. Venanzi, *J. Chem. Soc.,* **1955**, 4461; **1956**, 2712.
47. F. A. Cotton, "Modern Coordination Chemistry," eds. J. Lewis and R. G. Wilkins, Interscience, New York, 1960.
48. B. M. Gatehouse, S. E. Livingston, and R. S. Nyholm, *J. Chem. Soc.,* **1957**, 4222; C. C. Addison and B. M. Gatehouse, *J. Chem. Soc.,* **1960**, 613; J. R. Ferraro, *J. Inorg. Nucl. Chem.,* **10**, 319 (1959).
49. J. P. Faust and J. V. Quagliano, *J. Am. Chem. Soc.,* **76**, 5346 (1954); K. Nakamoto, J. Fujita, and H. Murata, *J. Am. Chem. Soc.,* **80**, 4817 (1958).
50. K. Nakamoto, et al., *J. Am. Chem. Soc.,* **79**, 4904 (1957); C. G. Barraclough and M. L. Tobe, *J. Chem. Soc.,* **1961**, 1993.
51. B. J. Hathaway and A. E. Underhill, *J. Chem. Soc.,* **1961**, 3091.
52. N. A. Matwiyoff and R. S. Drago, *Inorg. Chem.,* **3**, 337 (1964).
53. H. Kriegsman and S. Pischtschan, *Z. Anorg. Chem.,* **308**, 212 (1961); W. F. Edgell and C. H. Ward. *J. Mol. Spectry.,* **8**, 343 (1962).

GENERAL REFERENCES

A. In the area of infrared, highly recommended references dealing with theory are as follows:

Introductory

R. P. Bauman, "Absorption Spectroscopy," Wiley, New York, 1962.

G. Barrow, "Introduction to Molecular Spectroscopy," McGraw-Hill, New York, 1962.

J. C. D. Brand and J. L. Speakman, "Molecular Structure," E. Arnold, London, 1960.

P. Wheatley, "The Determination of Molecular Structure," Clarendon, Oxford, 1960.

Advanced

A. B. F. Duncan, "Theory of Infrared and Raman Spectra" in "Chemical Applications of Spectroscopy," ed. W. West (vol. IX, "Technique of Organic Chemistry," ed. A. Weissberger) Interscience, New York, 1956.

G. Herzberg, "Infrared and Raman Spectra," Van Nostrand New York, 1945.

E. B. Wilson, J. C. Decius, and P. C. Cross, "Molecular Vibrations," McGraw-Hill, New York, 1955.

G. W. King, "Spectroscopy and Molecular Structure," Holt, Rinehart and Winston, New York, 1964.

B. References dealing with applications are as follows:

F. A. Cotton, "Infrared of Transition Metal Complexes," in "Modern Coordination Chemistry," ed. J. Lewis and R. G. Wilkins, Interscience, New York, 1960.

M. Davies (ed.), "Infrared Spectroscopy and Molecular Structure," Elsevier, Amsterdam, 1963.

K. Nakamoto, "Infrared Spectra of Inorganic and Coordination Compounds," Wiley, New York, 1963.

K. Nakanishi, "Infrared Absorption Spectroscopy–Practical," Holden-Day, San Fransisco, 1962. This reference contains many problems (with answers) involving structure determination of organic compounds from infrared spectra.

M. K. Wilson, "Determination of Organic Structures by Physical Methods," eds. F. C. Nachod and W. D. Phillips, Academic New York, 1962.

C. References 14–20 provide a good key to the literature.

8 Nuclear Magnetic Resonance Spectroscopy*

In the discussion of NMR and EPR (Chapter 10) it will be assumed that the reader has some familiarity with the interaction between a molecule and a magnetic field. The treatment of magnetism (Appendix A) provides a very brief review of some of the very elementary considerations of magnetism necessary for an understanding of the spectroscopic methods treated herein. Appendix A should be read prior to reading this chapter if the reader is not familiar with this subject.

THEORY OF NMR SPECTROSCOPY

Two properties of nuclear particles pertinent to an understanding of nuclear magnetic resonance spectroscopy are the net spin associated with the protons and neutrons (both have a spin quantum number of $\frac{1}{2}$) and the distribution of positive charge. Several different types of nuclei are represented in Fig. 8-1. If the spins of all the particles are paired, there will be no net spin and the *nuclear spin quantum number, I*, will be zero. The distribution of positive charge is spherical, so the nucleus is said to possess a zero nuclear quadrupole moment, eQ, where e is the unit of electrostatic charge and Q is a measure of the deviation of the charge distribution from spherical symmetry (which in this case is zero). The spherical, nonspinning nucleus in Fig. 8-1a is a representation of nuclei where I and eQ are zero. In Fig. 8-1b a nucleus with $I = \frac{1}{2}$ is represented. The charge distribution is spherical, i.e., eQ is zero, but the net spin of all the nuclear particles is $\frac{1}{2}$. The presence of an unpaired spin imparts to nuclei with $I = \frac{1}{2}$, a *nuclear magnetic moment,* **M**. Since nuclei with $I = 0$ have no net spin, $\mathbf{M} = 0$ for such cases.

In cases where $I \geqslant 1$, not only will the nucleus have spin associated

---

*Consult the General References for general reviews on NMR. The references by Gutowsky and by Pople, et al., contain an advanced treatment of this subject and are highly recommended reading.

with it, but the distribution of protonic charge will be nonspherical. A positive value of Q indicates that the protonic charge is oriented along the direction of the applied field vector (Fig. 8-1c), while negative values for Q indicate charge accumulation perpendicular to the principal axis (Fig. 8-1d).

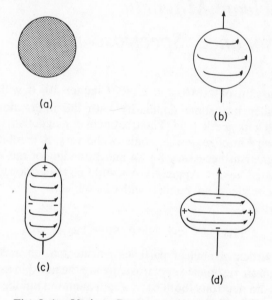

(a)

(b)

(c)

(d)

Fig. 8–1. Various Representations of Nuclei:
(a) $I = 0$, $eQ = 0$; (b) $I = 1/2$, $eQ = 0$; (c) $I \geqslant 1$,
$eQ > 0$; and (d) $I \geqslant 1$, $eQ < 0$.

Nuclei with even numbers of both protons and neutrons all belong to the type represented in Fig. 8-1a. The values for I, M and eQ for many other nuclei have been tabulated.[1,2]

NMR spectroscopy is most often concerned with nuclei with $I = \frac{1}{2}$, examples of which include H^1, P^{31}, F^{19}. Spectra cannot be obtained on nuclei with $I = 0$ and only in special cases can spectra result from nuclei where $I \geqslant 1$.

For a nucleus with $I = \frac{1}{2}$, two values for the *nuclear spin angular momentum quantum number*, $m_I = +\frac{1}{2}$ or $-\frac{1}{2}$, indicate the allowed orientations of the nuclear magnetic moment vector in an external magnetic field. The value $+\frac{1}{2}$ corresponds to alignment of the vector with the applied magnetic field and $-\frac{1}{2}$ opposed to it. The quantum number, m_I, has values: $I, (I - 1), ..., (-I + 1), -I$. For $I = 1$, m has values of $+1$, 0, and −1, corresponding respectively, to alignments with, perpendicular to, and opposed to the field. In the absence of a magnetic field, all orientations of the nuclear moment are degenerate. In the presence of an external field, however, this degeneracy will be destroyed. For a nucleus with $I = \frac{1}{2}$, the $m_I = +\frac{1}{2}$ state will be lower in energy and the $-\frac{1}{2}$ state higher, as indicated in Fig. 8-2. The energy difference between the two states,

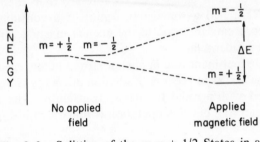

Fig. 8-2. Splitting of the $m = \pm 1/2$ States in a
Magnetic Field.

ΔE, is not very large compared to thermal energies, kT. Consequently, thermal agitation reduces the excess of nuclei in the lower energy state, and the two states are nearly equally occupied at normal temperatures. For example, at room temperature and at a magnetic field strength of 10,000 gauss, calculations employing the Boltzmann distribution law indicate that the ratio of protons in the lower energy state ($m_I = +\frac{1}{2}$) to those in the higher energy state ($m_I = -\frac{1}{2}$) is 1.0000066.

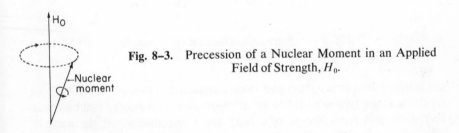

Fig. 8-3. Precession of a Nuclear Moment in an Applied
Field of Strength, H_0.

A nucleus with a magnetic moment can be treated as though it were a bar magnet which spins on its axis. When placed in an external field, the interaction of the magnetic moment with the external magnetic field produces a torque. This torque interacts with the angular momentum (in a classical way) and causes the magnetic moment to precess about the applied field vector, H_0, as indicated in Fig. 8-3. The angular frequency of the precession is referred to as the *Larmor frequency*, ω, (in radians sec^{-1}), the magnitude of which depends upon the applied field strength, H_0, the magnetic moment, and the spin angular momentum of the nucleus:

$$\omega = \gamma H_0 \tag{8-1}$$

The quantity, γ (radians gauss^{-1} sec^{-1}), referred to as the magnetogyric ratio (sometimes called gyromagnetic ratio), is a constant for a given nucleus and represents the ratio of the nuclear magnetic moment to the nuclear angular momentum.

In an NMR experiment one applies a strong homogeneous magnetic field causing the nuclei to precess. Radiation of energy comparable to ΔE is then imposed with a radio frequency transmitter. The experimental procedure for carrying out this operation is illustrated in Fig. 8-4. When

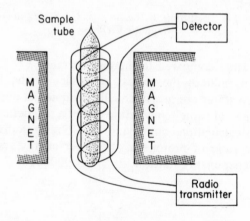

Fig. 8–4. Schematic Diagram of a Simple NMR Spectrometer.

the applied frequency from the radio transmitter is equal to the Larmor frequency, the two are said to be in *resonance,* and energy can be transferred to and from the source (i.e., the transmitter) and the sample. The net result of this resonance is that some nuclei are excited from the low energy ($m_I = +\frac{1}{2}$) state to the high energy state ($m_I = -\frac{1}{2}$; see Fig. 8-2) by absorption of energy from the source at a frequency equal to the Larmor frequency. Since $\Delta E = \mathbf{h}\nu$ and $\nu = 2\pi\omega$, ΔE is proportional to the Larmor frequency, ω. Energy will be extracted from the rf source only when this resonance condition ($\nu = 2\pi\omega$) is fulfilled. If a third electronic component, namely a detector, is added to the apparatus (see Fig. 8-4), one can observe the frequency at which the loss in energy from the transmitter occurs, allowing the resonance frequency to be measured. For a more complete discussion of the experimental procedure, see Pople, et al.[2]

It is possible to match the Larmor frequency and the applied radio frequency either by holding the field strength constant (and hence ω constant) and scanning a variable applied radio frequency until matching occurs or, as is done in the more common NMR apparatus, by varying the field strength until ω becomes equal to a fixed applied frequency. In this case there is no net change in the number of nuclei in the excited coils) are employed and the field strength at which resonance occurs is measured.

If the populations of nuclei in the ground and excited states were equal, then the probability that the nucleus would emit energy under the resonance condition would equal the probability that the nucleus would absorb energy [i.e., transitions $m_I(+\frac{1}{2}) \rightarrow m_I(-\frac{1}{2})$ would be as probable as $m_I(-\frac{1}{2}) \rightarrow m_I(+\frac{1}{2})$]. No net change would then be detected by the radio frequency probe. As mentioned earlier, in a strong magnetic field there will be a slight excess of nuclei aligned with the field (lower energy state) and consequently a net absorption of energy results. As energy is absorbed from the rf signal, enough nuclei could be excited after a finite period of time so that the population in the lower state would be equal to that in the higher state. Initially, absorption might be detected but this absorption would gradually disappear as the population of ground and excited states became equal. When this occurs, the sample is said to be saturated. If the NMR instrument is operated properly, saturation usually does not occur, because there are mechanisms for allowing nuclei to return to the lower energy state without emitting radiation. Two mechanisms whereby a given nucleus in the excited state can return to the ground state are referred to as: (1) spin-spin relaxation and (2) spin-lattice relaxation. In spin-spin relaxation the nucleus of one atom in the high energy state imparts its energy to another atom in the low energy state. In this case there is no net change in the number of nuclei in the excited state. This mechanism is not pertinent to the problem at hand but will be of importance for phenomena to be discussed later and is mentioned here for the sake of completeness. Spin-lattice relaxation involves transfer of energy to the lattice. The term lattice refers to the solvent, to the electrons in the system, or to other *different* kinds of atoms or ions in the system. This energy is converted into translational or rotational energy, and the nucleus returns to the lower state. Because of this mechanism, there is always an excess of nuclei in the lower energy state and a net absorption of energy from the rf source by the sample. We shall have more to say about relaxation processes later.

THE CHEMICAL SHIFT

The NMR phenomenon has significance to the chemist because the energy of the resonance (i.e., the field strength required to attain a Larmor frequency equal to the fixed frequency) is dependent upon the electronic environment about the nucleus. The electrons shield the nucleus, so that the magnitude of the field seen at the nucleus, H_N, is different from the applied field, H_0:

$$H_N = H_0(1 - \sigma) \qquad (8\text{-}2)$$

where σ, the shielding constant, is a dimensionless quantity which represents the shielding of the nucleus by the electrons. The value of the shielding constant, σ, depends on several factors, among which are the hybridization and electronegativity of the groups attached to the atom containing the nucleus being studied. As a result, many problems of interest to the chemist can be investigated by NMR. The proton resonance spectrum (i.e., an NMR spectrum of hydrogen nuclei) of C_2H_5OH obtained at low resolution is indicated in Fig. 8-5. The least shielded

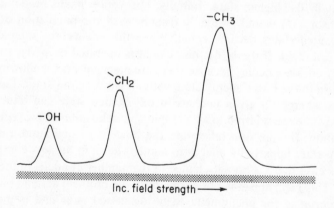

Fig. 8–5. Low Resolution Proton NMR Spectrum of C_2H_5OH.

proton (smallest σ) on the electronegative oxygen atom interacts with the field at lowest applied field strength. The areas under the peaks are in direct proportion to the numbers of equivalent hydrogens, $1:2:3$, on the hydroxyl, methylene, and methyl groups. Note that the separation of absorption peaks from $-CH_3$ and $-CH_2-$ hydrogens in this spectrum is greater than that in the infrared spectrum.

The next concern is to calibrate the horizontal axis of Fig. 8-5 so that the field strength (or some. function of it) at which the protons absorb energy from the radiofrequency probe can be recorded. Equation (8-2) could be employed, but accurate measurement of H_N and H_0 is difficult. Instead, a reference material is employed, and the difference between the field strength at which the sample nucleus and the nucleus in the reference compound absorbs is measured. For a given probe, the field experienced by the nucleus that is necessary for any proton to undergo resonance, H, is a constant. According to equation (8-2), the applied field necessary to cause the sample and reference protons to undergo resonance, H_S and H_R, respectively, is given by:

$$H_S - H_R = H_0(\sigma_R - \sigma_S)$$
$$H = H_S(1 - \sigma_S) \quad \text{and} \quad H = H_R(1 - \sigma_R)$$

where σ_S and σ_R are the shielding constants for the sample and reference. Consequently,

$$H_S(1 - \sigma_S) = H_R(1 - \sigma_R)$$

or

$$\frac{1 - \sigma_R}{1 - \sigma_S} = \frac{H_S}{H_R}$$

Subtracting one from both sides and rearranging, one obtains:

$$\frac{\sigma_S - \sigma_R}{1 - \sigma_S} = \frac{H_S - H_R}{H_R} \tag{8-3}$$

Since $\sigma_S <<< 1$, equation (8-3) becomes

$$\delta = \sigma_S - \sigma_R = \frac{H_S - H_R}{H_R}$$

where δ, the *chemical shift,* is defined as the difference in the shielding constants of the sample and reference. The relationship between H and frequency in cps is given by $\nu = \gamma H/2\pi$. Since the separation of the reference and sample signals is often measured in units of frequency (cps), the above equation for δ is more conveniently written as

$$\delta = \sigma_S - \sigma_R = \frac{\nu_S - \nu_R}{\nu_R} \tag{8-4}$$

The quantities ν_R and ν_S are very large numbers which are only slightly different than ν_0, the fixed frequency of the probe (commonly 40 or 60 mc sec^{-1} for protons). As a result, equation (8-4) can be rewritten as:

$$\delta = \frac{\nu_S - \nu_R}{\nu_0} \tag{8-5}$$

The quantity δ is referred to as the chemical shift. The quantity $\nu_S - \nu_R$, the difference between the resonance frequencies of the sample and reference, is often referred to by the symbol Δ. The quantity ν_0 refers to the constant probe frequency employed. The quantity $\nu_S - \nu_R$ is obtained by varying the field strength as in Fig. 8-5 and calibrating the horizontal axis of this figure (and hence the difference in the positions of the peaks) in terms of frequency. The following experimental procedure can be employed to accomplish this calibration and to determine the chemical shift of a sample relative to a standard (Fig. 8-6). The compound $Si(CH_3)_4$

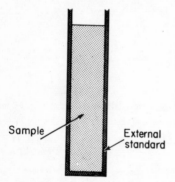

Sample

External standard

Fig. 8–6. NMR Sample Tube Containing an External Standard. For illustrative purposes the external standard compartment size is exaggerated. This is really just large enough for 2 to 3 drops of standard.

(abbreviated TMS), in which the protons are very highly shielded, can be employed as a standard. The spectrum of CH_3I relative to TMS is represented by solid line in Fig. 8-7. The field axis, H_0, is calibrated by displacing part of this spectrum electronically by imposing on the rf field a fixed audio frequency field. Part of the intensity of all the lines in the spectrum will be displaced a certain number of cycles per second equal to the audio frequency. The spectrum indicated by the dashed line will result. If the audio frequency were 300 cps, the distance on the chart paper between the original and the displaced peaks would be 300 cps. The displaced peaks are referred to as *side bands*. The distance between the $Si(CH_3)_4$ and CH_3I peaks is divided by the distance between one of

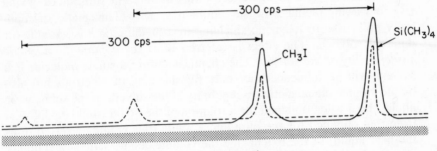

Fig. 8-7. Proton NMR Spectrum of CH_3I with $Si(CH_3)_4$ as an Internal Standard (Solid Line). The dashed line is the same spectrum with a 300 cps side band.

the main peaks and its side band. Multiplication of this ratio by 300 cps (or by whatever imposed frequency is selected) gives the value, Δ, in cycles per second, for the difference between the sample signal (CH_3I) and the reference signal ($Si(CH_3)_4$). It is required that the rate at which the field changes be constant. The quantity δ is calculated from Δ by use of equation (8-6):

$$\delta = \frac{\Delta \times 10^6}{\text{fixed frequency of the probe, } \nu_0} \tag{8-6}$$

The frequency of a commonly employed probe for protons is 60,000,000 cps (i.e., 60 mc sec^{-1}). The factor 10^6 is employed in equation (8-6) to give convenient numbers for δ in units of parts per million, ppm. The quantity Δ is directly related to the probe frequency, i.e., at 60 mc sec^{-1} it is $\frac{3}{2}$ that at 40 mc sec^{-1}. The chemical shift, δ, is independent of the probe frequency employed. If the sample resonance peak occurs at a lower field strength than the reference, Δ is negative by the conventions outlined above. When $Si(CH_3)_4$ is employed as a standard, almost all δ values are negative and the larger negative numbers refer to lesser shielding. Procedures, other than the sideband technique, have been outlined[2] for obtaining very accurate chemical shift data. With the A-60 spectrometer, commercially available from Varian Associates, it is possible to read δ directly from the chart paper if the instrument is calibrated periodically.

As mentioned in Appendix A, magnetic field-induced circulations give rise to a magnetic moment which is opposed to the applied field. This is the principal effect in diamagnetic substances and accounts for the repulsion experienced by these materials when placed in a magnetic field. The magnitude of this effect varies in different substances, giving rise to varying diamagnetic susceptibilities. This diamagnetic susceptibility gives rise to magnetic shielding in a medium, and is variable for different solvents. The effect is referred to as the *volume diamagnetic susceptibility of the solvent*. The chemical shift of a solute molecule in a solvent will be influenced not only by shielding of electrons but also by the volume diamagnetic susceptibility of the solvent. If the solute were liquid, the δ value obtained for a solution of the liquid would be different from that obtained for the pure liquid solute (this is often referred to as the neat liquid) to the extent that the volume diamagnetic susceptibility of the solvent and neat liquid were different. Because of the variation in the contribution from volume diamagnetic susceptibility, the chemical shifts of neat liquids relative to an external standard are difficult to interpret. Problems are also encountered when substances are examined in solution. The diamagnetic contributions to the shielding of the solute would depend upon the average number of solute and solvent molecules, i.e., the number of solvent and solute neighbors. Consequently the chemical shift will be concentration dependent. To get a meaningful value for δ, it is therefore necessary to eliminate or keep constant the contribution to δ from the diamagnetic susceptibility of the solvent. This can be accomplished by measuring δ at different concentrations and extrapolating to infinite dilution, in effect producing a value for δ under volume susceptibility conditions of the pure solvent. If all values for different solutes are compared in this solvent, the effect is constant.

Contributions to the measured δ from the volume diamagnetic susceptibility of the solvent can be minimized by using an *internal standard*. The internal standard is dissolved in the solvent along with the sample. It must, of course, be unreactive with the solvent and sample. Under these conditions the standard is subjected to the same field (from solvent molecules) as the solute (i.e., same volume susceptibility), and the effects will tend to cancel when the difference, Δ, is calculated. (Due to variation in the arrangement of solvent around different solutes, an exact cancellation is often not obtained.) Cyclohexane and $Si(CH_3)_4$ are commonly employed as internal standards for protons. In order for the results from an internal and an external standard to be strictly comparable, δ for the standard as a pure liquid must be identical with δ for the standard in the solvent. It is now common practice to employ an internal standard for accurate work. Several spectra at different concentrations should be run as checks and the results relative to two internal standards compared.

The solvent employed for an NMR experiment should be chemically inert, and should have symmetrical electron distribution. Carbon tetrachloride is ideal for proton resonance. Chemical shift values close to those obtained in carbon tetrachloride are obtained in chloroform, deuterochloroform, and carbon disulfide. Acetonitrile, dimethylformamide, and acetone are frequently used but can be employed satisfactorily only if there are no specific interactions (H bonding or other Lewis acid-base interactions) and if an internal standard is employed. It is also possible to measure δ in such a solvent for compounds whose chemical shifts in CCl_4 are known, to determine a correction factor for the volume susceptibility of the solvent. This is then applied to the chemical shifts of other solutes in that solvent.

As seen in the above discussion, the solvent in which the chemical shift is examined has a pronounced effect on the value obtained. It is found that even the relative values of δ for the different protons in a given molecule may vary in different solvents. A quantity σ_{solv} has been proposed[3] to encompass all types of shielding from solvent effects. This quantity is constituted of the following:

$$\sigma_{solv} = \sigma_B + \sigma_A + \sigma_W + \sigma_E$$

where σ_B is the shielding contribution from the bulk magnetic susceptibility of the solvent, σ_A arises from anisotropy of the solvent, σ_W arises from van der Waals interactions between the solvent and solute, and σ_E is the shielding contribution from a polar effect caused by charge distribution induced in neighboring solvent molecules by polar solutes (i.e., an induced solvent dipole–solute interaction). As mentioned above, σ_B is eliminated by the use of internal standards. Some indication of the importance of the other effects for a given solute can be obtained by determining δ in different solvents.

Instead of δ, τ values are often employed to report chemical shifts. The τ scale is designed to give positive numbers for most chemical shifts. When δ is defined, as above, by $\sigma_S - \sigma_R$ the value for τ can be obtained from:

$$\tau = 10 + \delta \tag{8-7}$$

where $Si(CH_3)_4$ is employed as the internal standard and δ is usually a negative number. The larger values for τ indicate a more shielded proton.

The spectrum in Fig. 8-7 has been drawn to scale (a 60 mc sec^{-1} probe was employed), so with a ruler and the information given, the reader should be able to calculate the value: $\tau = 7.8$. Appendix F contains data to permit conversion of δ relative to various standards to δ relative to $Si(CH_3)_4$ as the reference.

Researchers in the field of NMR have been most effective in devising confusing ways of presenting chemical shift data. The chemical shift is sometimes presented as $\sigma_R - \sigma_S$, and one can also find the chemical shift reported as the quantity Δ, defined above, in either units of gauss or cps. A whole host of different external standards have been employed. When the convention $\delta = \sigma_R - \sigma_S$ is employed, Δ values for peaks on the low field side of the standard are positive and those on the high field side negative. This is just the opposite of the δ convention described above where peaks on the low field side of $Si(CH_3)_4$ have negative Δ values and the larger negative δ values correspond to less shielding. For most fluorine and phosphorus shifts the convention employed involves negative Δ values for peaks on the low field side, i.e., $\sigma_S - \sigma_R$. Using F_2 as the standard for fluorine shifts, most Δ values are positive and the larger positive δ values correspond to more shielding. Care should be exercised to state the convention when reporting δ values and to determine the convention employed before comparing literature data from different sources.

CHEMICAL SHIFTS OF SOME SYSTEMS STUDIED BY NMR

The main concern in this section will be with demonstrating the wide range of systems that can be studied by NMR. Only the simplest kinds of applications will be discussed. The nuclei which have been most frequently studied are H^1, F^{19}, and P^{31}. There are also extensive reports of C^{13}, B^{11}, O^{17}, N^{15} and Co^{59} NMR spectra. The total range of the NMR spectral region is so large that overlap of the absorption from nuclei of two different elements is not a problem. Modification of the equipment (i.e., use of different radio frequency probes) is necessary to obtain the spectrum of more than one element.

The range of proton chemical shifts measured on pure liquids[4] for a series of organic compounds is illustrated in Fig. 8-8. Proton shifts outside this total range have been reported, and sometimes shifts outside the range indicated for a given functional group occur. In general, the data in Fig. 8-8 serve to give a fairly reliable means of distinguishing protons on quite similar functional groups. Note the difference in CH_3—C, CH_3C=, CH_3—O, HC=, HCO, etc. Care must be exercised with

—OH groups, for the shift is very concentration- and temperature-dependent. For example, when the spectrum of ethanol is examined as a function of concentration in an inert solvent (e.g., CCl_4), the total change in chemical shift in going from concentrated to dilute solution amounts to about 5 ppm. When the data are extrapolated to infinite dilution, the

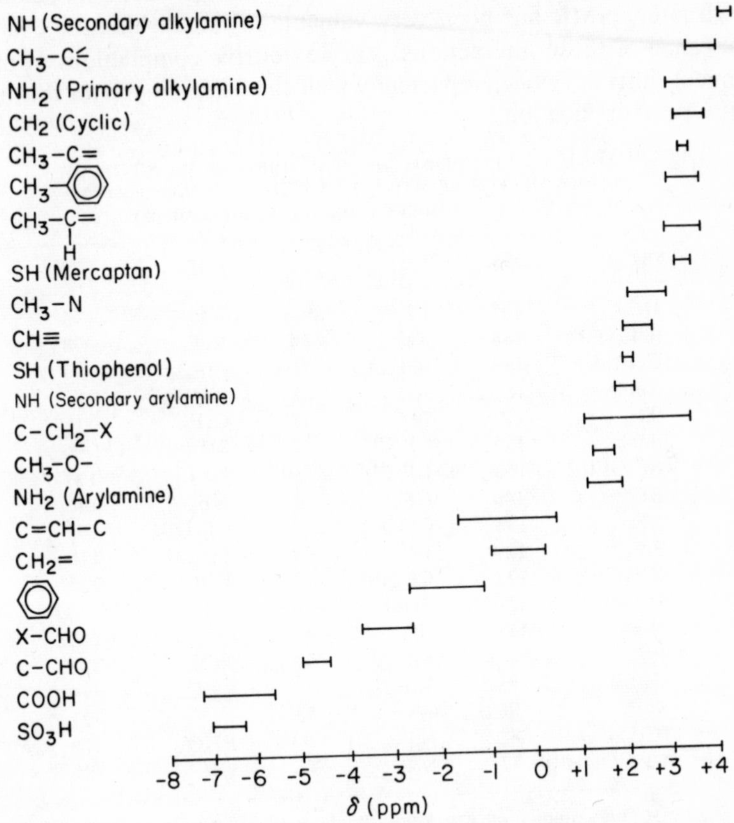

Fig. 8–8. Range of Proton NMR Signals for Various Functional Groups. δ is relative to water; this convention is that previously described, in that peaks on the low field side of water have negative Δ values and those on the high field side positive Δ values.

hydroxyl proton appears at a higher field than the methyl protons, in contrast to the spectrum of pure ethanol represented in Fig. 8-5. These changes are due to differing degrees of hydrogen bonding. There is more hydrogen bonding in concentrated than in dilute solutions. The effect of this interaction is to reduce the screening of the proton, causing a shift to lower field. This behavior on dilution can be employed to verify the assignment of a peak to a hydroxyl group. This dilution technique has been used to investigate the existence of steric effects in hydrogen bonding[5] and should aid in distinguishing between intermolecular and intramolecular hydrogen bonding. Solvent effects are quite large whenever hydrogen bonding or other specific interactions occur and, as will be shown later, NMR has been very valuable in establishing the existence or absence of these interactions. Very extensive compilations of proton chemical shifts have been reported[6] which can be employed for this fingerprint type of application.

TABLE 8-1.[a] FLUORINE CHEMICAL SHIFTS OF SELECTED COMPOUNDS (IN PPM RELATIVE TO $CFCl_3$ — LARGER POSITIVE NUMBERS INDICATE HIGHER FIELD)

CH_3F	278	CF_4	70	SOF_2	−70
HF	203	PF_3	68, 12	TiF_6^{2-}	−75
$(CF_3)_3CF$	188	TeF_6	64	XeF_6	−78
CeF_4	187	$(CF_3)_4C$	61.5	ClF_3	−80
XeF_4	182,27	AsF_3	48	$XeOF_4$	−89
SiF_4	177	BrF_3	38	ClF_3	−116
BeF_2	155	CF_3Cl	32	BrF_5	−132,−269
BF_3OEt_2	153	CF_2Cl_2	9	NF_2Cl	−137
BF_4^-	149	CF_3I	4	NF_3	−140
BF_3	133	$CFCl_3$	0	CF_3OF	−142
SiF_6^{2-}	129	IF_5	−4	SF_5OF	−178
$(CF_3CF_2)_2$	127	CF_3NSF_2	−33	$FOClO_3$	−225
$F^-(aq)$	120	SO_2F_2	−36	IF_7	−238,−274
SbF_3	117	SF_6	−42	OF_2	−250
PF_5	96, 62	SF_5OF	−48	$FClO_2$	−288
CF_3H	88	SeF_6	−50	FNO_2	−394
SbF_3	86	IF_5	−53	F_2	−422
$(CF_3)_2CO$	82	N_2F_4	−60	FNO	−478
CF_3COOH	77	NSF_3	−66	UF_6	−746

[a]This compilation was kindly made available by Dr. B. Stewart of the General Chemical Division of the Allied Chemical Company.

For a limited number of compounds a correlation has been reported between the electronegativity of X and the proton chemical shift of the CH_3 group in CH_3X compounds,[7] and also between the electronegativity of X and $\delta CH_3 - \delta CH_2$ for a series of C_2H_5X compounds.[8] The more electronegative X is, the less shielded are the protons. The severe limitations of such a correlation are discussed in the next section.

The range of fluorine chemical shifts is an order of magnitude larger than that normally encountered for protons. The difference between the fluorine resonance in F_2 and in F^-(aq) is 542 ppm compared to the range of about 12 ppm for proton shifts (see Fig. 8-8). A compilation of fluorine shifts is contained in Table 8-1. A wide range (~500 ppm) of phosphorus chemical shifts has also been reported. The recent literature and Fluck[9] can be consulted for compilations. The fingerprint application is immediately obvious for compounds containing these elements. Before additional applications are discussed, it is necessary to consider in more detail some other effects influencing the NMR spectrum.

Mechanism of Electron Shielding and Factors Contributing to the Magnitude of the Chemical Shift

Our next concern is with the factors that contribute to the chemical shift (δ in ppm) when it is measured under conditions which eliminate contributions from σ_{solv}. If the shielding of the nucleus were related only to the electron density about the nucleus in the ground state molecule, δ values could be employed to measure electron distribution and answer questions about inductive effects, electronegativity, acidity, basicity, etc. Even though this often is not the case, much useful information can be obtained from the chemical shift, but it is necessary to appreciate the various effects that contribute to the magnitude of the chemical shift.

Effects which generate magnetic fields whose direction is opposed to the applied field will shield the nucleus (i.e., higher external fields will be required to obtain the precession frequency). These are referred to as *diamagnetic effects*. Effects which generate magnetic fields whose direction is parallel to the applied field "deshield" the nucleus and are referred to as *paramagnetic effects*. The following four contributions to the chemical shift will be discussed: (1) local diamagnetic shielding, (2) local paramagnetic shielding, (3) remote shielding from neighbor anisotropy, and (4) interatomic ring currents.

Local effects arise from the electron distribution on the atom whose δ value is being measured, while remote effects include contributions to δ from electron density on other atoms.

LOCAL DIAMAGNETIC SHIELDING. Local diamagnetic shielding is best explained by considering what happens when an atom with a spherical distribution of electron density is placed in a magnetic field. Since the diamagnetic susceptibility is identical in all directions, the susceptibility is said to be *isotropic*, in contrast to an *anisotropic* case in which the susceptibility is different in different directions. When an atom with isotropic susceptibility is placed in a magnetic field, the field will induce electron circulations in the atom in such a direction as to generate a magnetic field opposed to the applied field (see Fig. 8-9). This will be a diamagnetic effect, and the nucleus is said to be shielded. The applied field, H_0, must be increased by the amount of this diamagnetic shielding

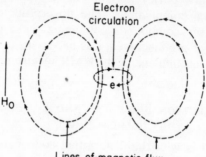

Fig. 8–9. Local Diamagnetic Contribution to the Shielding. Electron circulations occur in a plane perpendicular to the plane of the page.

(over what would be required for the nucleus in the absence of this effect) in order for the Larmor precession to occur at the fixed frequency. The magnitude of the field generated at the nucleus by electron circulations is directly proportional to the strength of the applied field, and also will depend on the electron density surrounding the nucleus. As a consequence of the former effect, the chemical shift is field dependent. When the atom is present in a molecule, this spherical symmetry does not exist, and the total induced electron circulations do not follow simple paths. The electron cloud surrounding the nucleus being investigated can be arbitrarily divided into an isotropic and an anisotropic part. The behavior of the isotropic part is identical with that discussed above for the symmetrical atom. The anisotropic contribution is included in the *local paramagnetic shielding*.

When electron-donating groups are attached to the proton, the shielding from the diamagnetic effect is increased by the increased electron density. Decreased shielding results from attachment of electron-withdrawing groups. The contribution to the shielding of protons from the local diamagnetic effect, σ_{LD}, is given by:

$$\sigma_{LD} = 21.4\lambda \times 10^{-6} \tag{8-8}$$

where λ measures the effective number of electrons in the hydrogen $1s$

atomic orbital .It can be seen that if this were the only effect influencing chemical shift, δ could be correlated with the electron density around the proton and with the electronegativity of the attached groups.

LOCAL PARAMAGNETIC SHIELDING. Local paramagnetic contributions arise from the anisotropy in the electron distribution about the atom whose chemical shift is being measured. Electron circulations develop about the nucleus which either produce a secondary magnetic field in the same direction as the applied field or are less effective in producing a diamagnetic field because of restrictions on circulation. Quantum mechanically, this anisotropy is described by a mixing, under the influence of the applied magnetic field, of the ground state and a low-lying electronically excited state of appropriate symmetry. This provides a mechanism for anisotropic electron circulation. Since the excitation energies to the empty higher energy hydrogen orbitals are large, the excited state is far removed from the ground state, and hence this effect makes an insignificant contribution to most proton chemical shifts. In the case of nuclei in which the ground and excited states are closer in energy (e.g., C, N, F, O) this effect is responsible for significant contributions to the chemical shifts.

REMOTE SHIELDING FROM NEIGHBOR ANISOTROPY. Remote effects have their origin at an atom other than the one whose chemical shift is being investigated. As illustrated in Fig. 8-10, the field at the proton in HX from the currents on X will be strongly dependent upon the orientation of the HX molecule with respect to the direction of the applied field, H_0. When the applied field is parallel to the internuclear axis, the magnetic field generated from electron circulations on X (indicated by the dotted line) will shield the proton (Fig. 8-10a), while a perpendicular orientation (Fig. 8-10b) will result in deshielding. The magnitude of the induced moment on atom X (and hence the shielding at the proton) for the parallel and perpendicular orientations will depend upon the susceptibility of

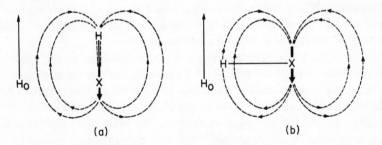

(a)   (b)

Fig. 8–10. Neighbor anisotropy in HX for Different Orientations.

X for parallel, $\chi_{\parallel}$, and perpendicular, $\chi_{\perp}$, orientations. Since only the mean contribution to the shift is measured, i.e., the average overall directions of the applied field relative to the X–H line, the effects would cancel if $\chi_{\perp}$ were equal to $\chi_{\parallel}$. The resultant contribution to the shielding at the proton from this effect will depend upon the anisotropy in the susceptibility, $\Delta\chi$, which equals $\chi_{\parallel} - \chi_{\perp}$ for an axially symmetric molecule. The same considerations apply to a system in which the source of anisotropy is located in the H—X bond instead of at X.

The above treatment for HX can be extended to other molecules. For a molecule in which the bond or atom making the remote contribution has equal susceptibilities in all directions perpendicular to the bond axis (i.e., it has axial symmetry as for example the iodine in CH_3I), the following equation can be derived for $\Delta\sigma$, the net contribution of this remote effect to the shielding:

$$\Delta\sigma = (\Delta\chi/3R^3)(1 - 3\cos^2\theta) \qquad (8-9)$$

where R is the distance from the location of the point dipole representing $\Delta\chi$ to the proton being investigated, θ is the angle formed between the line R and the C—I bond, and $\Delta\chi = \chi_{\parallel} - \chi_{\perp}$. The quantities θ and R are illustrated in Fig. 8-11. Values of $\Delta\chi$ for various bonds can be found in

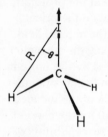

Fig. 8–11. Illustration of the Parameters θ and R of Equation (8–9).

the literature. The quantity $\Delta\sigma$ can then be calculated if the structure is known and the point dipole can be located. With large atoms, e.g., chlorine or iodine, the dipole is located at the atom.

If $\Delta\chi$ is zero, $\Delta\sigma$ is zero and there is no contribution to the shielding from neighbor anisotropy. In CH_4, for example, the carbon has spherical symmetry, $\Delta\chi$ is zero, and the contribution $\Delta\sigma$ from carbon is zero. There has been considerable discussion of the above equation and the reader is referred to an article[10] and some comments[11] by Musher for further study. Procedures have been described[12] for the experimental evaluation of $\Delta\chi$. In general, reported values for a given bond differ widely.

It is possible to divide the anisotropy contribution from a remote atom, $\Delta\chi$, into two parts: (1) a diamagnetic effect due to the field induced circulation of electrons on the remote atom and (2) a paramagnetic effect. Since the electron distribution around most atoms is close to spherical symmetry, the contribution from the diamagnetic effect will be small but that from the paramagnetic effect is often large. The paramagnetic effect is accounted for by the mechanism of magnetic-field-induced mixing of the ground state with a paramagnetic excited electronic state. *In contrast to local effects, both the diamagnetic and paramagnetic remote effects arise from anisotropy.*

With regard to the diamagnetic contribution, it is often found that $\chi_\perp$ is greater than $\chi_\parallel$. As a result there is less electron circulation when the bond is perpendicular to the field, and the contribution to $\Delta\sigma$ is less for this orientation than for the parallel orientation. *In most compounds the greatest contribution to the shielding from the neighbor effect arises from the paramagnetic part.* The magnetic field which results in ethyl iodide from the paramagnetic effect is illustrated in Fig. 8-12. *If the bond has cylindrical symmetry with regard to its orientation with the field* (i.e., C—I bond parallel to the field), this effect is not operative. Only when the C—I bond has a component perpendicular to the field will the field-induced coupling of the ground and paramagnetic excited states occur. As illustrated in Fig. 8-12, this effect causes shielding of the protons. Since the parallel orientation makes no contribution, the net effect

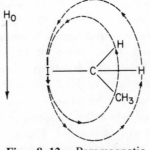

Fig. 8–12. Paramagnetic Part of Magnetic Anisotropy in C_2H_5I.

is shielding. It is interesting to note that the C^{13} resonance of the α carbon occurs at a higher field than the β carbon, as would be expected from the magnetic anisotropy* resulting from the iodine.

*Usually the paramagnetic term makes the most significant contribution to anisotropy and unless otherwise stated this will be the effect implied by the term magnetic anisotropy.

INTERATOMIC RING CURRENTS. Interatomic ring currents develop in cyclic, conjugated systems. Field-induced electron circulations occur in a loop around the ring and extend over a number of atoms. The moment induced at the center of the ring is opposed to the field, but in benzene, for example, the magnetic lines of flux at the protons are parallel to the applied field, and these protons are deshielded. This is the explanation for the low π value (equation 8-7) observed for the protons in benzene.[13]

CHEMICAL SHIFTS FOR WHICH THE LOCAL DIAMAGNETIC TERM DOES NOT PREDOMINATE

One important generalization can be drawn from the preceding and subsequent discussion, viz., chemical shift data are not reliable indications of the electron density around the nucleus being measured.

At the present state of development, the above division of factors contributing to τ must be regarded as a simplified physical model for problems that are treated more elegantly by quantum mechanics. The next step, the quantitative quantum mechanical evaluation of shielding in various molecules, appears formidable at present. After a discussion of spin-spin splitting, an empirical approach, with theoretical justification, will be presented for estimating the contribution to τ from anisotropy. Prior to this empirical method and for systems which cannot be evaluated by this empirical approach, contributions from anisotropy have been invoked when needed to account for differences between measured τ values and those expected on the basis of chemical behavior. When suspected deviations are encountered, the molecule is examined to see what property it possesses that could account for the observed discrepancies. For example, the τ value for HCl (in the vapor phase) indicates this proton is more shielded than those in methane. This is in contrast to the greater acidity of HCl. Since HCl is linear and cylindrically symmetrical about the hydrogen-chlorine bond, a paramagnetic contribution is expected when the molecule is perpendicular to the applied field and none when it is parallel. The net effect will be a shielding of the proton in HCl. This effect is greater than and in a direction opposite to the local (proton) diamagnetic effect, which is related to electronegativity of the attached atom and the removal of electrons from the hydrogen orbitals.

In the series HF, HCl, HBr, and HI, the magnitude of the paramagnetic contribution, $\Delta\sigma_p$, giving rise to anisotropy increases with increasing atomic number of the halogen. This is due to the decreased difference in the energy of the ground and excited states, ΔE, making more favorable a field-induced mixing of ground and excited states in the compounds of the higher atomic number atoms.

$$\Delta\sigma_p \propto 1/\Delta E \qquad (8\text{-}10)$$

The acidity of the compounds in the series $C_2H_6 < C_2H_4 < C_2H_2$ increases in the order listed. The τ values decrease in the order $C_2H_6 < C_2H_2 < C_2H_4$, indicating decreased shielding. Acetylene is more highly shielded than expected on the basis of its acidity and the shielding is attributed to two effects: (i) Remote diamagnetic shielding from electron circulations in the triple bond (Fig. 8-13a)(this effect is a maximum when the molecular axis is aligned with the field and is classified here as a diamagnetic effect because the moment arising from the electron circulations opposes the applied field). (2) Remote paramagnetic shielding from higher state mixing (Fig. 8-13b). Both of these effects provide shielding at the proton and contribute to the observed experimental chemical shift.

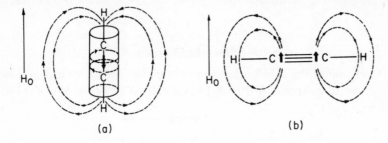

Fig. 8–13.   Contributions to the Shielding in Acetylene.

As mentioned earlier, local paramagnetic shielding is not important in proton nuclear magnetic resonance but is for magnetic resonance studies on larger atoms. Since the s orbital is spherically symmetrical, the electron density shielding the hydrogen is isotropic. The $2p$ orbitals could be used to destroy spherical symmetry, but since their energy is so high compared to $1s$, this mixing mechanism is not very important (see equation 8-10). In the case of nuclear magnetic resonance of other nuclei the highest energy–filled and lowest energy–empty orbitals are not so widely separated in energy. Calculations indicate[14] that the variation in the local paramagnetic term is the principal cause of the variation in the chemical shift for fluorine. As discussed earlier in connection with remote paramagnetic effects, field-induced mixing of a paramagnetic excited state does not occur for a symmetrical species, F^-, and is greatest in

F_2 when the fluorine bond axis is perpendicular to the applied field. Since this effect is a local paramagnetic effect, the net result will be to deshield the fluorine nuclei in F_2. For a bond with an intermediate amount of ionic character, the paramagnetic contribution would be decreased and may be a function of the electronegativity of the neighboring atom. A quantitative estimate of the magnitude of the paramagnetic shielding, σ_p, in fluorine compounds can be obtained from the equation:

$$\sigma_p = -\tfrac{2}{3}(e^2\mathbf{h}^2/m^2c^2)\ \langle 1/r^3 \rangle\,(1 - I)/\Delta E \tag{8-11}$$

where $\langle 1/r^3 \rangle$ is the average of $1/r^3$ for a fluorine $2p$ electron which is taken as equal to 8.89 divided by the Bohr radius, I is the ionic character of the bond, and ΔE is the average triplet excitation energy. Thus correlations of the fluorine chemical shift with electronegativity of the attached atom (i.e., ionic character) must be carried out on systems in which ΔE is a constant or is linearly related to σ_p. The local paramagnetic term also appears to be the dominant factor with C^{13}, N^{14}, and Co^{59} chemical shifts.

SPIN-SPIN SPLITTING

If one examines the NMR spectrum of ethyl alcohol under high resolution, the spectrum shown in Fig. 8-14 is obtained, in contrast to the low

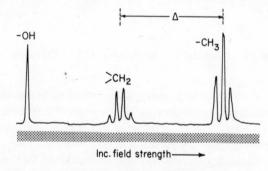

Fig. 8-14. High Resolution NMR Spectrum of a Sample of Ethanol (Acidified).

resolution spectrum in Fig. 8-5. The chemical shift of the CH_2 group relative to the CH_3 group is indicated by Δ (measured from the band centers). The fine structure in the $-CH_3$ and $-CH_2-$ peaks arises from the phenomenon known as *spin-spin splitting*, and the separation, J, between the peaks comprising the fine structure is referred to as the spin-spin coupling constant. This parameter is usually expressed in cycles per second. As mentioned earlier, the magnitude of Δ depends upon the applied field strength.* However, the magnitude of the spin-spin coupling constant in cps is field independent.

The cause of the fine structure and the reason for the field-independent character of J can be understood by considering an H—D molecule. If by some mechanism the magnetic moment of the proton can be transmitted to the deuteron, the field strength at which the deuteron precesses at the probe frequency will depend upon the magnetic quantum number of the neighboring hydrogen nucleus. If the proton nucleus has a spin of $+\frac{1}{2}$, its magnetic moment is aligned with the field so that the field experienced by the deuterium is the sum of the proton and applied fields. A lower applied field strength, H_0, will be required to attain the precession frequency of the deuterium nucleus in this molecule than in the one in which the hydrogen has a magnetic quantum number of $-\frac{1}{2}$. In the latter case the field from the proton opposes the applied field and must be overcome by the applied field to attain a precessional frequency equal to the probe frequency. The hypothetical spectrum that would result for the deuterium resonance is indicated in Fig. 8-15a. The magnetic quantum numbers for the hydrogen nuclei in the molecules giving rise to the

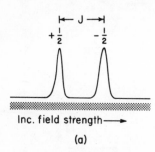

Inc. field strength⟶

(a)

Fig. 8–15. NMR Spectra for the Hypothetical HD Experiment. (a) Deuterium resonance for HD; (b) Proton resonance for HD.

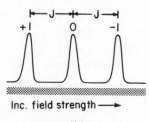

Inc. field strength ⟶

(b)

*Different values for Δ are obtained when different frequency probes are employed because the chemical shift is field dependent; see discussion under section on Local Diamagnetic Shielding for an explanation.

different peaks are indicated. The two peaks are of equal intensity because there is practically equal probability that the hydrogen will have $+\frac{1}{2}$ or $-\frac{1}{2}$ magnetic quantum numbers. The proton resonance spectrum is indicated in Fig. 8-15b. These proton resonance peaks correspond to magnetic quantum numbers of $+1$, 0, and -1 for the attached deuterium nuclei in different molecules. The spin-spin coupling constant J_{DH} or J_{HD} in Fig. 8-15a and 8-15b, respectively, have the same value. Subsequently, we shall discuss a mechanism for transmitting the magnetic moment of a neighboring atom to the nucleus undergoing resonance.

Returning to ethyl alcohol we shall examine the splitting of the methyl protons by the methylene protons. The two equivalent protons on the $-CH_2-$ group can have the various possible combinations of nuclear orientations indicated by the arrows in Fig. 8-16a. In case 1 both nuclei have m values of $+\frac{1}{2}$ giving a sum of $+1$ and accounting for the low field peak of the $-CH_3$ resonance. Case 2 is the combination of $-CH_2-$

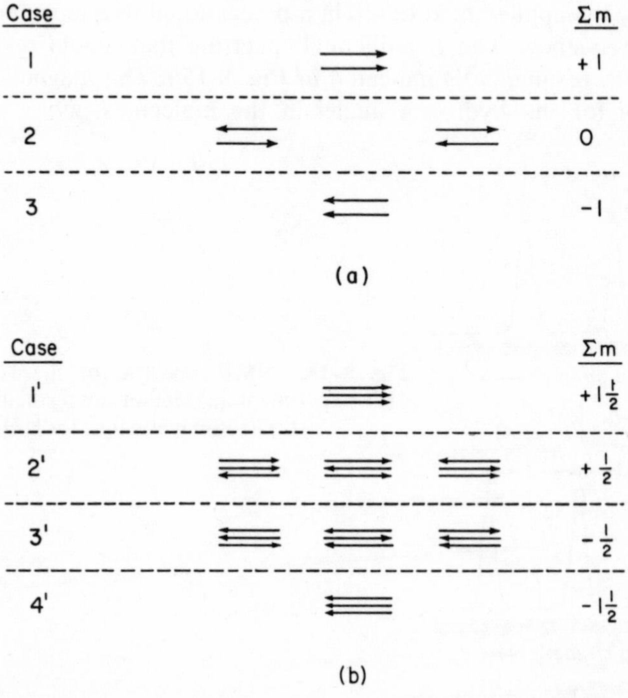

Fig. 8-16. Possible Orientations of Proton Nuclear Magnetic Moments for (a)—CH_2— and (b) —CH_3 Groups.

nuclear spins that gives rise to the middle peak and case 3 the high field peak. The probability that the spins of both nuclei will cancel (case 2) is twice as great as the combinations represented by case 1 or case 3. (There are an equal number of $+\frac{1}{2}$ and $-\frac{1}{2}$ spins.) As a result, the area of the central peak will be twice that of the others (see Fig. 8-14).

The nuclear configurations of the $-CH_3$ group which cause splitting of the $-CH_2-$ group are indicated in Fig. 8-16b. The four different total net spins give rise to four peaks (Fig. 8-14) with relative areas in the ratio $1:3:3:1$. Because of the selection rules for this process, equivalent nuclei do not split each other; e.g., one of the protons in the $-CH_3$ group cannot be split by the other two protons. A general rule for splitting can be formulated which eliminates the necessity for going through a procedure such as that in Fig. 8-16. For the general case of the peak from atom A being split by a nonequivalent atom B, the number of peaks, n, in the spectrum due to A is given by the formula

$$n = 2\Sigma S_B + 1 \qquad\qquad (8\text{-}12)$$

where ΣS_B equals the sum of the spins of equivalent B nuclei. The application of this formula is illustrated by the examples in Table 8-2. The relative intensities of the peaks can be obtained from the coefficients of the terms that result from the binomial expansion of $(r+1)^m$, where $m = n-1$; e.g., when $m = 3$, $r^3 + 3r^2 + 3r + 1$ or $1:3:3:1$.

TABLE 8-2. SPIN-SPIN SPLITTING IN VARIOUS MOLECULES[a]

Molecule	Groups Being Split (A)	Groups Doing the Splitting (B)	ΣS_B	n
CH_3CH_2OH	CH_3	CH_2	1	3
CH_3CH_2OH	CH_2	CH_3	3/2	4
PF_3	P	F	3/2	4
PF_3	F	P	1/2	2
$(CH_3)_4N^+$	CH_3	N	1	3

[a]Spin quantum numbers for the most abundant isotopes of nuclei contained in the above compounds are $H = \frac{1}{2}$, $P = \frac{1}{2}$, $F = \frac{1}{2}$, $N = 1$.

Rapid intermolecular chemical exchange has a profound effect on spin-spin splitting, as demonstrated by the NMR spectrum of ethanol. If a very pure sample of alcohol is obtained which contains no acidic or basic impurities, the O—H peak is resolved into a triplet, as expected for splitting of this proton by the CH_2 group. In addition to —CH_3 splitting, the CH_2 peak is split by the proton on the oxygen. Any acidic or basic impurity catalyzes a very rapid proton exchange among the hydroxyl groups. This rapid proton exchange occurs at such a rate that in a short time interval many different protons occupy a site on the oxygen, and only the average of their nuclear spins is seen in the methylene proton spectrum. An average peak devoid of fine structure from O—H splitting is obtained.

In order to demonstrate one further point, it is interesting to speculate about the phosphorus nuclear magnetic resonance spectrum of the compound HPF_2 (which has not yet been reported). The spectrum in Fig. 8–17a represents the splitting of the phosphorus signal by the two fluorine atoms, while Fig. 8-17b results by adding the splitting by the hydrogen to the spectrum in Fig. 8-17a. If instead we have a large splitting of the

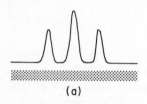

(a)

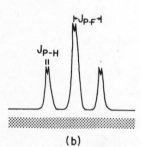

(b)

Fig. 8–17. P^{31} NMR Spectrum Expected for HPF_2 if $J_{P-F} > J_{P-H}$. (a) F splitting P. (b) H and F splitting P.

phosphorus signal by the proton, the spectrum in Fig. 8-18a arises while Fig. 8-18b results by incorporating subsequent smaller splitting of Fig. 8-18a by the fluorines. The actual spectrum is expected to be Fig. 8-17b or 8-18b, and Fig. 8-17a or 8-18a are indicated to show how the actual spectrum arises. The spectrum obtained depends upon the magnitude of J_{P-F} vs. J_{P-H}. If the P—F coupling constant is greater than the P—H coupling constant, Fig. 8-17b will result; while Fig. 8-18b results if J_{P-H} is much greater than J_{P-F}. If the two coupling constants were similar, the spectrum would be a complex pattern intermediate between Fig. 8-17b and 8-18b. In most compounds studied $J_{P-F} > J_{P-H}$ ($\sim$1500 cps vs. $\sim$200 cps), so the spectrum in Fig. 8-17b is expected.

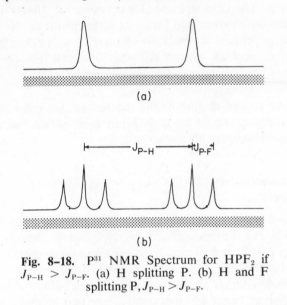

Fig. 8-18. P^{31} NMR Spectrum for HPF_2 if $J_{P-H} > J_{P-F}$. (a) H splitting P. (b) H and F splitting P, $J_{P-H} > J_{P-F}$.

SPIN-SPIN COUPLING MECHANISM FOR TRANSMITTING NUCLEAR SPINS

In the preceding section the splitting in the spectrum of the HD molecule by the magnetic moment of the attached nucleus was discussed. We shall now be concerned with the mechanism whereby information regarding the spin of the nucleus causing the splitting is transmitted to the nucleus whose resonance is split. A model has been proposed by Ramsay.[15] Consider a proton split by the nucleus X (which has a spin of $\frac{1}{2}$) in the hypothetical molecule HX. The nuclear spin of X is transmitted to H by polarization of the bonding electrons. This phenomenon is the principal mechanism for spin-spin splitting. If X has a nuclear magnetic quantum number $+\frac{1}{2}$ the electron with spin of $-\frac{1}{2}$ will have the highest probability of being found near X. Since all the electron spins are paired, the electron with spin $+\frac{1}{2}$ remains, to be found near the proton. Consequently, the spin of X is transmitted to H. The two different spin states of X give rise to two different energy transitions. The nuclear moment of X is transmitted through the bonding electrons and affects the proton regardless of the orientation of the molecule in the field. It can also be appreciated that the value of J will simply depend upon the energy difference of the two different kinds of molecules containing X in different spin states. This energy difference will be independent of the field strength. The field strength independence of J provides a criterion for determining whether two peaks in a spectrum are the result of two nonequivalent protons or spin-spin coupling. The peak separation for two nonequivalent protons will be different when 40 mc sec^{-1} and 60 mc sec^{-1} probes are employed, but the separation will be the same if the two peaks arise from spin-spin splitting.

The above representation of the mechanism for transmitting nuclear spin-spin splitting should be considered a simplified incomplete treatment of a more complex phenomena.

APPLICATIONS OF SPIN-SPIN COUPLING TO STRUCTURE DETERMINATION

There have been many applications of spin-spin coupling to determination of structures. For example, if the spectrum of a sample contains the very characteristic fine structure of the —CH_2—and—CH_3 resonances of an ethyl group, this is a good indication of the presence of this group in the molecule. Other applications involve variations in the magnitude of J in different types of compounds. For two nonequivalent protons on the same carbon, e.g., $ClBrC = CH_2$, proton-proton spin coupling constants, J_{H-H}, of 1 to 3 cps are observed. Coupling constants for nonequivalent *trans* ethylenic protons have values in the range of 17 to 18 cps, while *cis* protons give rise to coupling constants of 8 to 11 cps. These differences aid in determining the structures of isomers.

Protons attached to metal ions are in general very highly shielded, the resonance often occurring 10 to 20 ppm on the high field side of the water peak (which lies about 5 ppm to the low field side of TMS). The metal atom gives rise to local environments of high diamagnetic shielding. It has been concluded[16] that the shielding can be attributed to the electron density on H from the nonpolar nature of the M—H bond and from shielding resulting from electron density in the large and diffuse $4s$ and $4p$ levels of the metal. The proton NMR in $HRh(CN)_5^{3-}$ is a doublet (rhodium $I = \frac{1}{2}$), the center of which occurs at 15.6 ppm on the high field side of water. This splitting and shift establishes the existence of a bond between rhodium and hydrogen.[17]

The characteristic chemical shift of hydrogens attached to phosphorus occur in a limited range, and the peaks have fine structure corresponding to J_{P-H} (phosphorus $I = \frac{1}{2}$). The phosphorus resonance[18] of $HPO(OH)_2$ and $H_2PO(OH)$ is reported to be a doublet in the former and a triplet in the latter compound supporting the structures in Fig. 8-19. The coupling of the hydroxyl protons with phosphorus is either too small to be resolved,

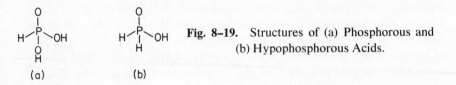

Fig. 8–19. Structures of (a) Phosphorous and (b) Hypophosphorous Acids.

(a)   (b)

for they are far removed or it is not observed because of a fast proton exchange reaction, a phenomenon to be discussed shortly. Similar results obtained from fluorine NMR establish the structures of $FPO(OH)_2$ and $F_2PO(OH)$ as containing, respectively, one and two fluorines attached to phosphorus. The P^{31} resonance in P_4S_3 consists of two peaks with intensity ratios of three to one.[19] The more intense peak is a doublet and the less intense a quadruplet. Since $I = 0$ for S^{32}, both the spin-spin splitting and the relative intensities of the peaks indicate three equivalent and one unique phosphorus atoms. It is concluded that P_4S_3 has the structure in Fig. 8-20.

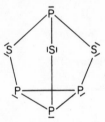

Fig. 8–20. The Structure of P_4S_3.

The fluorine resonance in BrF_5 consists of two peaks with an intensity ratio of four to one. The intense line is a doublet and the weak line is a quintet (1:4:6:4:1). This indicates that the molecule is a symmetrical tetragonal pyramid.

Solutions of equimolar quantities of TiF_6^{2-} and TiF_4 in ethanol give fluorine NMR spectra[20] consisting of two peaks with the intensity ratio 4:1 ($I = 0$ for Ti^{48}). The low intensity peak is a quintuplet and the more intense peak a doublet. The structure $[TiF_5(HOC_2H_5)]^-$ containing octahedrally coordinated titanium was proposed.

Complications are often encountered which make spectral interpretation more difficult than in the examples mentioned above. These complications also often provide much additional information about the system. The first of these to be discussed briefly here and in more detail in a later section is chemical exchange. When fast exchange occurs, the NMR spectrum measures only the average environment of the nucleus. For example, ammonia dissolved in water undergoes very rapid proton exchange reactions with water. The proton NMR spectrum consists of only one peak, which is the average resonance frequency of all the protons on nitrogen and oxygen. Spin-spin splitting will also disappear if the exchange is fast enough, because the NMR spectrometer detects only the average spin state of the nucleus doing the splitting. (Recall the earlier discussion of the splitting of $H_2P(OH)$.) The spectra of solutions of TiF_4 in donor solvents taken at $-30°C$ consist of two triplets of equal intensity.[21] This is the expected spectrum for the *cis* structure (Fig. 8-21) which contains two sets of nonequivalent fluorine atoms with

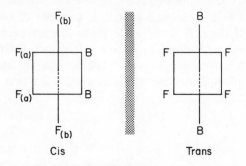

Fig. 8–21. *Cis* and *Trans* Structures for $TiF_4 \cdot 2B$. B is a donor molecule, and $F_{(a)}$ and $F_{(b)}$ represent nonequivalent fluorines.

two equivalent fluorines in each. However, at $0°C$ only a single fluorine peak is obtained, and it is proposed that a rapid dissociation reaction occurs making all fluorines equivalent. At the lower temperature this

$$TiF_4 \cdot 2B \rightleftharpoons TiF_4B + B$$

reaction is slowed down so that the nonequivalence can be detected by NMR. Internal rearrangements and ionic exchange mechanisms are also possible. By considering this example, we can illustrate one of the possible pitfalls in structure determination using NMR spectroscopy. If only the high temperature ($0°$ C) spectrum had been investigated or if rapid exchange occurred at $-30°$ C, it could have been incorrectly assumed that the adduct had the *trans* structure on the basis of the single NMR peak. If the actual structure were *trans*, only a singlet fluorine resonance would be detected at the lower temperature and the higher temperature. It would have been difficult to draw any structural conclusion because of the possibility that rapid exchange might be occurring at both temperatures. Problems concerning chemical exchange and procedures for calculating rates of exchange from NMR spectra will be discussed in more detail in a later section.

Another effect that gives rise to spectra other than those predicted by equation (8-12) is *nuclear quadrupole relaxation*. Often splittings do not occur because the nucleus to which the element being investigated is attached undergoes rapid relaxation, which causes a rapid change in the spin state of the nucleus. This is equivalent to rapid exchange which places the nucleus whose spectrum is being studied on many different splitting nuclei with different spin states. Only the average spin state is detected in both instances. Intermediate exchange rates between slow exchange, where equation (8-12) applies, and rapid exchange often result in a broadening of the resonance line. In some instances the proton resonance absorption is broadened by this effect to such an extent that the signal cannot be distinguished from the background. Relaxation effects are often encountered for nuclei which have a quadrupole moment because these nuclei are very efficiently relaxed by the fluctuating *electric* field gradients which arise from the thermal motion of the polar solvent and solute molecules. As a result of this effect the proton spectrum of $N^{14}H_3(N^{14}, I = 1)$ consists of three very broad signals while in the absence of this effect, the spectrum of $N^{15}H_3(N^{15}, I=\frac{1}{2})$ consists of a sharp doublet. In cases of other nuclei where there is even more rapid relaxation than in N^{14}, a broad signal is commonly obtained with no fine structure.

The nature of the spectra of complex molecules will depend on the number of bonds through which spin-spin coupling can be transmitted. For proton-proton coupling in saturated molecules of the light elements, the magnitude of J falls off rapidly as the number of bonds between the two nuclei increases and usually is negligible for coupling of nuclei separated by more than three bonds. Long-range coupling (coupling over more than three bonds) is often observed in unsaturated molecules. A number of examples are contained and discussed in articles by Hoffman and Gronowitz.[22] In unsaturated molecules the effects of nuclear spin are transmitted from the C—H σ bond by coupling of the resulting electron spin on carbon with the π electrons. This π electron spin polarization is easily spread over the whole molecule because of delocalization and can couple back into the σ system, in the same way, several atoms distant from the splitting nucleus. This problem has been treated quantitatively.[23]

When spin-spin coupling involves an atom other than hydrogen, long-range coupling can occur by a coupling mechanism different from that described above, namely, through-space coupling. This interaction is again one of spin polarization, but it occurs through nonbonding pairs of electrons, and the coupling is *through space* instead of through σ or π bonds. In the compound $CF_3CF_2SF_5$ the coupling constant for the fluorines of the CF_2 group and the *trans* fluorine of the SF_5 group is about 5 cps, much smaller than that for the CF_2 group coupling to the *cis* fluorines (~16 cps), because of the contribution from through-space coupling in the latter case.[24]

If two nuclei splitting another group in a molecule are magnetically nonequivalent, the spectrum will be very much different from that in which there is splitting by two like nuclei. Four lines of equal intensity will result from splitting by two nonequivalent nuclei with $I = \frac{1}{2}$, and three lines with an intensity ratio $1:3:1$ will be observed for splitting by two equivalent nuclei. Consequently, we must determine what constitutes magnetically nonequivalent nuclei. Nonequivalence may arise because of differences in the chemical shifts of the two splitting nuclei or because of differences in the J values of the two splitting nuclei with the nucleus being split. An example of the latter is found in the molecule $H_2C=CF_2$, where neither the two hydrogens nor the two fluorines can be considered equivalent. Each proton sees two nonequivalent fluorines (one *cis* and one *trans*) which have identical chemical shifts but different J_{HF} coupling constants. The simple $1:2:1$ triplet expected when both protons and both fluorines are equivalent is not observed in either the fluorine or proton NMR because of the nonequivalence that exists in the J values.

Applications Involving the Magnitude of Coupling Constants

The factors that determine the magnitude of the coupling constant are not well understood for most systems. It has been shown that in the Hamiltonian describing the interaction between the C^{13} nucleus and a directly bonded proton, the *Fermi contact term* is the dominant one. Qualitatively, this term is a measure of the probability of the bonding pair of electrons existing at both nuclei. The need for this can be qualitatively appreciated for those cases where electron spin polarization by the nuclei is the principal coupling mechanism. The greater the electron density at both nuclei, the greater will be the interaction of the nuclear moments with the bonding electrons and hence with each other through electron spin polarization. Since an s orbital has a finite probability at the nucleus and p, d, etc., orbitals have nodes (zero probability) at the nucleus, the Fermi contact term will be a measure of the s character of the bond at the two nuclei.

Since the s orbital of hydrogen accommodates all of the proton electron density, the magnitude of $J_{C^{13}-H}$ for directly bonded carbon and hydrogen will depend upon the fraction of s character, ρ, in the carbon hybrid orbital bonding the hydrogen. The following equation permits calculation of ρ from $J_{C^{13}-H}$ data.

$$J_{C^{13}-H}(\text{cps}) = 500\rho_{C-H} \qquad (8\text{-}13)$$

Since $\rho = 0.33$ for an sp^2 hybrid and 0.25 for an sp^3 hybrid, it can be seen that $J_{C^{13}-H}$ should be a sensitive measure of carbon hybridization. The natural abundance of C^{13} ($I = \frac{1}{2}$) is 1.1 per cent, and the two peaks resulting from this splitting can be seen in spectra of concentrated solutions of nonenriched compounds. The use of $J_{C^{13}-H}$ to measure the hybridization of carbon in a C—H bond was studied in detail by Muller[25] and is supported by valence bond calculations.[26]

It has been shown that a linear relationship exists between $J_{C^{13}-H}$ and τ for a series of methyl derivatives in which the contribution to τ from magnetic anisotropy is approximately constant,[27,28] or varies with electronegativity of the group attached to methyl. The plot[28] is contained in Fig. 8-22 where the plus sign is used to indicate those points employed to construct the line. There are many compounds which would fall close to this line and consequently do not have abnormal anisotropic contributions to the chemical shift, but this could not be determined a priori with confidence. Those compounds represented by points which deviate from this line have appreciable contributions to τ from anisotropy. The following explanation is offered for the existence of this relationship. Isovalent hybridization arguments[29] indicate that as X becomes more electronegative in the compounds CH_3X, more p character is employed in the C—X orbital, and there is a corresponding increase in the s character in the C—H orbitals. It has been shown that carbon electronegativity increases as the hybridization changes from sp^3 to sp^2 to sp.[30] If there are no anisotropic contributions (or if the contribution varies with electronegativity), a correlation would be expected between carbon electronegativity and τ. Since carbon electronegativity is related to carbon hybridization which is in turn related to $J_{C^{13}-H}$, a correlation is expected between $J_{C^{13}-H}$ and τ for compounds in which the contributions to τ from magnetic anisotropy are constant (or vary linearly with the electronegativity of group X). In view of the difficulty in assessing the existence of even large anisotropic contributions to the chemical shift (see section on chemical shifts which are greatly influenced by anisotropy), this relationship is of considerable utility. Certainly the chemical shift of compounds that do not fall on the line cannot be interpreted in terms of inductive or electronegativity arguments, i.e., a local diamagnetic effect. It is not possible to check calculated anisotropies by the deviation of a compound from the line because the

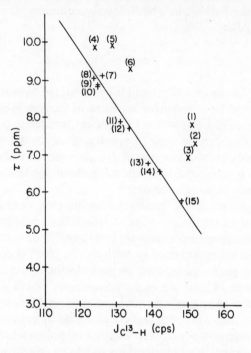

Fig. 8–22. Relationship Between $J_C{}^{13}{}_{-H}$ and τ. X indicates points for compounds known to contain anisotropic contributions the shift: (1) CH_3I, (2) CH_3Br, (3) CH_3Cl, (4) $Ge(CH_3)_4$, (5) $Sn(CH_3)_4$, and (6) $Pb(CH_3)_4$. + indicates points used to construct the line: (7) C_2H_6, (8) $(CH_3)_4C$, (9) $(\underline{CH_3}CH_2)_2O$, (10) $\underline{CH_3}CH_2OH$, (11) $(CH_3)_3N$, (12) $(CH_3)_2NH$, (13) $(CH_3)_2O$, (14) CH_3OH, and (15) CH_3F.

possibility does exist that the line in Fig. 8-22 contains contributions from neighbor anisotropy which vary linearly as the electronegativity of X varies.

Many applications of $J_{C^{13}-H}$ data are suggested by this correlation. It has been shown that the carbon hybridization in $Si(CH_3)_4$, $Ge(CH_3)_4$,

$Sn(CH_3)_4$, and $Pb(CH_3)_4$ changes in such a way as to introduce more s character into the C—H bond as the atomic number of the central element increases. An explanation for this change in terms of changing bond energies is proposed, and it is conclusively demonstrated that chemical shift data for these compounds cannot be correlated with electronegativities of the central element,[28] because large anisotropic contributions to the proton chemical shift exist in $Ge(CH_3)_4$, $Sn(CH_3)_4$, and $Pb(CH_3)_4$.

The proton chemical shifts of the two methyl groups in $CH_3C(O)SCH_3$ are almost the same and the peaks cannot be assigned directly. However, the $J_{C^{13}-H}$ values for CH_3 groups on sulfur vary considerably from those on the acetyl carbon, and this allows unequivocal assignment of the high field signal to the S-methyl group.[31] The carbon-13-proton coupling constants for the N-methyl groups in $CH_3C(S)N(CH_3)_2$ and $(CH_3)_2NC(S)N(CH_3)_2$ are very close, respectively, to those in N,N-dimethylacetamide and tetramethylurea. These data were employed in conjunction with other arguments to indicate that the nitrogen atoms in the sulfur compounds would be poor donor sites. Sulfur coordination occurs with the Lewis acids iodine and phenol.[32] The $J_{C^{13}-H}$ values for $(CH_3)_2S$, $(CH_3)_2SO$, $(CH_3)_2SO_2$, and $(CH_3)_3S^+$ support the existence of some sulfur-oxygen π bonding in $(CH_3)_2SO$ and an even larger amount in $(CH_3)_2SO_2$.[33]

It has been proposed[34] that a relationship exists between J_{Sn-H} and the hybridization of tin in the tin-carbon bonds of compounds of the type $(CH_3)_{4-n}SnX_n$. This relationship and results from other physical methods were employed to establich the existence and structure of a five-coordinate tin addition compound $(CH_3)_3SnCl \cdot B$[35] where B, the base, is $(CH_3)_2SO$ or $(CH_3)C(O)N(CH_3)_2$. The J_{Sn-H} values suggest that tin employs essentially sp^2 orbitals in bonding to carbon and consequently p-d orbitals in bonding to the donor and chlorine. Similar results were obtained for J_{Pb-H} in the analogous lead compounds.[35]

The Pt-P spin-spin coupling constants have been evaluated in a series of platinum complexes.[36] The most abundant platinum nucleus has zero spin but two lower intensity peaks appear, one on each side of the main phosphorus resonance, as a result of the splitting of phosphorus by the Pt^{195} isotope with spin $\frac{1}{2}$. The coupling constants for a series of compounds of the general formula $(R_3P)_2PtX_2$ have been reported. When both cis and $trans$ complexes are available, the coupling constant can be used to distinguish the two, for J_{Pt-P} is greater for the cis complex. For $(n\text{-}Bu_3P)_2PtCl_2$, J_{Pt-P} is 3.62 cps for the cis complex and 2.46 cps for the $trans$. It is proposed that π bonding has the greatest effect on J_{Pt-P}. The d orbitals of two $trans$-phosphorus atoms π overlap only d_{xz} and d_{xy}

orbitals on platinum (P located on the x axis). Since two *cis*-phosphorus atoms can overlap d_{xy}, d_{yz}, and d_{xz}, metal ligand π bonding is greater in the *cis* complex than in the *trans* and consequently J_{Pt-P} is greater in the *cis* complex.

The fluorine NMR spectra of a large number of compounds of general formula $R_{5-n}PF_n$ (where R is a hydrocarbon, fluorocarbon, or halide other than fluorine) have been reported.[37] The number of peaks in the spectrum and the magnitude of the coupling constants are employed to deduce structures. For a series of compounds of the type R_2PF_3, a trigonal bipyramidal structure is proposed, and it is found that the J_{P-F} values for apical fluorines are~170 cps less than those for equatorial ones. The most electronegative groups are found in the apical positions. The spectra and coupling constants, obtained on these compounds at low temperature, indicate that the two methyl groups in $(CH_3)_2PF_3$ are equatorial and the two trifluoromethyl groups in $(CF_3)_2PF_3$ are axial. At room temperature, rapid intramolecular exchange occurs and the effect of this exchange is to average the coupling constants.

COMPLEX SPECTRA OBTAINED WHEN J ~ Δ

Complications in interpreting NMR spectra also arise when the spin-spin coupling constant between two nonequivalent nuclei is of the same order of magnitude as the chemical shift between them. Spectra of ClF_3 obtained by using two different probes illustrate these complications. With a high frequency probe (40 mc sec^{-1}), $J \ll \Delta$ and the spectrum in Fig. 8-23a is obtained. The molecule ClF_3 has two long Cl—F bonds and one short one, giving rise to nonequivalent fluorines. The spectrum obtained at 40 mc sec^{-1} (Fig. 8-23a) is that expected for nonequivalent fluorines splitting each other. As expected the triplet is half the intensity of the doublet. Using a lower frequency probe (10 mc sec^{-1}), the difference in Δ for the nonequivalent fluorines is of the order of magnitude of J_{F-F} (recall that Δ is field dependent) and the complex spectrum in Fig. 8-23b is obtained. Complex patterns of this sort result whenever the coupling constants between nonequivalent nuclei are of the order of magnitude of the chemical shift. Meaningful coupling constants or chemical shifts *cannot* be calculated directly from the complex patterns by using the procedures previously outlined. It is often possible to calculate the J and Δ values from these complex patterns by involved procedures that have been treated in detail in various texts[2,38,39] and review articles.[40] This subject cannot be treated in detail in the space allotted here. A simple system will be discussed here to illustrate the evaluation of

J and Δ and to illustrate the effects which similar Δ and J values have on the spectrum of a simple system.

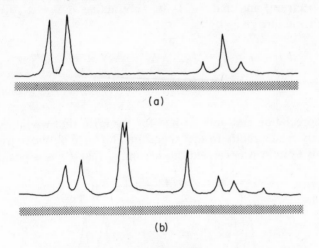

(a)

(b)

Fig. 8–23. Fluorine NMR Spectra of ClF_3. (a) at 40 mc sec^{-1} and (b) at 10 mc sec^{-1}.

Various structures are classified into different systems by employing the following conventions: equivalent nuclei are symbolized by a single letter A_n, etc., where n is an integer refering to the number of equivalent nuclei; a second set of equivalent nuclei would be labeled B_n, etc.; and by convention the nuclei are labeled A, B, etc., in order of increased shielding. If the chemical shifts of some of the nuclei are very much different from others, the symbols X and Y are employed. The molecule ClF_3 (consider only fluorines) would be classified as an AB_2 molecule (at 10 mc sec^{-1}). The phosphorus NMR of the tetrapolyphosphate anion, $P_4O_{13}^{6-}$, would yield an A_2B_2 spectrum, and P_4S_3 is an A_3X system.

An AB system, where both A and B have $I = \frac{1}{2}$, will be treated here. The two extremes of the A—B system are the A—X (where X has a spin of $\frac{1}{2}$) and the A_2 system. Spectra corresponding to these extremes are indicated as (a) and (d), respectively, in Fig. 8-24. When the ratio of $J_{A-B}/(\Delta_B - \Delta_A) = 0.33$, the spectrum in (b) is obtained, while a $J_{A-B}/(\Delta_B - \Delta_A)$ ratio of 1.4 gives rise to the spectrum in (c). The chemical shift for (a) is indiacted by δ. If the peaks in the first three spectra are labeled $1, 2\ 3$, and 4 from left to right, $J_{A-B} = (1-2) = (3-4)$ in *all* spectra. The quantity $\Delta_B - \Delta_A$ is obtained from the expression:

$$(1 - 3) = (2 - 4) = [(\Delta_B - \Delta_A)^2 + (J_{A-B})^2]^{\frac{1}{2}}$$

where all quantities are in units of cps and $(\Delta_B - \Delta_A)$ is the unknown. The value for Δ_A is found by adding $\frac{1}{2}(\Delta_B - \Delta_A)$ to e (the Δ value of the center of the spectrum) and that for Δ_B by subtracting $\frac{1}{2}(\Delta_B - \Delta_A)$ from e. The line intensities are given by

$$1 = 4 = 1 - J_{A-B}[(\Delta_B - \Delta_A)^2 + (J_{A-B})^2]^{-\frac{1}{2}}$$

$$2 = 3 = 1 + J_{A-B}[(\Delta_B - \Delta_A)^2 + (J_{A-B})^2]^{-\frac{1}{2}}$$

An appreciation can now be had for the error that would exist in δ if incorrectly read directly from a spectrum like (c). The above treatment of the A—B system was carried out assuming that J has a positive value.

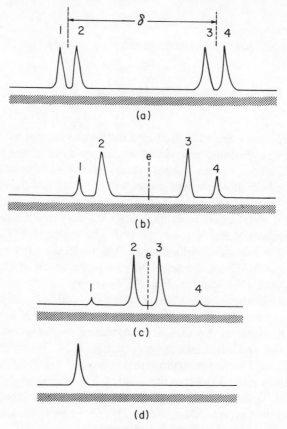

Fig. 8–24. Spectra for (a) A—X, (b) A—B, $J_{A-B}/\Delta_B-\Delta_A \sim 0.33$, (c) A—B, $J_{A-B}/\Delta_B-\Delta_A \sim 1.4$, and (d) A_2.

Actually the sign of the coupling constant can be plus or minus. It is impossible to tell from the spectrum of A—B system what the sign of the coupling constant is. If J were negative, the two more intense middle peaks would correspond to those labeled *1* and *4* in Fig. 8-24 and the two less intense outside ones would be *2* and *3*. This can be made clear as follows. The splitting of A and B to produce a spectrum like that in Fig. 8-24c can be illustrated as in Fig. 8-25a. In Fig. 8-25 line I represents the chemical shift difference between A and B and line II the spin-spin

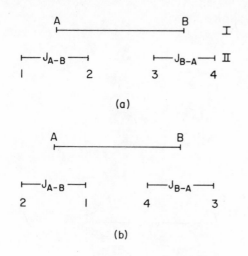

Fig. 8–25. Effect of the Sign of J_{AB} on the Splitting of an A—B System.

splitting of A by B when J_{AB} is positive. If J_{AB} were negative the result in Fig. 8-25b would be obtained. The equations for the intensity indicate that the two center peaks are more intense than the outer ones for both situations, and consequently it is impossible to tell the sign of J from the spectrum. A negative coupling constant reverses the combination of nuclear spins that gives rise to the low energy state.

Procedures for analyzing more complex systems (i.e., ABX_n, ABC, AB_2, A_2B_2, etc.) have been described.[2,38–40] In very complex systems, estimated J and Δ values are sometimes used in the equations (which are often solved by a computer) and the resulting spectra calculated. The quantities J and Δ are then varied until the calculated and experimental spectra agree both from the standpoint of the peak separations and relative line intensities of all the peaks. Once the above calculations are completed, the interpretation of the spectrum can be illustrated as has

been done for the P^{31} spectrum of the anion $H-\underset{\underset{O}{|}}{\overset{\overset{O}{\|}}{P}}-\underset{\underset{O}{|}}{\overset{\overset{O}{\|}}{P}}-O^{3-}$ indicated in

Fig. 8-26. The actual spectrum, IV, can be generated in three stages. The first consideration, I, consists of two lines from the two nonequivalent phosphorus atoms, $P_{(a)}$ and $P_{(b)}$, and their separation is the chemical shift difference. The second consideration, II, includes splitting by hydrogen.

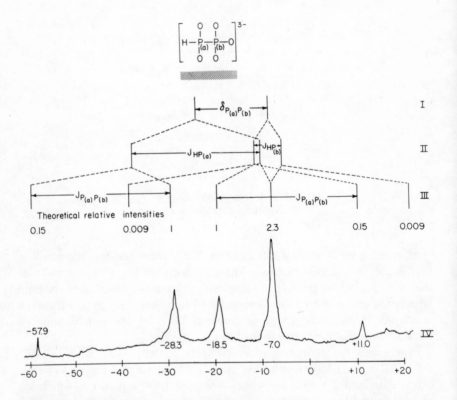

Fig. 8-26. The Phosphorus NMR Spectrum of the Diphosphate Anion $HP_2O_5^{3-}$ and Its Interpretation. I. Chemical shift differences in P_a and P_b. II. H—P splitting. III. P—P splitting. IV. Observed spectrum. From C. F. Callis, et al., *J. Am. Chem. Soc.*, **79**, 2722 (1957) with permission.

Since the hydrogen is on $P_{(a)}$, $J_{P(a)-H} > J_{P(b)-H}$. The four lines which result are included in II. The third consideration, III, includes $P_{(a)}-P_{(b)}$ splitting and accounts for the final spectrum for this A—B—X case. Two of the expected lines are not detected in the final spectrum because they are too weak to be detected and another pair fall so close together that they appear as a single peak (the most intense peak). The analysis of the $HP_2O_5^{3-}$ spectrum to yield the interpretation contained in Fig. 8-26 is carried out[41] by procedures similar to, but more complex than, those described above for the A—B system.

CHEMICAL EXCHANGE AND OTHER FACTORS AFFECTING LINE WIDTH

As mentioned above, certain chemical exchange processes are found to have a very pronounced effect on the appearance of NMR spectra. As both the number of peaks and the fine structure for a given compound depend upon the effects to be discussed, an understanding of these effects is necessary in order to interpret spectra obtained for many systems. Furthermore, it will be seen that line-broadening caused by rapid chemical exchange provides kinetic data on very fast reactions and other information of significance to inorganic chemists.

The natural width of a spectral line, W, is proportional to the reciprocal of the average time, t, the system spends in the excited state.

$$W \ \alpha \ 1/t \tag{8-14}$$

This important statement can be understood by a consideration of the Uncertainty Principle:

$$\Delta E \ \Delta t \sim h \tag{8-15}$$

As the lifetime of the excited state becomes very short (i.e., Δt is small), the uncertainty in the energy of this state, ΔE, becomes great. The lifetime of a nucleus in a particular spin state will be determined by the relaxation processes already discussed. According to equation (8-14), when ΔE is large, a wide range of frequencies is absorbed in transitions, resulting in a broad line.

In infrared, visible, and ultraviolet spectroscopy, the limit of resolution of commonly available instruments is not sufficient to allow measurement of the natural line width. In NMR spectroscopy, the natural line width often can be obtained, and as a result information about the lifetime of a state can be deduced from the observed line width. The lifetime of the state will depend upon the efficiency of the spin-lattice and spin-spin relaxation processes. Since both of these effects control the natural line width, we shall review and discuss these mechanisms in more detail.

Spin-lattice relaxation will be considered first. Since molecules contain magnetic *nuclei,* the random molecular motion will cause these nuclei to give rise to fluctuating *magnetic* fields. When this field is properly phased (to match the precessional frequency) and properly oriented, a nucleus which is in an upper spin state can be relaxed to the ground state by imparting its excess energy to the lattice as rotational and translational energy. This mechanism for spin-lattice relaxation is referred to as *nuclear-dipolar* interaction. The total energy of the system is unchanged by this process, and the efficiency of the relaxation mechanism will depend upon (a) the magnitude of the local fields and (b) the rate of fluctuation of the local fields. A quantity referred to as the *spin-lattice relaxation time,* T_1, can be defined to indicate the rate of this process. A large value for T_1 indicates an inefficient relaxation process, and a long lifetime for the excited state. In the absence of other effects, a sharp line results as predicted by equation (8-14) when T_1 is large.

There are other relaxation mechanisms that decrease T_1 and result in line broadening. One particularly effective mechanism involves paramagnetic substances. The mechanism is similar to that discussed above except that since the magnetic moment of an unpaired electron is about 10^3 times as large as the moment of a nucleus, very low values for T_1 and consequently very broad lines result when paramagnetic species are present. Other mechanisms by which paramagnetic species contribute to the relaxation time have been proposed (see Pople, et al.,[2] p.211).

As previously mentioned, nuclei with quadrupole moments can interact with local fluctuating *electric-field* gradients (which arise from the motion of polar solvent molecules and solute molecular vibrations) and undergo spin-lattice relaxation. This is a very effective process, and as a result deuterium (spin: $I = 1$) undergoes spin-lattice relaxation much more rapidly than a proton.

Three processes are included in *spin-spin relaxation.* As indicated in Fig. 8-27, precession of a magnetic nucleus (a) can be resolved into the rotating (b) and static components. At the nucleus being examined, the static component of another nucleus causes a slight variation in the effective field at this nucleus. The contribution to the effective magnetic field by this second nucleus varies with the angle, distance, and magnitude of the field of this second nucleus. Since the effect drops off sharply with distance, only neighboring molecules will have an appreciable effect on the effective field. A variation in the environments of nuclei undergoing

the NMR transition exists because of the random arrangments of neighboring molecules. This results in a range of energies over which the transition can occur, and a broad line results. A second cause of broadening

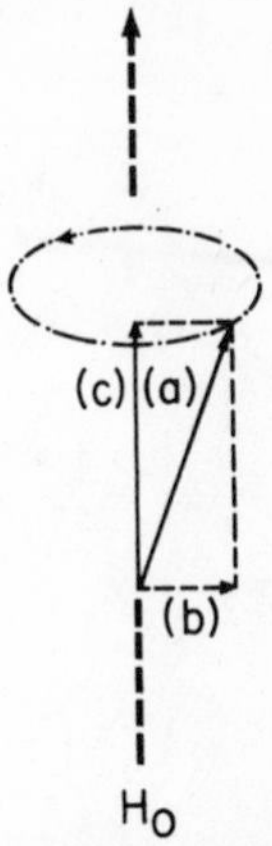

Fig. 8–27. Larmor Precession (a) and the Rotating
         (b) and Static (c) Components.

included in T_2 results from the variation in the applied field H_0 over
the sample dimensions. The observed spectrum is a superposition of
several spectra corresponding to the different values of H_0 in the different parts of the sample. Finally, line broadening can be effected by a
third mechanism. If the rotating component of a neighboring molecule
has a frequency equivalent to the Larmor frequency of the nucleus
undergoing the transition, this rotating component can induce a transition
of the neighboring nucleus to a different spin state. The nucleus inducing
the transition simultaneously undergoes a change in its spin state in this
process. This decreases the lifetime of the excited state and results in
broadening. The efficiency of these two processes is described by the
spin-spin relaxation time, T_2, which corresponds to an average lifetime for
a given spin state. The NMR spectra of solids are very broad because
T_2 is short. The fixed positions of the atoms in the solid give rise to some
very large, oriented local fields. Both of the spin-spin processes are more
efficient and T_2 is smaller. *Because of the very broad lines usually obtained when solid spectra are examined, most inorganic applications
have been carried out on gases, liquids, or solutions.* A sample-spinning
procedure has been reported to reduce slightly line widths in solids.[42]

Effect of Chemical Exchange on Spectra and the Evalua-tion of Reaction Rates for Fast Reactions

The NMR spectrum may be drastically affected if the molecules
being studied are undergoing very rapid exchange reactions. As an

example,[43] consider the spectra in Fig. 8-28. The spectra of acetic acid and water are represented, respectively, in parts (a) and (b). The mixture

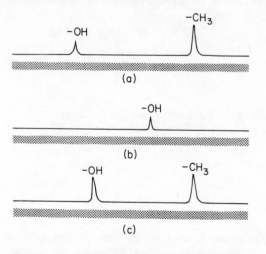

Fig. 8–28.   NMR Spectra of (a) CH_3COOH, (b) H_2O, and (c) a Mixture of the Two.

(c) does not show two separate O—H resonances from the water and the acid but instead shows only one. The position of this one average resonance is a linear function of the mole fraction, N, of CH_3COOH in the mixture: $\delta_{avg} = N_A\delta_A + N_B\delta_B$. In the mixture, the —OH protons are exchanging positions very rapidly between the acid and the water. The time for the NMR transition is much longer than the time required for proton exchange, and the method measures the average hydroxyl proton environment in the system. The proton exchange between water and acetic acid is always too fast to be studied by NMR techniques and is mentioned simply to illustrate the effects of fast exchange on the NMR spectrum.

For the purpose of demonstrating the calculation of rates from NMR spectra, a simple case will be discussed involving exchange between two sites that are equally populated and have equal lifetimes. We will further impose the condition of long spin-lattice relaxation time in the absence of exchange so that the signal width is small compared to separation of the two signals.* The hypothetical spectra obtained for the proton exchange in molecules A—H and B—H are indicated in Fig. 8-29. In

---

*For a treatment where this is not the case, see reference 44.

(a) the mean lifetime of the protons on A and B is long compared to the NMR transition time. In the sequence (b) to (f), spectra are indicated for increasing rates of proton exchange between the two sites. In the region of partial collapse [spectra (b) to (d)], *the lifetime of the proton on A, τ_A'*, which is equal to the *lifetime on B* (there are two equally populated sites with equal lifetimes), τ_B', can be obtained from the expression:

$$\frac{(\nu_A - \nu_B)_{obs}}{\nu_A{}^0 - \nu_B{}^0} = [1 - \frac{1}{2\pi^2\tau^2(\nu_A{}^0 - \nu_B{}^0)^2}]^{1/2} \qquad (8\text{-}16)$$

where $(\nu_A{}^0 - \nu_B{}^0)$ is the separation of peaks for long mean lifetimes, as in (a); $(\nu_A - \nu_B)_{obs}$ is the separation of peaks which have begun to coalesce as in (b), (c), and (d), and τ' equals $\tau'_A/2$ (the values of $\nu_A - \nu_B$ are expressed in cps).

In the spectrum (e), where the two peaks have just merged, $(\nu_A - \nu_B)_{obs}$ equals zero and the expression

$$\tau' = \frac{\sqrt{2}}{2\pi(\nu_A{}^0 - \nu_B{}^0)} \qquad (8\text{-}17)$$

results.

From these equations it can be seen that in order for two separate peaks to be observed at frequencies ν_A and ν_B, the lifetimes of the two states (A and B) must be greater than $1/(\nu_A - \nu_B)$; i.e., $1/(\Delta_A - \Delta_B)$. For smaller values of τ' (i.e., shorter lifetimes of a given state, as in (d)), the breadth of the merged peak can be used to calculate the lifetime.[44] If the exchange rate falls outside the limit which permits measurement by this technique, the rate may possibly be measured if conditions (temperature, concentration) are changed to alter the rate. Sometimes, with weak signals and large differences in Δ, rapid exchange $(\tau' \sim 1/\Delta)$ results in such extensive broadening that a peak cannot be detected.

There have been several reports of rate studies by the above technique. In general, changes in the concentrations of reagents, increasing acidity or basicity for acid– or base-catalyzed reactions, or increasing temperature can give rise to the series of spectra, (a) to (f) of Fig. 8-29, representing increasing rates of exchange. As a specific example, the protons in the system H_2O—H_2O_2 are found to undergo rapid exchange and to give rise to a single proton peak at room temperature under all conditions[45]. From the width of the single peak (which varies with exchange rate), it is found that acids and bases catalyze the exchange reaction. A procedure for calculating the lifetime from the width of the peak is described and a mechanism for the exchange proposed. A complete and rigorous analysis of exchange broadening has been reported.[46]

The spectrum of *N,N*-dimethylacetamide, $CH_3C(O)N(CH_3)_2$, has three peaks at room temperature, two of which correspond to the different environments of the two methyl groups on the nitrogen (one *cis* and one *trans* to oxygen). The C—N bond has multiple bond character and gives rise to an appreciable barrier to rotation about this bond. As a result of this barrier, the two nonequivalent N—CH_3 groups are detected. As the temperature is increased, the rate of rotation about the C—N bond increases and the *N*-methyl resonances merge, giving rise to a series

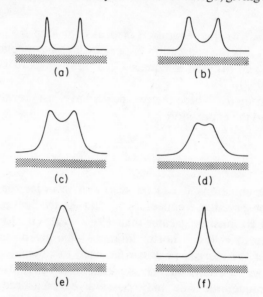

Fig. 8–29. Change in Spectra with Change in Rate of a Nucleus Undergoing Exchange Between Two Sites. (a) Slow exchange, (b) to (e) increasing rate, and (f) very rapid exchange. From *High Resolution Nuclear Magnetic Resonance* by J. A. Pople, W. G. Schneider, and H. J. Bernstein. Copyright 1959. McGraw-Hill Book Company. Used by permission.

of spectra similar to those in Fig. 8-29a to 8-29f. The lifetime of a particular configuration can be determined as a function of temperature and the activation energy for the barrier to rotation evaluated.[44] Similar studies have been carried out on other amides[47] and on nitrosamines.[48] The rates of inversion of substituted 1,2-dithianes and 1,2-dioxanes[49] are among the many other rates that have been studied. Caution should be employed in interpreting these results because the assumption is often made that δ does not change with temperature.

For a first-order process in substance A, as for example the rotation about the C—N bond in amides, the average residence time, τ_A', is related to the specific rate of exchange by:

$$1/\tau_A' = (1/[A]) \times (d[A]/dt) \qquad (8\text{-}18)$$

Combination of (8-18) with the first order rate equation, $d[A]/dt = k[A]$, yields

$$1/\tau_A' = k \qquad (8\text{-}19)$$

For a second order reaction such as A + B, the rate equation is:

$$d[A]/dt = k[A][B] \qquad (8\text{-}20)$$

Combination with (8-18) produces the equation:

$$1/\tau_A' = k[B] \qquad (8\text{-}21)$$

Usually, determinations of exchange rates by NMR involve assuming an exchange mechanism. In order to determine the order of a reaction to obtain mechanistic information, the rate must be investigated as a function of the concentration of the reagents. There are experimental limitations to doing this in many of the systems discussed in this section.

The next point to be discussed is the effect of chemical exchange on spin-spin splitting. As an example, consider the spectrum of CH_3OH (Fig. 8-30) in the absence of exchange. The doublet methyl group results

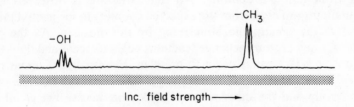

Inc. field strength⟶

Fig. 8–30. Proton NMR Spectrum of Methanol.

from the OH splitting and the quartet hydroxyl from the splitting by the three equivalent protons on carbon.[50] The exchange of hydroxyl protons may result in a change in the nuclear spin state of the proton attached to the oxygen. When rapid exchange occurs, this results in the presence on the oxygen of many different protons with both spin states and when the frequency of the exchange is greater than $\sqrt{2}\pi \, (\nu_A{}^0 - \nu_B{}^0)$ (see equation 8-17), only the average effect of the two spin states is observed. The spectrum obtained under conditions of rapid exchange consists of only two sharp peaks with no fine structure. The —O—H peak is a singlet because each hydroxyl proton spends some time on a large number of different molecules and the resonance is affected by an average of the methyl proton nuclear spins of all these molecules. The methyl group of each molecule experiences the effect of the nuclear spin of the many different hydroxyl protons on the oxygen. An average effect and a single line results for the methyl group. As the exchange rate increases, the fine structure present in the spectrum obtained under conditions of no exchange gradually collapses to give a broad line and then sharpens. Rate data can be obtained as described above by replacing the chemical shift by the coupling constant. Since J_{H-H} is the same for both the methyl and hydroxyl protons in methanol, both peaks will collapse to the same extent as the exchange reaction is catalyzed. In the methanol–water system the collapse of the methyl peak can be used to calculate the total proton exchange (i.e., CH_3OH with CH_3OH and CH_3OH with H_2O). The broadening of the water line can be employed to calculate the exchange rate of methanol with water.

The mechanism of proton exchange for solutions of methyl ammonium chloride[51] in water as a function of pH was evaluated by a procedure similar to that described above. In acidic solution (pH = 1.0) the NMR spectra of these solutions consist of a quadruplet methyl peak (split by the three ammonium protons), a sharp water peak, and three broad peaks from the ammonium protons. The triplet for the ammonium protons results from nitrogen splitting. No fine structure is observed in the ammonium proton peak from the expected coupling to the methyl protons because of the quadrupole broadening by the nitrogen. As the pH is increased, rapid proton exchange reactions begin to occur and the —CH_3, H_2O, and —$NH_3{}^+$ bands begin to broaden. Eventually, at about pH 5, two peaks with no fine structure remain, one from the protons on the —CH_3 group and the other a broad peak from an average of all other proton shifts. As the pH is raised to 8, the broad proton peak sharpens again. The —CH_3 broadening yields the exchange rate of protons on nitrogen; the broadening of the water line measures the lifetime of the proton on water and the broadening of the —$NH_3{}^+$ triplet measures the lifetime of the proton on the nitrogen. An analysis of the kinetic data yields: (1) the rate law and a consistent mechanism for the exchange

$$CH_3NH_3^+ + B \xrightarrow{k_1} CH_3NH_2 + BH^+$$

where the base $B = H_2O$, CH_3NH_2, or OH^-; (2) the fraction of the above protolysis that involves water; (3) the contribution to the exchange reaction from:

$$CH_3NH_2 + BH^+ \rightarrow CH_3NH_2H^+ + B$$

and

$$CH_3NH_2 + B \rightarrow CH_3NH_2 + B'$$

(B' is B with one hydrogen replaced by a different hydrogen). The details of this analysis can be obtained from the reference by Grunwald et al.[31] which is highly recommended reading. In subsequent studies the rates of proton exchange in aqueous solutions containing NH_4^+, $(CH_3)_2NH_2^+$, and $(CH_3)_3NH^+$ were measured and compared.[52]

The methods described above for studying exchange processes are not limited to proton exchange. Sulfur tetrafluoride has a C_{2v} structure with two sets of two nonequivalent fluorine atoms. At room temperature a single sharp peak is obtained for the fluorine NMR spectrum. As the temperature is lowered, the peak first broadens and then splits into two broad peaks. At $-98°$ C the spectrum consists of two separate triplets.[53,54] It was found that the exchange rate in solution was a function of SF_4 concentration, supporting a bimolecular mechanism. It was proposed that the intermediate

is involved. A series of group VI fluorides were studied and it was found that the rate of exchange increases in the order: $SF_4 < SeF_4 < TeF_4$.

Another example of information obtained from rate studies is reported by Muetterties and Phillips.[54] They found that SiF_6^{2-} in aqueous solution gives rise to the spectrum in Fig. 8-31. The main peak arises from fluorines on Si^{28} ($I = 0$), and the two small peaks result from spin-spin splitting of the fluorine by Si^{29} ($I = \frac{1}{2}$). The appearance of the satellites corresponding to J_{Si-F} indicates that the rate of exchange of fluorine atoms must be less than 10^3 sec^{-1} $[\tau' < 1/(\nu_A - \nu_B)]$. It is also found that the spectrum of solutions of SiF_6^{2-} containing added F^- contains two separate

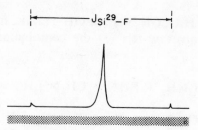

Fig. 8–31. The Flourine NMR
Spectrum of SiF_6^{2-}.

fluorine resonances. These are assigned to the F^- and SiF_6^{2-}. There are satellites (J_{Si-F}) on the SiF_6^{2-} peak. When a solution of SiF_6^{2-} is acidified, rapid exchange occurs, the satellites disappear, and the central peak broadens. The following reactions are proposed:

$$SiF_6^{2-} + H_3O^+ \rightarrow HFSiF_5^- \xrightarrow{H_2O} H_2OSiF_5^- \xrightarrow{HF} SiF_6^{2-} + H_3O^+$$

The C^{13} spectrum of CO_2 in water gives rise to two peaks,[55] one from dissolved CO_2 and a second for H_2CO_3, HCO_3^-, and CO_3^{2-}. Rapid proton exchange gives rise to a single C^{13} peak for these latter three species. The reaction $CO_2 + H_2O \rightarrow H_2CO_3$ has a half-life of about 20 sec, so a separate peak for dissolved CO_2 is detected.

The NMR spectrum of $B_3H_8^-$ is of interest because it demonstrates the effect of intramolecular exchange on the NMR spectrum. The structure of $B_3H_8^-$ is illustrated in Fig. 8-32 along with a possible mechanism for the intramolecular hydrogen exchange.[56] The B^{11} spectrum is a

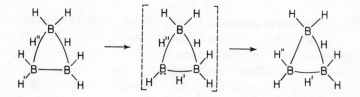

Fig. 8–32. The Structure of $B_3H_8^-$ and a Proposed Step for
the Intramolecular Exchange.

nonet which results from a splitting of three equivalent borons by eight equivalent protons. It is proposed that the frequency of steps similar to those in Fig. 8-32 is large, making the three borons equivalent and the eight protons equivalent in the NMR spectrum. In this example the eight hydrogens remain attached to the borons and cause splitting. Contrast this to rapid intermolecular exchange where a single boron resonance signal would result if exchange made all protons equivalent.

There is another possible explanation leading to the observed spectrum which does not involve exchange. When a particular set of nuclei are *strongly coupled together* (e.g., the eight hydrogens and also the three borons of $B_3H_8^-$), these nuclei can behave as a single set of equivalent nuclei in coupling to nuclei outside the set. Strong coupling of the eight protons would give rise to the observed nonet in the B^{11} resonance. This effect has been discussed quantitatively.[57]

An interesting example of a system in which rapid rotation does not remove nonequivalence is seen[58] in the methylene protons of $(CH_3 CH_2O)_2SO$. The two protons of a given methylene group are not stereochemically equivalent because of the lack of symmetry of the sulfur atom with respect to rotation about the S—O—C bonds. One of the possible rotamers is depicted in Fig. 8-33. The small dot in the center

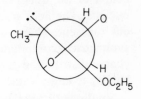

Fig. 8–33. Nonequivalence of the Two Protons of a Given Methylene in One of the Rotamers of $(CH_3CH_2O)_2SO$.

represents the sulfur with lines connecting the oxygen, the lone pair, and the ethoxyl groups. The large circle represents the methylene carbon with two hydrogens, an oxygen, and a methyl group attached. The molecule is so oriented that we are looking along a line from sulfur to carbon. The nonequivalence of the two methylene hydrogens of a given —CH_2— group is seen in this rotamer. To treat this problem completely, all possible rotamers must be considered. Nonequivalence in the chemical shift is said to arise if the populations of the different rotamers vary. If rapid interconversion between rotamers is taking place, nonequivalence can arise if the molecule spends a longer time in one of the lower energy confirmations, i.e., one must perform a time average to determine the chemical shifts of the nonequivalent protons. However, the fact remains that symmetry considerations[58] indicate the hydrogens can never be equivalent in any rotamer in this system. Gutowsky[59] has treated a similar problem, that of the chemical shift in substituted ethanes of the type:

$$
\begin{array}{ccc}
A & & X \\
& \diagdown & \diagup \\
B-&C-C&-H. \\
& \diagup & \diagdown \\
D & & H
\end{array}
$$

The two protons are not equivalent from symmetry arguments, and it is proposed that this intrinsic asymmetry will result in different chemical shifts which, if large enough, will be observable. The same explanation can be applied to diethylsulfite, and it is difficult to distinguish between intrinsic asymmetry and rotamer populations.[59]

CONSEQUENCES OF NUCLEI WITH QUADRUPOLE MOMENTS IN NMR

As mentioned earlier, many nuclei with quadrupole moments undergo spin-lattice relaxation readily and have very small values for T_1. When the nucleus with a quadrupole moment is attached to another atom whose spectrum is being measured, we have seen that rather extensive broadening occurs. When one attempts to obtain an NMR spectrum on a nucleus with a quadrupole moment that undergoes relaxation readily, the signals are sometimes broadened so extensively that no spectrum is obtained. This is the case for most halogen (except fluorine) compounds. The effectiveness of the quadrupole relaxation process depends upon the interaction of the quadrupole moment with the electric field gradient at the nucleus. The field gradient is caused by the asymmetry of the electronic environment. Sharp signals have been obtained for the halide ions and symmetrical compounds of the halogens (e.g., ClO_4^-), where the spherical charge distribution gives rise to only small field gradients at the nucleus, leading to larger values for T_1.

Solutions of I^- (I^{127}, $I = \frac{5}{2}$) give rise to an NMR signal. When iodine is added, the triiodide ion, I_3^-, is formed, destroying the cubic symmetry of the iodide ion so that quadrupole broadening becomes effective and the signal disappears. Small amounts of iodine result in a broadening of the iodide resonance and the rate constant for the reaction $I^- + I_2 \rightarrow I_3^-$ can be calculated from the broadening.[60] It is interesting to note that chlorine chemical shifts have been observed[61] for the compounds: $SiCl_4$, CrO_2Cl_2, $VOCl_3$, and $TiCl_4$.

An interesting effect has been reported for the fluorine NMR spectrum of NF_3. The changes in a series of spectra obtained as a function of temperature are opposite to those normally obtained for exchange processes. At $-205°$ C a sharp single peak is obtained for NF_3 and as the temperature is raised the line broadens and a spectrum consisting of a sharp triplet ($I = 1$ for N^{14}) results at $20°$ C. It is proposed that at low temperature the slow molecular motions are most effective for quadrupole relaxation of N^{14}; and, as a result, a single line is obtained. At higher temperatures, relaxation is not as effective and the lifetime of a given state for the N^{14} nucleus is sufficient to cause spin-spin splitting. A similar effect is observed for pyrrole.[62]

The N^{14} resonance of azoxybenzene,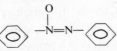

exhibits only a singlet. The nitrogens are not equivalent and it is proposed that the field gradient at the N—O nitrogen is so large as to make this resonance unobservable.

THE DOUBLE-RESONANCE TECHNIQUE

This technique can be used to great advantage to simplify complex spectra. The method involves application of a second strong rf field whose frequency is adjusted to cause saturation of a second nucleus which is splitting the nucleus being measured. This saturation causes the second nucleus to undergo frequent transitions so that the effect from

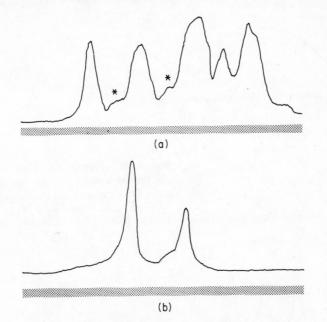

Fig. 8–34. Proton NMR Spectrum of B_2H_6. (a) Proton NMR with B^{11} and B^{10} splitting. (b) Proton NMR with B^{11} nucleus saturated. From J. N. Shoolery, *Disc. Faraday Soc.*, **19**, 215 (1955).

spin-spin splitting caused by this nucleus disappears. The second nucleus is, in effect, *decoupled* from the rest of the system. The proton NMR spectrum of diborane is indicated in Fig. 8-34a. This spectrum results from two sets of nonequivalent protons (bridge and terminal protons) being split by the B^{11} nucleus. The asterisk denotes fine structure arising from the smaller abundance of protons on B^{10} nuclei. (B^{10} has a natural abundance of 18.83 per cent and $I = 3$ compared to 81.17 per cent for B^{11} with $I = \frac{3}{2}$.) In Fig. 8-34b, the splitting caused by B^{11} has been removed by saturation of the boron nucleus by the double resonance technique. Two peaks of intensity ratio 2 : 1 are obtained, corresponding to the four terminal and two bridge protons.[63]

The double resonance technique has been successfully used on the proton NMR spectrum of $Al(BH_4)_3$. This molecule contains six Al—H—B bridge bonds. Both B and $Al^{27}(I = \frac{5}{2})$ have quadrupole moments. The proton NMR at 30 mc sec^{-1} consists[64] of a single broad line (Fig. 8-35a). When the B^{11} nucleus is saturated, the proton resonance spectrum in Fig. 8-35b results. Examination of the proton resonance while saturating B^{11} is symbolically designated as: $H^1 - \{B^{11}\}$. Fig. 8-35c

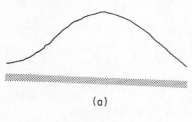

(a)

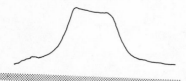

(b)

Fig. 8–35. Proton NMR of $Al(BH_4)_3$. (a) Proton resonance. (b) Proton resonance, B^{11} saturated. (c) Proton resonance, Al^{27} saturated. From R. A. Ogg, Jr., and J. D. Ray, *Disc. Faraday Soc.*, **19**, 239 (1955).

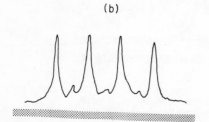

(c)

represents the proton NMR spectrum when the sample is irradiated with frequency corresponding to that of $Al^{27}(H^1 - \{Al^{27}\})$. The four large peaks arise from B^{11} splitting of the proton and the smaller peak from B^{10} splitting. The bridging and terminal hydrogens are not distinguished because of a rapid proton exchange reaction which makes all hydrogens equivalent.

Two isomers have been obtained in the preparation of N_2F_2. One definitely has a *trans* structure with one fluorine on each nitrogen. In conflicting reports, the structure of the second isomer has been reported to be the *cis* isomer and also $F_2N{=}N$. An excellent discussion of the results obtained by employing several different physical methods in an attempt to resolve this problem has been reported along with the fluorine NMR spectrum and results from a double resonance experiment.[65] Saturation of the N^{14} nucleus in this second isomer with a strong rf field causes collapse of all nitrogen splitting. It is concluded that the chemical shift of the two nitrogens must be equivalent and this eliminates the $F_2N{=}N$ structure. Additional evidence is obtained for this structure from a complete spectral interpretation. The value for J_{N-F} calculated in this study for a *cis* structure is reasonable when compared to J_{N-F} for NF_3.

Although the above examples of double resonance involve different nuclei, this is not a requirement. The technique has been used to great advantage to simplify proton spectra by saturating a set of proton nuclei which differ in chemical shift from another set and which are splitting that set (i.e., A or B of ABX, A_2B, etc.). A convenient procedure in which double resonance techniques can be employed to evaluate chemical shifts for complex spectra (where $J \sim \Delta$) has been reported.[66] The shift is evaluated from the frequency of the audio side band on the strong rf field which is most effective for decoupling.

The double resonance technique has been successfully employed to determine the relative sign of coupling constants. This can be illustrated by considering the proton NMR spectrum[67] of $(C_2H_5)_2Tl^+$ in Fig. 8-36 (I for $Tl = \frac{1}{2}$). If $J_{Tl\text{-}CH_3}$ and $J_{Tl\text{-}CH_2}$ are both positive, both low field peaks correspond to interaction with positive nuclear magnetic quantum numbers of Tl. If the signs of J are different, one low field peak corresponds to interaction with the moment from thallium nuclei where $m = +\frac{1}{2}$ and the other to $-\frac{1}{2}$. By irradiation at the center of gravity of each of the multiplets, it was shown that each CH_3 triplet was coupled to the distant methylene quartet and vice versa. For example, irradiation with a frequency corresponding to the low field triplet resulted in the disappearance of the fine structure of the high field methylene signal. This result indicates that $J_{\text{Tl-CH}_3}$ and $J_{\text{Tl-CH}_2}$ have opposite signs, for if the sign were the same, the two low field multiplets would be coupled together as would the two high field multiplets and saturation of the low field

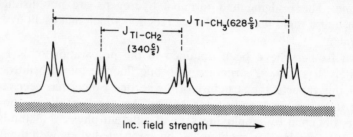

Inc. field strength ⟶

Fig. 8–36.   NMR Spectrum of $(C_2H_5)_2Tl^+$ (Facsimile).

triplet would cause collapse of the fine structure in the low field methylene signal.

A more complete discussion of the theory of the double resonance technique and many more examples of its application are contained in a review article[68] by Baldeschwieler and Randall.

The application of coupling constant information is an area which is still in its infancy. The above applications involving $J_{\text{Sn-H}}$ and $J_{\text{Pt-P}}$ are empirical in nature, and a rigorous application of the concepts must await further theoretical development leading to a complete understanding of all the effects that influence the magnitude of J.

NMR STUDIES OF EXCHANGE REACTIONS BETWEEN LIGANDS AND METAL IONS

The presence of paramagnetic ions in aqueous solution causes a broadening of the water line in the NMR spectrum (see section on chemical exchange). Both the longitudinal, T_1, and tranverse, T_2, relaxation times are affected.* Several different effects must be considered in the complete analysis of this problem. The water molecules in the system can be roughly divided into two categories: (1) those molecules in the coordination sphere and (2) the bulk solvent molecules. Coordinated molecules are held more firmly in place and may be less free to undergo proton exchange by the water-water exchange mechanism than those of the bulk solvent. On the other hand, the magnetic field of the ion has a greater effect on the coordinated solvent molecules and hence on relaxation

*For a more complete analysis see reference 69.

induced by the ion. The line width will depend upon the following relaxation mechanisms: (1) $1/\tau_B$, the exchange rate constant for the reaction between coordinated and bulk water molecules (τ_B is the lifetime of a coordinated water molecule); (2) $1/T_{2A}$, the relaxation rate constant for a bulk solvent molecule; (3) $1/T_{2B}$, the relaxation rate constant for a coordinated water molecule, which is not the same as (2) because of the relatively greater effect of the magnetic field of the metal ion; (4) $1/\tau_S$, the spin relaxation time for the unpaired electrons. In most instances there is very rapid spin exchange for the electron and no appreciable line broadening from this effect. In subsequent discussion this will be assumed, but it should be mentioned that Mn^{2+} has a very large value for τ_S and the subsequent treatment does not apply to that ion.

The experimental line width, $1/T_2$, observed for H_2O is given by the following expression:

$$1/T_2 = P_A/T_{2A} + P_B/(T_{2B} + \tau_B) \qquad (8\text{-}22)$$

where P_B is the fraction of protons on coordinated water molecules, P_A the fraction of protons on bulk solvent molecules (which is approximately one), and the other terms have been defined above. For a metal ion concentration of M moles liter^{-1} and a coordination number of six:

$$P_B = 6M/55$$

If $T_{2B} \gg \tau_B$, relaxation is rate-determining and (8-22) becomes:

$$1/T_2 = 1/T_{2A} + P_B/T_{2B} \qquad (8\text{-}23)$$

Under these conditions $1/\tau_B$ is large (i.e., rate of exchange is fast) and the rate of relaxation slow. Nearly all solvent molecules will be influenced by the ion in a short time and the relaxation is said to be rate-controlling. If $\tau_B \gg T_{2B}$, the exchange is line-width determining and the line width is given by:

$$1/T_2 = 1/T_{2A} + P_B/\tau_B \qquad (8\text{-}24)$$

when $\tau_B \gg T_{2B}$, the rate of exchange is controlling ($1/\tau_B$ is small), and the effect of the paramagnetic ion is limited because a limited number of water molecules will be subjected to the field of the ions.

If the rate of exchange is studied as a function of temperature, it can be determined whether τ_B or T_{2B} is greater. Since $1/\tau_B$ is the rate constant for a chemical process, it will increase with temperature, while $1/T_{2B}$

will decrease with temperature. If electron spin relaxation, τ_S, is controlling, $1/T_{2B}$ increases slightly with temperature. These considerations indicate whether equation (8-23) or (8-24) should be employed. The quantity $1/T_2$ is measured from the line width, and P_B can be easily determined. Evaluation of T_{2A} by the following procedure permits calculation of either τ_B or T_{2B}, the information being sought. The quantity, $1/T_{2A}$, the relaxation rate constant for the bulk solvent, cannot be evaluated from the pure solvent because water molecules in the second, third, etc., solvent layers around the ion are not in the same environment as water molecules in pure solvent. The relationship between $1/T_{2A}$ and $1/T_{2A}°$, where $T_{2A}°$ is the relaxation time constant for pure solvent, is:

$$1/T_{2A} = 1/T_{2A}° + P_B/T_{2A}'$$

where $1/T_{2A}'$ is the average contribution to $1/T_{2A}$ from solvent molecules estimated from the effect of substitution-inert complexes on the line width of pure solvent. In general, $1/T_{2A}$ is only one-tenth $1/T_{2B}$ so the crude estimate from the above experiment suffices.[69]

Exchange reactions have been investigated[69] in which OH^- removes a proton from a coordinated ammonia or ethylenediamine molecule.[69] For $Cr(NH_3)_6^{3+}$ the rate constant at 25° C is 2×10^6 liters mole^{-1} sec^{-1}, while $Cr(NH_3)_2(SCN)_4^-$ exchanges at a rate some one hundred times slower. In view of the negative charge on the latter species, a slower reaction is expected. Several other examples of studies of this type of reaction and rapid ligand replacement reactions have been summarized.[69a]

In an interesting study,[70] the O^{17} ($I = \frac{5}{2}$) NMR spectrum of enriched $[Co(NH_3)_5OH_2]F_3$ was found to contain a peak at $+1.3$ gauss in addition to the solvent peak (see Fig. 8-37). Addition of Co^{2+} ion caused a shift in the peak assigned to solvent water to -3.3 gauss, but the coordinated water peak (at $+1.3$ gauss) is not shifted. The shift in the solvent water peak is due to the coordination of water by Co^{2+} and rapid exchange of the water coordinated with Co^{2+} and solvent water. The water in $[Co(NH_3)_5O^{17}H_2]^{3+}$ does not undergo rapid exchange with Co^{2+}, and this peak is not shifted but is broadened slightly. The broadening is attributed to the species $[(H_3N)_5Co^{III}-O\underset{\textstyle\diagdown H}{\overset{\textstyle\diagup H}{-}}Co^{II}(H_2O)_5]^{5+}$.

The above result suggests[70] an interesting technique for determining solvation numbers of ions. For example, when aluminum(III) is dissolved in H_2O^{17}, only a single O^{17} peak is found. The coordinated and free water resonances overlap. When cobalt(II) is added, this peak is diminished in intensity and a second-peak at higher field is observed for the free water rapidly exchanging with cobalt(II). The spectrum is illustrated in Fig. 8-37b. There is residual absorption at the same resonance position as in the solution containing only aluminum(III), and this is attributed to water coordinated to this ion. Separate resonances for bound and free water upon the addition of cobalt(II) were not observed when labile ions

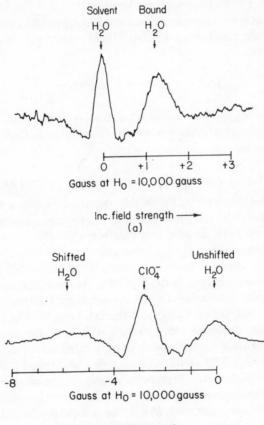

Fig. 8-37. The O^{17} NMR Spectrum of (a) $[Co(NH_3)_5H_2O^{17}]F_3$ in H_2O^{17} and of (b) $Al(ClO_4)_3 + Co(ClO_4)_2$ in H_2O^{17}. From J. A. Jackson, J. F. Lemons, and H. Taube, *J. Chem. Phys.*, **32**, 554 (1960).

(e.g., Li^+) were substituted for aluminum(III). At the O^{17} enrichment available at the time of this experiment, the sensitivity of the experiment was not great enough to permit calculation of coordination numbers from the peak areas.

Subsequently, Connick and Fiat[71] using enriched H_2O^{17} were able to calculate coordination numbers by this technique. There have also been extensive studies reported[71] on the rate of substitution of coordinated water molecules by bulk water molecules from the broadening of the O^{17} resonance in H_2O^{17} by paramagnetic ions.

The Cu^{63} nuclear magnetic resonance spectrum has been employed[72] to measure a rate constant of 0.5×10^8 liters mole^{-1} sec^{-1} for the electron exchange reaction:

$$Cu^{2+} + Cu^+ \rightarrow Cu^+ + Cu^{2+}$$

The resonance signal for diamagnetic Cu^+ is broadened by the rapid exchange reaction that occurs when small amounts of Cu^{2+} are added to a solution of the ion.

NMR OF PARAMAGNETIC COMPLEXES – CONTACT SHIFTS

As mentioned previously, the NMR spectrum of many paramagnetic compounds cannot be obtained because the unpaired electron broadens the spectrum by both dipolar and electron spin–nuclear spin coupling mechanisms. Since the magnetic moment of an electron is $\sim 10^3$ times larger than the nuclear magnetic moment, tumbling of paramagnetic ions produces large magnetic fields which are very effective in causing dipolar spin-lattice relaxation, i.e., T_1 is decreased. (see section on Chemical Exchange and Other Factors Affecting Line Widths.) If the wave function for the unpaired electron has a finite value at the nucleus, electron spin–nuclear spin coupling occurs. This can also give rise to a fluctuating magnetic field at the nucleus, which shortens T_1. If the electron relaxation is very slow, the lifetime of an ion in a given spin state will be long, and two resonances, corresponding to $S = \pm\frac{1}{2}$, will be observed. This case is not very common. When the paramagnetic state has a very short lifetime, the magnetic nucleus senses only the time-averaged magnetic field of the two spin states of the electron and a single peak is observed. Often electron spin relaxation is of such a rate as to be intermediate between these two extremes, in effect shortening T_2 and causing severe broadening. When electron relaxation is very rapid, broadening is minimized, and the major effect on the spectrum from the presence of unpaired electrons is to change the magnetic field experienced by the magnetic nucleus. This causes a very large chemical shift (sometimes 3000 to 5000 cps) of the resonance in the NMR spectrum. This shift is referred to as a *contact NMR shift*.

The following relationship can be derived between the contact shift, $\Delta\nu/\nu$, and the electron spin–nuclear spin coupling constant, A_N:[73]

$$\frac{\Delta H}{H} = \frac{\Delta\nu}{\nu} = -2A_N \frac{\gamma_e}{\gamma_N} \frac{g\beta I(I+1)S(S+1)}{9kT} \tag{8-25}$$

Equation (8-26) is for the specific case of proton magnetic resonance.

$$\frac{\Delta H}{H} = \frac{\Delta\nu}{\nu} = -\tfrac{1}{6}A_N \frac{\gamma_e}{\gamma_N} \frac{g\beta S(S+1)}{kT} \tag{8-26}$$

where γ_e is the magnetogyric ratio for the electron, γ_N is the magnetogyric ratio for the magnetic nucleus, I is the nuclear spin, S is the electron spin multiplicity, ΔH is $H_{\text{complex}} - H_{\text{ligand}}$ or $\Delta\nu = \nu_{\text{complex}} - \nu_{\text{ligand}}$, β is the Bohr magneton, and g is the ratio of the magnetic moment to the total angular momentum of the electron.

Since the contact shift is to lower fields when A_N is positive and to higher fields when A_N is negative, the sign of the electron spin–nuclear spin coupling constant can be obtained from NMR. Often all terms in (8-26) can be evaluated for a complex ion, so A_N can be calculated from the measured contact shift.

The conditions requisite to observing a contact shift in NMR are that either of the following inequalities be satisfied:

$$\frac{1}{\tau_S} \gg A_N \quad \text{or} \quad \frac{1}{\tau_e} \gg A_N \tag{8-27}$$

where τ_S is the electronic relaxation time, τ_e is the chemical exchange time, and A_N is the contact interaction constant (electron spin–nuclear spin coupling constant). Fortunately, most of the paramagnetic metal ions of the first transition series have sufficiently short electron spin lifetimes or sufficiently fast ligand exchange rates to allow NMR studies to be made on their complexes.

Much information about bonding can be obtained from the electron spin-nuclear spin coupling constants (A_N), often called the contact interaction constant. The magnitude of this quantity is related to the unpaired spin densities in π orbitals of sp^2 carbons by equation (8-28).[74–76]

$$A_N = Q\rho_N \tag{8-28}$$

where ρ_N is the spin density at carbon, Q is the proportionality constant (-22.5 gauss for an aromatic C—H fragment and $+27$ gauss for C—CH_3 fragment). Spin density (ρ_N) is defined as that fraction of an unpaired electron which appears to be localized at site N. Spin densities may be either positive or negative. A negative spin density results when the electron spin at site N is antiparallel to the net spin of the paramagnetic species as a whole and the opposite is true for positive spin density. Negative spin density is a concept foreign to Huckel molecular orbital theory. Molecular orbital theory must be modified by addition of $\pi-\pi$ exchange interaction in order to account for negative spin densities. Exchange interaction is the unpairing of electron spins so as to reduce the energy of the system through exchange interaction of electrons having the same spin (as discussed in Chapter 1 for the first excited state of He).

The allyl free radical, the molecular orbitals of which are described in Fig. 8-38, will be briefly discussed in order to demonstrate the affects of exchange interaction on the spin densities of conjugated radicals.

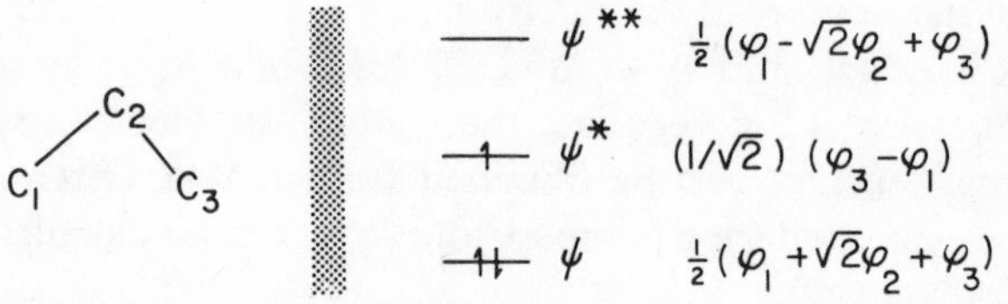

$$\psi^{**} \quad \tfrac{1}{2}(\varphi_1 - \sqrt{2}\varphi_2 + \varphi_3)$$

$$\psi^{*} \quad (1/\sqrt{2})\,(\varphi_3 - \varphi_1)$$

$$\psi \quad \tfrac{1}{2}(\varphi_1 + \sqrt{2}\varphi_2 + \varphi_3)$$

Fig. 8–38. The Combination of Carbon Atomic Orbitals φ_1, φ_2; φ_3 Constituting the Molecular Orbitals of Allene. The subscripts on carbon in the structural formula correspond to atomic orbitals φ_1, φ_2, and φ_3.

The odd electron in ψ^* gives rise to positive spin (α) densities at carbons 1 and 3. Exchange interactions between the odd electron in ψ^* of spin α and the paired electron in ψ of spin α enhances the positive spin density at C_1 and C_3 and leaves a net spin β (negative spin density) at C_2. Valence bond theory accommodates negative spin densities quite naturally. The valence bond wave function for the allyl radical (CH_2=CH—$CH_2 \cdot \leftrightarrow$ $\cdot CH_2$—CH=CH_2) predicts the same electron spin at atoms 1 and 3 and antiparallel spin at position 2 because of exchange interactions. A simple rule for predicting the signs of spin densities comes from valence bond theory. All positions at which a major contributing resonance form places the unpaired electron have positive spin density. Any position where no important resonance form places the odd electron has negative spin density. For example, the allyl radical has positive spin density at positions 1 and 3 and negative spin density at position 2.

In paramagnetic complexes the effects of unpaired electrons in the metal ion are transferred to the ligand through the formation of covalent bonds. Charge transfer mechanisms offer a convenient way to look at the transfer of the effects of unpaired electrons from the metal to the ligand. For the purpose of predicting how the unpaired electron density on the ligand will distribute itself, the ligand can be treated as a free radical. To demonstrate the mechanism for this, the complex nickel(II) aminotroponeimineate (Fig. 8-39a) will be considered.[77] In valence bond structures (b) and (c) in Fig. 8-39 an electron is added to the d orbital

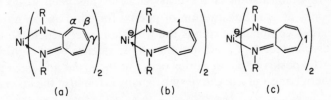

Fig. 8–39. The Structure of Nickel(II) Aminotroponeimi-neate (a) including Resonance Forms (b) and (c) which Place Odd Electron Density on the Ligand.

of nickel and the odd electron on the ligand is delocalized on the ring in the α and γ positions. There is another structure similar to (b) which places the odd electron on the other α position but this is not indicated. This complex is tetrahedral and the valence bond structures (b) and (c) put two electrons in the particular nickel orbital which contributes to the π system of the overall molecule (d_{xz}, d_{xy}, or d_{yz}). In effect, the nickel is reduced in these resonance forms. The spin magnetic moment of the electron on nickel in the ground state is aligned with the field. Because the d orbitals of Ni^{2+} are more than half filled, the electron transferred from the ligand into the d orbitals must pair up with the d electrons (which are aligned with the field) and so must have opposite spin. As a result, the odd electron remaining on the ligand will have its spin moment aligned with the field. Valence bond structures (Fig. 8-39) place the unpaired electron at the α and γ positions of the seven-membered ring. No structure placing the odd electron at the β position can be written without recourse to long bonds. The ligand as a whole has spin parallel to the nickel ion. Positive spin densities are thus predicted for the α and γ carbons and a negative spin density is expected for the β carbon. Since the spin density at the proton is antiparallel to that on the carbon, the

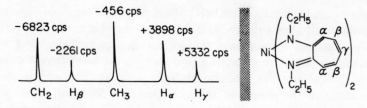

Fig. 8-40. Proton Magnetic Resonance Spectra of Ni^{II} N,N'-diethylaminotroponeimineate.

α and γ protons are expected to be shielded while the β proton should be deshielded. These considerations lead to the NMR assignment in Fig. 8-40. Confirmation of these assignments has been made by other independent means. Substitution of phenyl for ethyl on the nitrogens of the previous compound extends the π system over which the unpaired spin is distributed. As expected from simple valence bond considerations (Fig. 8-41), positive spin densities occur at the *ortho* and *para* positions of the phenyl ring and a negative spin density is found at the *meta* position.

Fig. 8-41. Valence Bond Structures for the Phenyl group in the Phenyl Substituted Aminotroponeimineate Complex.

Valence bond calculations of spin densities have been useful for predicting spin densities at atoms not readily observable in the NMR. The calculations are made assuming the ligand to be a free radical. The values obtained are then scaled down to correspond to the transfer of that fraction of an electron which best agrees with the observed spin densities. Results presented in Fig. 8-42 for the N, N'-diethylaminotroponeimineate system, assuming transfer of 0.10 electrons in the complex, are in extremely good agreement with spin densities experimentally determined from the contact shift.[77]

Contact interactions have been observed in a large number of systems. By virtue of the fact that the sign of the spin density can be determined, one can obtain information regarding the mechanism of electron delocalization onto the ligand. For example, in some octahedral Ni^{II} complexes of benzonitrile, it was shown that the principal mechanism

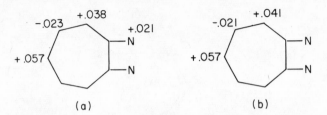

Fig. 8–42. Calculated and Experimental Spin Densities.
(a) Spin densities calculated for transfer of 0.10 electrons.
(b) Experimental spin densities.

involved back bonding from the metal with the ligand π system.[78a] In the case of the octahedral complex of nickel(II) with $CH_3CON(CH_3)_2$, the principal mechanism involved charge transfer in the nickel-oxygen σ bond. Also, by comparing the magnitude of the contact shift for a series of different transition metal ions with the same ligand, the amount of charge transfer (i.e., covalence) in the metal-ligand bond can be estimated.[78b]

The O^{17} NMR spectra of aqueous solutions of rare earth perchlorates have been reported.[79] The observed magnitude and variation of the O^{17} contact shifts with the number of $4f$ electrons was interpreted as evidence for very weak covalent bonding of O^{17} $2s$ and $2p$ orbitals with the rare earth $6s$ orbitals. The $4f$, $5d$, and $6p$ orbitals play at most a minor role in the bonding.

It is apparent that NMR spin density determinations provide a promising new approach to the study of conjugation in molecules containing extended π electron systems. The ability of NH, O, S, and SO_2 groups to transfer electronic effects has been studied directly using this technique.[80] The importance of double bonding between fluorine and π systems has also been assessed.[80]

MISCELLANEOUS APPLICATIONS OF NMR TO INORGANIC PROBLEMS

The phosphorus and fluorine nuclear magnetic resonance spectra of $P_3N_3Cl_4F_2$ have been reported.[81] The complex spectra which result can be analyzed as an AB_2X_2 spin system in which the two fluorine atoms (Fig. 8-43) are X_2, the phosphorus to which the fluorines are attached is A, and the other two phosphorus atoms are B_2. It can be concluded that the compound is a 1,1-difluoride 3,3,5,5-tetrachloride.

The phosphorus nuclear magnetic resonance spectrum of $P_4N_4Cl_{6-}$ $(NHC_6H_5)_2$ consists of two triplets of approximately equal intensity.[84] This indicates that the compound has the structure in Fig. 8-44, with the

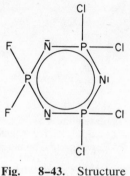

Fig. 8–43. Structure
of $P_3N_3Cl_4F_2$.

two aniline groups located on the *trans* phosphorus atoms. The groups
may be on the same or opposite sides. The phosphorus NMR spectra of
two isomers with composition $P_3N_3(C_6H_5)_3Br_3$ indicate that these
are *cis*-1,3,5 and *trans*-1,3,5 isomers.[83] The spectrum of the *cis* compound
consists of single peak while that of the *trans* consists of two peaks with
an intensity ratio of 2:1.

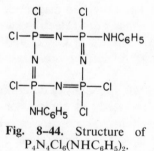

Fig. 8–44. Structure of
$P_4N_4Cl_6(NHC_6H_5)_2$.

In the reaction of SO_3 and SO_2 with CF_3OF, a series of compounds

can be separated, among which are the following:

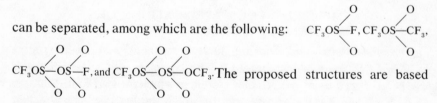

$CF_3OS{-}OS{-}F$, and $CF_3OS{-}OS{-}OCF_3$. The proposed structures are based
on the chemical shifts and peak areas of the fluorines.[84]

There has been some controversy[85,86] in the interpretation of the
fluorine NMR spectrum and the assignment of the structure for the
product of the reaction between AsF_3 and SO_3. A more recent article[86]
reported that several compounds exist depending upon the mole ratio

of starting materials. At a mole ratio of 1 $AsF_3 \pm 3 SO_3$ the NMR spectrum consists of two peaks, one assigned to As—F and one to S—F. The S—F peak has five times the intensity of the As—F peak. It was proposed that the mixture consists of equimolar quantities of (a) and (b) (Fig. 8-45). At a ratio 2 AsF_3: 3 SO_3 the spectrum consists of three peaks of relative intensity $3:2:1$. The most intense peak occurs in the S—F region and the others in the As—F region. Structure (c) of Fig. 8-45 is proposed to account for this result. At a mole ratio of $1:1$, two peaks are obtained in the spectrum and the one assigned to As—F has twice the intensity of the S—F peak. Structure (d) of Fig. 8-45 is proposed.

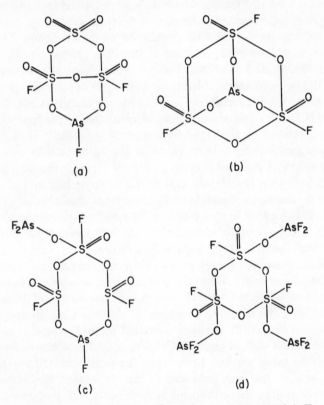

Fig. 8-45.   Possible Structures for the Adducts of AsF_3
and SO_3.

The Sn^{119} nuclear magnetic resonance spectra[87] of mixtures $SnCl_4$-$SnBr_4$, $SnCl_4$-SnI_4, $SnBr_4$-SnF_4, and $SnCl_4$-$SnBr_4$-SnI_4 indicate the existence of mixed halides in these systems. Compounds with the general formulas SnX_3X', SnX_2X_2' (where X and X' are different halogens) are found in the binary systems while $SnClBrI_2$, $SnClBr_2I$, and $SnCl_2BrI$ are reported along with mixed dihalides in the ternary system. There have been extensive studies of this type on many other systems.[88] For example, the P^{31} resonance spectrum has been employed to calculate equilibrium constants for the mixed species in the systems: PBr_3-PCl_3, $P(OC_6H_5)_3$-PCl_3, $P(OC_6H_5)_3$-PBr_3, and PCl_3-PBr_3-$P(OC_6H_5)_3$ systems.

Studies on hydrogen-bonding systems indicate that the proton resonance in the free acid is shifted to lower field in the hydrogen-bonded adduct.[89-91] The magnitude of the shift for different donors and a given acid has been reported to parallel qualitatively the shift in the N—H frequency of pyrrole dissolved in these donors.[90] It was proposed that the hydrogen bonding interaction lowers the local electron symmetry around the proton and inhibits diamagnetic circulation of the electrons. The O—H distance is also increased, so there is less diamagnetic shielding of the proton by the bonding electrons. Both of these effects shift the resonance to lower fields. In benzene, toluene or mesitylene as solvent it is observed that the protons of chloroform and related compounds ($CHCl_3$, $CHBr_3$, CHI_3, $SiHCl_3$) are considerably more shielded than in the free substances in dilute solutions of saturated hydrocarbon solvents.[92] It is proposed that a hydrogen bonded adduct exists in the aromatic solvents, and the chemical shift can only be accounted for by locating the acid hydrogen (of $CHCl_3$, etc.) on the sixfold axis of the benzene ring and in a similar position for toluene or mesitylene. Ring currents shield the acidic hydrogen when it is located in this position. Phase diagrams confirm the existence of $1:1$ complexes of chloroform with both toluene and mesitylene.

When the spectra of N,N-dimethylformamide in various aliphatic hydrocarbon solvents or even in water are measured, only small differences in chemical shift are observed. However, in aromatic solvents the formyl proton is shifted upfield, as are the resonances of both methyl groups.[93] Using the coupling constants of the N—CH_3 groups with the formyl proton to identify the nonequivalent methyl groups, it was found that the chemical shift of the N—CH_3 trans to the carbonyl was shifted more than the other methyl. In benzene the peaks crossed and the trans N—CH_3 was on the high field side of the cis methyl. Since the methyl groups were shifted more than the formyl proton, it was proposed that the formyl proton is near the edge of the ring and the methyls closer to the center. The structure in Fig. 8-46 was proposed.

The Co^{59} ($I = \frac{7}{2}$) nuclear magnetic resonance has been detected[94,95] and interpreted[96,97] for a series of cobalt complexes. The shifts are due to a paramagnetic term which arises from a magnetic field-induced mixing of the $^1T_{1g}$ state with the ground state of spin-paired Co^{III}.[96] (See the Tanabe and Sugano diagrams in Appendix C.) The contribution to the chemical shift from this effect is inversely proportional to the energy separation of the two states. Since this is the predominant term contributing to δ, the

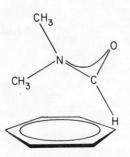

Fig. 8–46. Structure of the Adduct of Benzene with $HCON(CH_3)_2$.

value of δ will be related to the energy for this spectroscopic transition and the position of the ligand in the spectrochemical series. Some representative data[97] are listed in Table 8-3.

TABLE 8-3. RELATION OF δ TO THE ENERGY OF THE TRANSITION $^1A_{1g} \rightarrow {}^1T_{1g}$[97]

Compound[a]	E (cm^{-1})	Resonance Frequency (mc sec^{-1})
$Co(NH_3)_6Cl_3$	21,000	4.4534
$Co(en)_3Cl_3$	21,300	4.4488
$K_3Co(CN)_6$	32,100	4.4171
$Co(acac)_3$	16,900	4.7371

[a]en = ethylenediamine and acac = acetylacetonate

It has been reported that coordination of a donor molecule to a boron compound causes a shift in the B^{11} resonance to higher field in the adduct.[98-100] For example, the chemical shift of the B^{11} resonance in BCl_3 is -45.6, and this changes to -11 in BCl_4^-, to -10.5 in $BCl_3O(C_2H_5)_2$, and to -9.0 in $BCl_3C_5H_5N$. These δ values are in ppm relative to the B^{11} signal in $BF_3O(C_2H_5)_2$. Spacings are determined using $\delta = -85$ for $B(C_2H_5)_3$ and $\delta = -45.6$ for BCl_3 as internal standards. Shifts indicative of adduct formation are observed in several trialkylborate-amine systems and in mixtures of BI_3 or BF_3 with PCl_3.

These are but a few of the many applications of NMR to the solution of inorganic problems. A comprehensive treatment would require a book much larger than this one. Recent developments in this rapidly changing field are reviewed regularly in *Annual Reports of the Chemical Society* and in *Annual Reviews of Physical Chemistry*.

EXERCISES

1. Using the data in Appendix F, convert the τ value calculated from Fig. 8-7 to a δ value at infinite dilution toward the reference H_2O.

2. a. Using the Δ value from Fig. 8-7 calculate the Δ value for the peak separation of CH_3I and $Si(CH_3)_4$ at a probe frequency of 16 mc sec^{-1}.

   b. What field strength would be required for the $Si(CH_3)_4$ resonance at 16 mc sec^{-1}?

   c. What is the difference between the field strengths at which CH_3I and $Si(CH_3)_4$ undergo NMR transitions at 16 mc sec^{-1}, and what is the difference at 100 mc sec^{-1}? (Hint: Calculate the frequency difference and convert to field difference.)

3. The δ value of a substance relative to the external standard, methylene chloride, is -2.5. Calculate δ relative to external standards (a) benzene and (b) water using the data in Appendix F.

4. a. Would you expect the difference in $\delta_{CH_3} - \delta_{CH_2}$ in C_2H_5I to be a value which is independent of the remote anisotropy in the C—I bond? Why?

   b. Will this difference have a greater or smaller contribution from anisotropy than δ_{CH_2}?

   c. If in a series of compounds the δ_{CH_2} values showed a different trend than the $\delta_{CH_3} - \delta_{CH_2}$ values, what could you conclude about anisotropic contributions?

5. Combine in your thinking (reread if necessary) the discussion on interatomic ring currents with the relationship between $J_{C^{13}-H}$ and τ (discussed in the section on Correlations of τ with Coupling Constants and Other Applications of Coupling Constant Data). Using these concepts, propose a method for determining if there is anisotropy in the methyl chemical shift of *B*-trimethyl borazine.

6. Assuming the relationship discussed between J_{Sn-H} and hybridization, what would be the ratio of the coupling constants in a five-coordinate and six-coordinate complex of $(CH_3)_3SnCl$ [i.e., $(CH_3)_3SnCl \cdot B$ and $(CH_3)_3SnCl \cdot 2B$]?

7. In the hypothetical paramagnetic complex $M(en)_2Cl_2$ no species of the type $M(en)_2ClH_2O^+$ is detected spectroscopically. How could you ascertain whether or not the species formed very rapidly but underwent the reaction:

$$M(en)_2Cl\,H_2O^+ + Cl^- \rightarrow M(en)_2Cl_2 + H_2O$$

much more rapidly?

8. Consider the molecule

where M and X have $I = \frac{1}{2}$. Sketch the NMR spectra for the following conditions assuming $\Delta > J$ in all cases (when necessary to assume orders of magnitude for various coupling constants, state your assumption):

a. NMR spectrum of X, no exchange.
b. NMR spectrum of M, no exchange.
c. NMR spectrum of X with rapid intermolecular exchange.
d. NMR spectrum of M with rapid $[\tau' > 1/(\nu_A - \nu_B)]$ intermolecular exchange
e. NMR spectrum of X with rapid intramolecular exchange.
f. NMR spectrum of M with rapid intramolecular exchange.

9. In the absence of any exchange, two peaks A—H and B—H are separated by 250 cps. At room temperature, exchange occurs and the peaks are separated by 25 cps. The spin-lattice relaxation of A—H and B—H is long, and there are equal concentrations (0.2 M) of each. Calculate the lifetime of a proton on A, and from this the rate constant for the exchange (specify units).

10. In a given compound MF_4 (I, for $M = \frac{1}{2}$) the J_{M-F} value is 150 cps. In the absence of chemical exchange the F^- and M—F signals are separated by 400 cps. At room temperature the F^- and MF_4 exchange at a rate such that the fine structure just disappears. Assuming equal concentrations of M—F and F^- species and no stable intermediates, calculate τ' for F^-. What will be the separation of the MF and F^- peaks under these conditions?

11. The compound $B[N(CH_3)_2]_3$ is prepared and dissolved in a wide number of different solvents. Propose a method of determining in which ones the solvent is coordinated to the compound.

12. The spectrum of tetrahydrofuran, $(CH_2)_4O$, is a complex A_2B_2 type. Explain how the double resonance technique could be employed to aid in interpreting the spectrum.

13. Consider the diamagnetic complex $(Me_3P)_4Pt^{2+}$. Sketch the phosphorus resonance signal if
a. $J_{P-H} > J_{P-Pt}$.
b. $J_{P-Pt} > J_{P-H}$.

14. The spectrum in Fig. 8-47 is that of an A—B type molecule:
a. Calculate J and $\Delta_B - \Delta_A$.

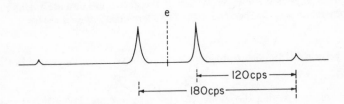

Fig. 8–47 Spectrum of an A—B molecule (Hypothetical).

b. A 40 mc probe was employed. Calculate the difference in δ for the two peaks.

c. If e occurs at a τ value of 7.2, what are the τ values for A and B?

15. Indicate the number of isomers for cyclic compounds of formulas $P_3N_3(CH_3)_2Cl_4$, and sketch the phosphorus resonance spectrum of each (assume $\Delta > J$, J_{P-H} is small, and J_{P-H} can be ignored for phosphorus atoms which do not contain methyl groups).

16. Consider the series i-propyl X (where X = Cl, Br, I).
    a. In which compound would the remote paramagnetic effect from the halogen be largest? Why?
    b. In which would the remote diamagnetic effect be largest?
    c. It is found that the α—H on the iodide is least shielded in this series. Explain.

17. Would you expect the N^{14} NMR spectrum to be sharper in NH_3 or NH_4^+? (for N^{14}, $I = 1$). Explain.

18. What would the NMR spectrum of PF_5 look like under the following conditions ($\Delta_{R(a)-F(b)} > J_{F(a)-F(b)}$):
    a. Very slow fluorine exchange.
    b. Rapid intermolecular fluorine exchange.
    c. Rapid intramolecular fluorine exchange.

19. The proton NMR spectrum of $\{Pt(H)(Cl)[P(C_2H_5)_3]_2\}$ in benzene is shown in Fig. 8-48. Recall (a) that there are two platinum nuclei, one with spin $\frac{1}{2}$ and one with zero spin, (b) Pt—H coupling constants are about 1000 to 1500 cps. Explain how the three peaks at high field arise and how it can be concluded that this complex has a *trans* structure.

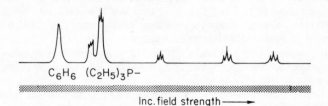

C_6H_6 $(C_2H_5)_3P-$

Inc. field strength ⟶

Fig. 8–48. Proton NMR Spectrum of Pt(H)(Cl)[P $(C_2H_5)_3]_2$ (Facsimilie).

20. Consider all possible isomers that could be obtained for the eight-membered ring compound $P_4N_4Cl_6(NHR)_2$ and indicate the ideal phosphorus resonance spectrum expected for each. Which of the above are definitely eliminated if the phosphorus resonance consists of two triplets of equal intensity?

21. The proton NMR spectrum of $\begin{matrix} CH_2-O \\ | \quad\quad\quad\searrow \\ \quad\quad\quad\quad S-O \\ | \quad\quad\quad\nearrow \\ CH_2-O \end{matrix}$ is not a singlet,[101]. Is the SO_3

group planar? Using the A, B, X, etc., terminology, classify this molecule and indicate the nonequivalent protons. What would the spectrum look like if the sulfur underwent very rapid inversion?

22. It is found that the methylene groups in $(CH_3CH_2)_2SBF_3$ give rise to a single methylene resonance. Explain.

23. a. Are the methyl groups in
$$(CH_3)_2 C \overset{\displaystyle H}{\underset{\displaystyle Cl}{\overset{\diagdown}{\underset{\diagdown}{-}}} P} \overset{\displaystyle O}{\overset{\diagup}{-}} C_6H_5 \quad \text{equivalent?}$$

b. Ignore the splitting of the methyl groups by the phenyl protons in the above compound and assume $J < \Delta$. What would the spectrum of the methyl groups look like?

REFERENCES CITED

1. H. S. Gutowsky, "Physical Methods of Organic Chemistry," 3rd ed., part 4, ed. A. Weissberger (Vol I of "Technique of Organic Chemistry"), Interscience, New York, 1960.
2. J. A. Pople, W. G. Schneider, and A. J. Bernstein, "High Resolution Nuclear Magnetic Resonance," McGraw-Hill, New York, 1959.
3. A. D. Buckingham, T. Schaefer, and W. G. Schneider, *J. Chem. Phys.,* **32**, 1227 (1960).
4. L. H. Meyer, A. Saika, and H. S. Gutowsky, *J. Am. Chem. Soc.,* **75**, 4567 (1953).
5. L. Eberson and S. Farsen, *J. Phys. Chem.,* **64**, 767 (1960).
6. N. S. Bhacca, L. F. Johnson, and J. N. Schoolery, "NMR Spectra Catalog," Varian Associates, Palo Alto, California, 1962; G. V. D. Tiers, "Exploratory NMR studies," Project 737602, Minnesota Mining and Manufacturing, St. Paul, Minn.
7. A. L. Allred and E. G. Rochow, *J. Am. Chem. Soc.,* **79**, 5361 (1957).
8. B. P. Dailey and J. N. Shoolery, *J. Am. Chem. Soc.,* **77**, 3977 (1955).
9. E. Fluck, "Anorganische und Allgemeine Chemie in Einzeldarstellungen. Band V. Die Kernmagnetische Resonanz und Ihre Anwendung in der Anorganischen Chemie," Springer-Verlag, Berlin, 1963.
10. J. I. Musher, *J. Chem. Phys.,* **35**, 1159 (1961) and errata in *J. Chem. Phys.,* **37**, 192 (1962).
11. J. I. Musher, *Disc. Faraday Soc.,* **34**, 67 (1962).
12. P. T. Narasimhan and M. T. Rogers, *J. Phys. Chem.* **63**, 1388 (1959).
13. A. A. Bothner-By and C. Naar-Colin, *J. Am. Chem. Soc.,* **80**, 1728 (1958); H. Spesecke and W. G. Schneider, *J. Chem. Phys.,* **35**, 722 (1961). A reasonably complete discussion of the above effects.
14. A. Saika and C. P. Slichter, *J. Chem. Phys.,* **22**, 26 (1954).
15. N. F. Ramsay, *Phys. Rev.,* **91**, 303 (1953).
16. R. M. Stevens, C. W. Kern, and W. N. Lipscomb, *J. Chem. Phys.,* **37**, 279 (1962).
17. W. P. Griffith and G. Wilkinson, *J. Chem. Soc.,* **1959**, 2757.
18. H. S. Gutowsky, D. W. McCall, and C. P. Slichter, *J. Chem. Phys.,* **21**, 279 (1953).
19. C. F. Callis, J. R. Van Wazer, J. N. Schoolery, and W. A. Anderson, *J. Am. Chem. Soc.,* **79**, 2719 (1957).
20. R. O. Ragsdale and B. B. Stewart, *Inorg. Chem.,* **2**, 1002 (1963).
21. E. L. Muetterties, *J. Am. Chem. Soc.,* **82**, 1082 (1960).

22. R. A. Hoffman and S. Gronowitz, *Arkiv. Kemi.*, **16**, 471, 563 (1961); **17**, 1 (1961); *Acta Chem. Scand.*, **13**, 1477 (1959).
23. M. Karplus, *J. Chem. Phys.*, **33**, 1842 (1960).
24. M. T. Rogers and J. D. Graham, *J. Am. Chem. Soc.*, **84**, 3666 (1962).
25. N. Muller, *J. Chem. Phys.*, **36**, 359 (1962).
26. H. S. Gutowsky and C. Juan, *J. Am. Chem. Soc.*, **84**, 307 (1962); *J. Chem. Phys.*, **37**, 2198 (1962).
27. J. H. Goldstein and G. S. Reddy, *J. Chem. Phys.*, **36**, 2644 (1962).
28. R. S. Drago and N. A. Matwiyoff, *J. Chem. Phys.*, **38**, 2583 (1963); *J. Organomet, Chem.*, **3**, 62 (1965).
29. H. A. Bent, *Chem. Revs.*, **61**, 275 (1961).
30. J. Hinze and H. H. Jaffe, *J. Am. Chem. Soc.*, **84**, 540 (1962).
31. R. L. Middaugh and R. S. Drago, *J. Am. Chem. Soc.*, **85**, 2575 (1963).
32. R. J. Niedzielski, R. S. Drago, and R. L. Middaugh, *J. Am. Chem. Soc.*, **86**, 1694 (1964).
33. R. L. Middaugh, and R. S. Drago; unpublished observations.
34. J. R. Holmes and H. D. Kaesz, *J. Am. Chem. Soc.*, **83**, 3903 (1961).
35. N. A. Matwiyoff and R. S. Drago, *Inorg. Chem.*, **3**, 337 (1964).
36. A. Pidcock, R. E. Richards, and L. M. Venanzi, *Proc. Chem. Soc.*, **1962**, 184.
37. E. L. Muetterties, W. Mahler, and R. S. Schmutzler, *Inorg. Chem.*, **2**, 613 (1963).
38. J. D. Roberts, "An Introduction to the Analysis of Spin-Spin Splitting in High Resolution Nuclear Magnetic Resonance," W. A. Benjamin, New York, 1961.
39. K. B. Wiberg and B. J. Nist, "The Interpretation of NMR Spectra," W. A. Benjamin, New York, 1962.
40. P. L. Corio, *Chem. Revs.*, **60**, 363 (1960).
41. C. F. Callis, J. R. Van Wazer, J. N. Shoolery, and W. A. Anderson, *J. Am. Chem. Soc.*, **79**, 2719 (1957).
42. E. R. Andrew, A. Bradbury, R. G. Eades, and G. F. Jenks, *Nature*, **188**, 1096 (1960).
43. H. S. Gutowsky and A. Saika, *J. Chem. Phys.*, **21**, 1688 (1953).
44. H. S. Gutowsky and C. H. Holm, *J. Chem. Phys.*, **25**, 1228 (1956).
45. M. Anbar, A. Loewenstein, and S. Meiboom, *J. Am. Chem. Soc.*, **80**, 2630 (1958).
46. J. Kaplan, *J. Chem. Phys.*, **28**, 278 (1958).
47. M. Rogers and J. C. Woodbrey, *J. Phys. Chem.*, **66**, 540 (1962).
48. C. Looney, W. D. Phillips, and E. L. Reilly, *J. Am. Chem. Soc.*, **79**, 6136 (1957).
49. G. Claeson, G. Androes, and M. Calvin, *J. Am. Chem. Soc.*, **83**, 4357 (1961).
50. Z. Luz, D. Gill, and S. Meiboom, *J. Chem. Phys.*, **30**, 1540 (1959).
51. E. Grunwald, A. Loewenstein, and S. Meiboom, *J. Chem. Phys.*, **27**, 630 (1957).
52. S. Meiboom, et al., *J. Chem. Phys.*, **29**, 969 (1958). And references contained therein.
53. F. A. Cotton, J. W. George, and J. S. Waugh, *J. Chem. Phys.*, **28**, 994 (1958).

54. E. L. Muetterties and D. W. Phillips, *J. Am. Chem. Soc.*, **81**, 1084 (1959).
55. A. Patterson, Jr., and R. Ettinger, *Z. Elektrochem.*, **64**, 98 (1960). In English.
56. W. D. Phillips, H. C. Miller, and E. L. Muetterties, *J. Am. Chem. Soc.*, **81**, 4496 (1959); W. N. Lipscomb, *Advan. Inorg. Chem. Radiochem.*, **1**, 132 (1959); B. M. Graybill, J. K. Rúff, and M. F. Hawthorne, *J. Am. Chem. Soc.*, **83**, 2669 (1961).
57. D. M. Grant and H. S. Gutowsky, *J. Chem. Phys.*, **34**, 699 (1961).
58. J. S. Waugh and F. A. Cotton, *J. Phys. Chem.*, **65**, 562 (1961).
59. H. S. Gutowsky, *J. Chem. Phys.*, **37**, 2136 (1962).
60. O. E. Myers, *J. Chem. Phys.*, **28**, 1027 (1958).
61. Y. Masuda, *J. Phys. Soc., Japan*, **11**, 670 (1956).
62. J. D. Roberts, *J. Am. Chem. Soc.*, **78**, 4495 (1956).
63. J. N. Shoolery, *Disc. Faraday.Soc.*, **19**, 215 (1955).
64. R. A. Ogg, Jr., and J. D. Ray, *Disc. Faraday Soc.*, **19**, 239 (1955).
65. J. H. Noggle, J. D. Baldeschwieler, and C. B. Colburn, *J. Chem. Phys.*, **37**, 182 (1962).
66. J. D. Baldeschwieler, *J. Chem. Phys.*, **36**, 152 (1962).
67. J. P. Maher and D. F. Evans, *Proc. Chem. Soc.*, **1961**, 208; D. W. Turner, *J. Chem. Soc.*, **1962**, 847.
68. J. D. Baldeschwieler and E. W. Randall, *Chem. Rev.*, **63**, 82 (1963).
69. a. R. G. Pearson, J. Palmer, M. M. Anderson, and A. L. Allred, *Z Elektrochem.*, **64**, 110 (1960). b. A. W. Nolle and L. O. Morgan, *J. Chem. Phys.*, **26**, 642 (1957).
70. J. A. Jackson, J. F. Lemons, and H. Taube, *J. Chem. Phys.*, **32**, 553 (1960).
71. R. E. Connick and R. E. Poulson, *J. Chem Phys.*, **30**, 759 (1959); T. J. Swift and R. E. Connick, *J. Chem. Phys.*, **37**, 307 (1962); R. E. Connick and D. N. Fiat, *J. Chem. Phys.*, **39**, 1349 (1963).
72. H. M. McConnell and H. E. Weaver, Jr., *J. Chem. Phys.*, **25**, 307 (1956).
73. N. Bloembergen, *J. Chem. Phys.*, **27**, 595 (1957).
74. H. M. McConnell, *Proc. Natl. Acad. Sci., U. S.*, **43**, 721 (1957).
75. H. M. McConnell, *J. Chem. Phys.*, **28**, 1188 (1958).
76. H. M. McConnell and D. B. Chestnut, *J. Chem.Phys.*, **27**, 984 (1957).
77. D. R. Eaton, A. D. Josey, W. D. Phillips, and R. E. Benson, *J. Chem. Phys.*, **37**, 347 (1962).
78. a. B. Wayland and R. S. Drago; to be published. b. B. Wayland and R. S. Drago, *J. Am. Chem. Soc.*, **87**, (in press) (1965).
79. W. B. Lewis, J. A. Jackson, J. F. Lemons, and H. Taube, *J. Chem. Phys.*, **36**, 694 (1962).
80. D. R. Eaton, A. D. Josey, W. D. Phillips, and R. E. Benson, *Mol. Phys.*, **5**, 407 (1962)
81. M. L. Heffernan and R. F. M. White, *J. Chem. Soc.*, **1961**, 1382.
82. K. John, T. Moeller, and L. F. Audrieth, *J. Am. Chem. Soc.*, **82**, 5616 (1960).
83. T. Moeller and P. Nannelli, *Inorg. Chem.*, **2**, 659 (1963).
84. W. P. Van Meter and G. H. Cady, *J. Am. Chem. Soc.*, **82**, 6005 (1960). See other papers by Cady for similar applications.
85. E. L. Muetterties and D. D. Coffman, *J. Am. Chem. Soc.*, **80**, 5914 (1958).
86. R. J. Gillespie and J. V. Oubridge, *Proc. Chem. Soc.*, **1960**, 309.
87. J. J. Burke and P. C. Lauterbur, *J. Am. Chem. Soc.*, **83**, 326 (1961).

88. E. Fluck, J. R. Van Wazer, and L. C. D. Groenweghe, *J. Am. Chem. Soc.,* **81,** 6363 (1959).And other papers by Van Wazer on redistribution reactions.
89. J. A. Pople, W. G. Schneider, and A. J. Bernstein;"High Resolution NMR," Chap. 9, McGraw-Hill, New York, (1959).
90. J. V. Hatton and R. E. Richards, *Trans. Farad. Soc.,* **57,** 28 (1961).
91. T. M. Connor and C. Reid, *J. Mol. Spectr.,* **7,** 32 (1961).
92. C. M. Huggins and D. R. Carpenter, *J. Phys. Chem.,* **63,** 238 (1959).
93. J. V. Hatton and R. E. Richards, *Mol. Phys.,* **3,** 253 (1960); J. V. Hatton and R. E. Richards. *Mol. Phys.,* **5,** 139 (1962).
94. W. G. Proctor and F. C. Yu, *Phys. Rev.,* **81,** 20 (1951).
95. R. Freeman, G. R. Murray, and R. E. Richards, *Proc. Roy. Soc. (London),* **A242,** 455 (1957).
96. J. S. Griffith and L. E. Orgel, *Trans. Faraday Soc.,* **53,** 601 (1957).
97. S. Dharmatti and G. R. Kanekar, *J. Chem. Phys.,* **31,** 1436 (1959).
98. H. Landesman and R. E. Williams, *J. Am. Chem. Soc.,* **83,** 2663 (1961).
99. T. P. Onak, H. Landesman, R. E. Williams, and I. Shapiro, *J. Phys. Chem.,* **63,** 1533 (1959).
100. W. D. Phillips, H. C. Miller, and E. L. Muetterties, *J. Am. Chem. Soc.,* **81,** 4496 (1959).
101. J. G. Pritchard and P. C. Lauterbur, *J. Am. Chem. Soc.,* **83,** 2105 (1961).

GENERAL REFERENCES

E. R. Andrew, "Nuclear Magnetic Resonance," Cambridge, New York, 1955.
E. Fluck, "Anorganische und Allgemeine Chemie in Einzeldarstellungen. Band V. Die kernmagnetische Resonanz und Ihre Anwendung in der Anorganischen Chemie," Springer-Verlag, Berlin, 1963.
H. S. Gutowsky, "Techniques of Organic Chemistry," vol. 1, part 4, 3rd. ed., ed. A. Weissberger, Interscience, New York, 1960.
L. M. Jackman, "Nuclear Magnetic Resonance Spectroscopy," Pergamon, New York, 1959.
J. A. Pople, W. G. Schneider, and H. J. Bernstein, "High Resolution Nuclear Magnetic Resonance," McGraw-Hill, New York, 1959.
J. C. Martin, *J. Chem. Educ.,* **38,** 286 (1961).
J. D. Roberts, "High Resolution Nuclear Magnetic Resonance," McGraw-Hill, New York, 1955.
J. A. S. Smith, *Quart. Revs.,* **7,** 279 (1953).

9

Nuclear Quadrupole Resonance Spectroscopy

INTRODUCTION

When a nucleus with an electric quadrupole moment (spin quantum number $I \gtrsim 1$, see the second paragraph of Chapter 8 and Fig. 8-1) is surrounded by an inhomogeneous electric field resulting from asymmetry in the electron distribution, the *quadrupolar nucleus will interact with this electric field* to an extent which is different for the various possible orientations of the elliptical quadrupolar nucleus. Since the quadrupole moment arises from an unsymmetrical distribution of electric charge in the nucleus, it is an electric moment rather than a magnetic moment. The allowed orientations are quantized, just as the energy of a spinning electron in the positive nuclear field is quantized. The nucleus has $2I + 1$ orientations, which are described by the nuclear magnetic quantum number m, where m has values $I, I - 1, ..., 0, ..., -I + 1, -I$. The quadrupole energy level that is lowest in energy corresponds to the orientation in which the greatest amount of positive nuclear charge is closest to the greatest density of negative charge in the electron environment. The energy differences between different orientations are not very great, and at room temperature a distribution of orientations exists in a group of molecules. If the nucleus is spherical ($I = 0$ or $\frac{1}{2}$) or if the electron environment around the nucleus is spherical (as in Cl^-), all nuclear orientations are equivalent and the corresponding quadrupole energy states are degenerate.

In a nuclear quadrupole resonance (NQR)* experiment, radiation in the radio frequency region is employed to effect transitions among the various orientations of a quadrupolar nucleus in an asymmetric field. Structural information about a compound can be obtained by considering

---

*For reviews of NQR see General References.

how different structural and electronic effects influence the asymmetry of the electron environment. In addition to this *direct measurement* of the quadrupole energy level difference by absorption of radio frequency radiation, the same information may also be obtained from the fine structure in the pure rotational (microwave) spectrum of a gas. The different nuclear orientations give slightly different moments of inertia, resulting in fine structure in the microwave spectrum. The direct measurement by absorption of radio frequency radiation must be carried out on a solid because molecular rotation in a gas or liquid averages the field gradient so that splitting of the quadrupole energy levels does not occur. Details regarding the instrumentation have been published.[1]

The energy difference between the various levels and hence, the frequency of the transition, will depend upon both the field gradient, q, produced by the valence electrons, and the quadrupole moment of the nucleus. The quadrupole moment, eQ, is a measure of the deviation of the electric charge distribution *of the nucleus* from spherical symmetry. For a given isotope this is a constant, and values for many isotopes can be obtained from several sources.[2,3] The units of eQ are charge times distance squared, but it is common to express the moment simply as Q in units of cm^2. For example, Cl^{35} with a nuclear spin $I = \frac{3}{2}$ has a quadrupole moment Q of -0.08×10^{-24} cm^2, the negative sign indicating that the charge distribution is flattened relative to the spin axis (see Fig. 8-1).

The second factor determining the extent of the splitting of the quadrupole energy levels is *the field gradient*, q, at the nucleus produced by the *electron distribution* in the molecule. The splitting of a quadrupole level will be related to the product eQq. By properly selecting the axes and defining the coordinate system, the components of the field gradient q (which is the second derivative of the time-averaged electric potential, V) along the x, y, and z axes can be labeled as q_{zz}, q_{yy}, and q_{xx}. By convention q_{zz} refers to the largest field gradient, q_{yy} the next largest, and q_{xx} the smallest when all three values are different. If $q_{zz} = q_{xx} = q_{yy}$, the field gradient *is spherical,* and all the quadrupole levels are degenerate (all orientations of the nucleus interact identically with the electronic charge). When $q_{zz} \neq q_{xx} = q_{yy}$, there is *axial symmetry* around the z axis. The NQR spectra of molecules of this type are easiest to interpret. For a molecule with axial symmetry, q_{zz} is abbreviated as q and the maximum field gradient lies along the z axis (i.e. the highest-fold symmetry axis) by convention. The chlorine atoms in Cl_2 and in CH_3Cl are axially symmetric, and the bond axis in Cl_2 and the C—Cl bond axis in CH_3Cl are the z axes in these molecules.

The energies of the various quadrupole states in an axially symmetric field are given by the following equation:

$$E_m = \frac{eQq[3m^2 - I(I + 1)]}{4I(2I - 1)} \qquad (9\text{-}1)$$

where I is the nuclear spin quantum number and m is the nuclear magnetic quantum number. For a nuclear spin of $I = \frac{3}{2}$, m can have values of $\frac{3}{2}, \frac{1}{2}, -\frac{1}{2}, -\frac{3}{2}$. For $m = \frac{3}{2}$, substitution into equation (9-1) produces the result $E_{3/2} = +eQq/4$. Since m is squared, the value for $m = -\frac{3}{2}$ will be identical to $m = +\frac{3}{2}$, and a doubly degenerate set of quadrupole energy states results. Similarly, the state from $m = \pm\frac{1}{2}$ will be doubly degenerate. The transition energy, ΔE, indicated by the arrow in Fig. 9-1, corresponds

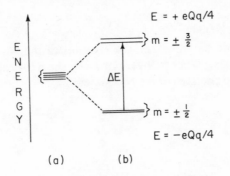

E = + eQq/4

m = ± 3/2

ΔE

m = ± 1/2

E = −eQq/4

(a)   (b)

Fig. 9-1. Quadrupole Energy Levels in a Spherical Field (a) and an Axially Symmetric Field (b).

to $eQq/4 - (-eQq/4)$ or $eQq/2$. Thus, for a nucleus with a spin $I = \frac{3}{2}$ in an axially symmetric field, a single transition is expected, and the quantity eQq expressed in energy units can be calculated directly from the frequency of absorption: $eQq = 2\Delta E = 2h\nu$. The quantity eQq is often expressed as a frequency (mc sec^{-1}). For the above case, eQq would be twice the frequency of the NQR transition. (Some authors use the symbol e^2Qq to represent the same quantity as eQq.)

The number of transitions and the relationship of the frequency of the transition to eQq can be calculated in a similar manner for other nuclei with different I values in axially symmetric fields by using equation (9-1). For $I = \frac{5}{2}$, three energy levels ($E_{\pm1/2}$, $E_{\pm3/2}$, and $E_{\pm5/2}$) and two transitions result. The selection rule for these transitions is $\Delta m = \pm1$, so the observed transitions are $E_{\pm1/2} \rightarrow E_{\pm3/2}$ and $E_{\pm3/2} \rightarrow E_{\pm5/2}$. (Recall that all levels are populated under ordinary conditions.) Substitution of I and m into equation (9-1) produces the result that the energy of the $E_{\pm 3/2} \to E_{\pm 5/2}$ transition is twice that of the $E_{\pm 1/2} \to E_{\pm 3/2}$ transition. In measured spectra, deviations from these predicted frequencies are attributed to deviations from axial symmetry in the sample, and, as will be seen shortly, this deviation can be used as a measure of asymmetry.

Field gradients about a nucleus described as $q_{xx} \neq q_{yy} \neq q_{zz}$, are termed *nonsymmetric*, and spectra obtained on these molecules are more complex than those obtained for molecules with axially symmetric environments. The molecule CH_3SH (C—S—H bond angle $\sim 90°$) has a sulfur atom with a nonsymmetric field gradient. The value of eQq cannot be calculated from the spectra of nuclei in nonsymmetric fields unless an asymmetry parameter, η, can be evaluated. It is defined as:

$$\eta = (q_{xx} - q_{yy})/q_{zz} \qquad (9\text{-}2)$$

In a nonsymmetric environment, the energies of the various quadrupole levels are no longer given by (9-1). For $I = \frac{3}{2}$, the following equations can be derived[4] for the energies of the two states:

$$E_{\pm 3/2} = \frac{3eQq\sqrt{1 + \eta^2/3}}{4I(2I - 1)} \qquad (9\text{-}3)$$

$$E_{\pm 1/2} = \frac{-3eQq\sqrt{1 + \eta^2/3}}{4I(2I - 1)} \qquad (9\text{-}4)$$

From the difference of equations (9-3) and (9-4) and $E = \mathbf{h}\nu$, it is seen that one transition with frequency $\nu = (eQq/2\mathbf{h})\sqrt{1 + \eta^2/3}$, is expected for $I = \frac{3}{2}$. Since there are two unknowns, η and q, the value for eQq cannot be obtained from a measured frequency. As will be seen shortly, this problem can be solved with results from NQR experiments on a sample in a weak magnetic field.

The equations for nuclei with I values other than $\frac{3}{2}$ have been reported, and in many instances where more than one line is observed in the spectrum, both the asymmetry parameter, η, and eQq can be obtained from the spectrum. For $I = 1$, the equations are:

$$E_0 = \frac{-2eQq}{4I(2I - 1)}$$

and

$$E_{\pm 1} = \frac{eQq(1 \pm \eta)}{4I(2I - 1)}$$

The corresponding energy levels are indicated in Fig. 9-2b where K stands for $(eQq/4I)(2I - 1)$. The pertubation of these levels by an applied magnetic field is indicated in Fig. 9-2c. This effect will be discussed in the next section. As can be seen in Fig. 9-2b, there will be two transitions for $I = 1$, $\eta \neq 0$, so the two unknowns, eQq and η, can be determined directly from the spectrum. It is interesting to point out that for a nucleus with $I = 1$ in an axially symmetric field only one line is expected in the spectrum (see Fig. 9-2a).

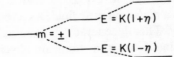

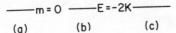

(a)   (b)   (c)

Fig. 9–2. Energy Levels for $I = 1$ under Different Conditions. (a) $\eta = 0$ and applied magnetic field, $H_0, = 0$. (b) $\eta \neq 0$, $H_0 = 0$. (c) $\eta \neq 0$, $H_0 \neq 0$.

The energies of the quadrupole levels as a function of η have been calculated[4] for cases other than $I = 1$ or $\frac{3}{2}$. Tables have also been reported[5] which permit calculations of η and eQq from spectral data for nuclei with $I = \frac{5}{2}, \frac{7}{2}$, and $\frac{9}{2}$. When η is appreciable, the selection rule $\Delta m = \pm 1$ breaks down, and complex spectra containing many bands are often obtained.

EFFECT OF A MAGNETIC FIELD ON THE SPECTRA

Considerable information can be obtained by determining quadrupole spectra of samples placed in a weak magnetic field. In general, *the applied magnetic field will shift the energy of a nondegenerate quadrupole level and split a doubly degenerate level* (i.e., one having $m \neq 0$ (equation 9-1)). This change in energy of the nondegenerate quadrupolar levels is indicated in Fig. 9-2(b) and (c) for a nucleus in which $I = 1$ and $\eta \neq 0$.

For a nucleus with $I = 1$, a quadrupole spectrum with two lines can arise from two distinct situations: for $\eta \neq 0$ as noted above (Fig. 9-2b), or for nuclei with $\eta = 0$ located in two nonequivalent lattice sites. Examination of the spectrum of the sample in an external magnetic field allows a distinction to be made between these two possibilities. In the former case ($\eta \neq 0$), two lines would again be observed, but with different energies than those obtained in the absence of the field; in the latter case, each doubly-degenerate level would be split giving a spectrum with four lines.

As mentioned earlier, the levels $E_{\pm 1/2}$ and $E_{\pm 3/2}$ are each doubly degenerate for $I = \frac{3}{2}$ in a nonsymmetric field. As a result eQq and η cannot be determined directly. This degeneracy is removed by a magnetic field, with four levels resulting. Four transitions are observed in the spectrum: $+\frac{1}{2} \rightarrow +\frac{3}{2}, +\frac{1}{2} \rightarrow -\frac{3}{2}, -\frac{1}{2} \rightarrow +\frac{3}{2}, -\frac{1}{2} \rightarrow -\frac{3}{2}$ ($\Delta|m| = +1$). The energy differences corresponding to these four transitions are functions of eQq and η (as indicated by equations 9-3 to 9-4), so these parameters can be evaluated[6] for this system from the spectrum of the sample with and without an applied magnetic field.

RELATIONSHIP BETWEEN THE ELECTRIC FIELD GRADIENT, q, AND MOLECULAR STRUCTURE

An analysis of the factors affecting the field gradient, q, in a molecule indicate[7,8] that for first and second row atoms, an important contribution will arise from the way in which the p orbitals are occupied by the valence electrons. Since the s orbital is spherically symmetrical, electron density in this orbital will not give rise to a field gradient. As long as the atom being studied is not the least electronegative in the bond to other atoms in the molecule, the maximum field gradient at this atom in any molecule, q_{mol}, is the atomic field gradient, q_{at}, for a single electron in a p_z orbital of the isolated atom. When the atom being investigated is more electronegative than the atom to which it is bonded, the quadrupolar atom has greater electron density around it in the molecule than in the isolated atom. The problem now becomes one of interpreting the relationship between the electron "occupation" of the p orbitals of a quadrupolar atom in a molecule, as given by q_{mol}, and structural considerations. The following equation relates structural considerations, the quantity eQq_{mol}, which is determined from the NQR spectrum of the molecule under consideration and eQq_{at} (eQ and q_{at} are defined above, and their product is the nuclear quadrupole coupling constant of the isolated atom):

$$eQq_{mol} = [1 - s + d - i(1 - s - d)]eQq_{at} \qquad (9\text{-}5)$$

where eQq_{at} is the quadrupole coupling constant for occupancy of the p orbital by a single electron, s is the fraction of s character employed by the atom in the bond to its neighbor, d is the amount of d character in this bond, and i is the fraction of ionic character in the bond (for a molecule A—B, $\psi^0 = c\psi_A + d\psi_B$ and $i = c^2 - d^2$). When the atom being studied is electropositive, i changes sign. Values for eQq_{at} and q_{at} have been tabulated for several atoms.[1,2,9,10] When π bonding is possible, this effect must also be included. Recently[8] a modified form of equation (9-5) has been employed:

$$eQq_{mol} = (1 - s + d - i - \pi)eQq_{at} \qquad (9\text{-}6)$$

where π is the extent of π bonding and all other quantities are as defined above.

As the amount of ionic character in a bond increases, the electronic environment approaches spherical symmetry (where $q_{mol} = 0$) and eqQ_{mol} decreases. Hybridization of the p orbital with an s orbital also decreases eQq_{mol}, as indicated by equation (9-6). Mixing of the s orbital with the p orbital decreases the field gradient, because the s orbital is spherically symmetrical. In a covalent molecule d orbital contribution to the bonding increases the field gradient. As can be seen from equation (9-6), the NQR spectrum of a molecule gives one measurable parameter, but there are four unknowns, s, d, π, and i. A rigorous solution is not possible unless additional equations relating other measurable variables to these parameters are discovered.

APPLICATIONS

NQR spectra of a number of molecules containing the following nuclei have been reported: As^{75}, B^{10}, B^{11}, Bi^{209}, Br^{79}, Br^{81}, Cl^{35}, Cl^{37}, Cu^{63}, Cu^{65}, Ga^{69}, Ga^{71}, Hg^{201}, I^{127}, I^{129}, In^{115}, N^{14}, S^{33}, Sb^{121}, Sn^{123}.

THE INTERPRETATION OF eQq DATA

As mentioned above it is not possible to interpret eQq values rigorously in terms of ionic character, π bonding, and s and d hybridization. For compounds in which there are large differences in ionic character, the effect can be clearly seen, as indicated by the data in Table 9-1. Smaller eQq_{mol} values are obtained for ionic compounds. Attempts have been made to "explain" eQq data for a large number of halogen compounds by assuming that d hybridization is not important and estimating ionic character or s hybridization. The lack of success is indicated by the divergence of opinion expressed by various authors[8,11] regarding the estimates of the quantities i, π, d, and s in equation (9-6). It can be con-

TABLE 9-1. VALUES OF eQq_{mol} FOR
SOME DIATOMIC HALIDES

Molecule[a]	eQq_{mol}	Molecule	eQq_{mol}
BrCl	−103.6	BrCl	876.8
ICl	−82.5	LiBr	37.2
TlCl	−15.8	NaBr	58
KCl	0.04	DBr	533
RbCl	0.774	FBr	1089
CsCl	3	DI	−1827
FCl	−146.0	NaI	−259.87

[a]Values for eQq_{at} are $Cl^{35} = -109.74$, $Br^{79} = 769.76$, and $I^{127} = -2292.84$. eQq_{mol} applies to the underlined atom.

cluded that the interpretation of these data, especially for systems in which eQq differences are small, is ambiguous. One of the more successful interpretations involves a study on a series of substituted chlorobenzenes. A linear relation is found between the Hammett σ constant of the substituent and the quadrupole resonance frequency.[12] The data obeyed the equation ν (mc sec^{-1}) = 34.826 + 1.024σ. The electron-releasing substituents have negative σ values and give rise to smaller eQq values, because the increased ionic character in the C—Cl bond makes the chlorine more negatively charged.

The general problem of covalence in metal-ligand bonds in a series of complexes has been investigated by direct measurement of the quadrupole resonance.[13] A rigorous interpretation of the data (especially where small differences are involved) is again hampered by the lack of information regarding the four variables in equation (9-6). In view of the ambiguity in interpretation, other quadrupole investigations concerned with elucidating ionic character, etc., from eQq data will not be presented here, nor will much faith be put in the conclusions regarding bond type that have been arrived at in these studies. Further developments are badly needed in this area of NQR.

As more data becomes available it may well become possible to correlate certain ranges of quadrupole coupling constants with specific functional groups, as has been done in infrared spectroscopy. For example, the eQq values (in mc sec^{-1}) for nitrogen in R—C—N groups are in the range −4.2 to −4.6, while those in R—N—C are about +0.5. The value of +1.2 for the nitrogen resonance in HNCS supports this structure instead of HSCN. The fingerprint application is also a possibility that may develop.

THE EFFECTS OF CRYSTAL LATTICE ON THE MAGNITUDE OF eQq

A further complication and limitation of the application of NQR spectroscopy result from the fact that direct measurement of nuclear quadrupole transitions can only be obtained on solids. For very complex molecules, this is the only source of nuclear quadrupole information because of the complexity of the microwave spectrum. Measurements on solids introduce the complexities of lattice effects. For those molecules which have been studied by both methods (direct measurement and microwave) it is found that eQq is usually 10 to 15 per cent lower in the solid state. It has been proposed[2] that the decrease is due to increased ionicity in the solid. There are several examples of molecules being extensively associated in the solid but not in the gas phase or in solution. (e.g., I_2 and CNCl). In these cases, considerable care must be exercised in deducing molecular properties from eQq values. Some examples where the crystal lattice affects the number of lines observed in a spectrum will be discussed in the next section.

STRUCTURAL INFORMATION FROM NQR SPECTRA

Since different field gradients will exist for nonequivalent nuclei in a molecule, we should expect to obtain a different line (or set of lines, depending on I) for each type of nuclear environment. In general, the environment of an atom as determined by NQR studies is in agreement with results obtained from x-ray studies. Only one line is found[13] in the halogen NQR spectrum of each of the following: K_2SeCl_6, Cs_2SeBr_6, $(NH_4)_2TeCl_6$, $(NH_4)_2SnBr_6$ and K_2PtCl_6. This is consistent with O_h structures for these anions.

As mentioned above, the following effects can give rise to multiple lines in the NQR spectrum:

(1) Chemically nonequivalent atoms in the molecule.

(2) Chemically equivalent atoms in a molecule occupying nonequivalent positions in the crystal lattice of the solid.

(3) Splitting of the degeneracy of quadrupole energy levels by the asymmetry of the field gradient. Splitting of the quadrupole levels by other

magnetic nuclei in the molecule, similar to spin-spin splitting in NMR, generally is not detected in NQR spectra. Usually these splittings are less than, or of the same order of magnitude as, the line widths. One case where such splitting has been reported[14] is in the spectrum of HIO_3. The I^{127} nucleus is split by the proton.

The nonequivalence of lattice positions (2) is illustrated in the bromine NQR spectrum of K_2SeBr_6 which gives a single line at room temperature and two lines at dry ice temperature. A crystalline phase change accounts for the difference. Although K_2PtI_6, K_2SnBr_6, and K_2TeBr_6 contain "octahedral" anions, the halides are not equivalent in the solid lattice, and the halide NQR spectra all consist of three lines, indicating at least three different halide environments.

Four resonance lines were found in the chlorine quadrupole spectra of each $TiCl_4$,[15] $SiCl_4$,[16] and $SnCl_4$.[16] It was concluded that the crystal structures of these materials are similar.

The problem of distinguishing nonequivalent positions in the lattice from chemical nonequivalence in the molecular configuration (which is related to the structure of the molecule in the gas phase or in a non-coordinating solvent) is difficult in some cases. In general, the frequency difference for lines resulting from nonequivalent lattice positions is small compared to the differences encountered for chemically nonequivalent nuclei in a molecule. When only slight separations between the spectral lines are observed, it is difficult to determine from this technique alone which of the two effects is operative. Another difficulty encountered in interpretation is illustrated by the chlorine spectrum of Nb_2Cl_{10}.[17] Even though this molecule has a structure containing both terminal and bridging chlorines, only a single chlorine resonance is observed in the spectrum. Consequently, arguments based on not observing certain lines may be of doubtful validity.

NQR studies of N^{14} ($I = 1$) are difficult to carry out but produce very interesting results. Since $I = 1$, both eQq and the asymmetry parameter η can be evaluated from the NQR spectrum. In BrCN the N^{14} NQR resonance is a doublet. This could result from two nonequivalent nitrogen atoms in the crystal lattice or from a splitting of the nitrogen resonance because of an asymmetric field gradient. The former explanation was eliminated by a single crystal x-ray study.[18] The structure of solid BrCN was found to consist of linear chains of the type:

$$\cdots Br—C \equiv N| \cdots \cdots Br—C \equiv N| \cdots Br—C \equiv N|$$

The nitrogen has axial symmetry here, and only one line is expected.

However, it is proposed that interactions between chains reduce the symmetry at the nitrogen and lead to the two lines. Various resonance forms can be written for BrCN, and the eQq values indicate that the bromine has a formal positive charge. An appreciable increase in eQq for bromine is observed in the solid relative to the gaseous state spectrum of BrCN. This could be due to increased contributions to the ground state from the structure Br^+CN^- in the solid because of stabilization of Br^+ by coordination. If the $N\cdots Br$—C bond is described as a pd hybrid, the increased d contribution in the bromine carbon bond will also increase eQq.

The iodine NQR spectrum of solid iodine indicates a large asymmetry parameter, η.[19] Since the iodine atom in an iodine molecule is axially symmetric, the large asymmetry is taken as indication of intermolecular bonding in the solid. A large η in the iodine NQR spectrum of the molecule HIO_3 supports the structure $IO_2(OH)$ instead of HIO_3. The structure HIO_3 has a C_3 axis so $q_{xx} = q_{yy}$. References 1 and 2 contain many additional examples of studies of this kind.

Information regarding π bonding can be obtained from the asymmetry parameter η. Methods for evaluating η for various nuclei have been discussed. A single σ bond to a halogen should give rise to an axially symmetric field gradient. Double bonding leads to asymmetry, and the extent of π bonding is related to η. It was concluded that there is appreciable (~ 5 per cent) carbon-halogen π bonding in vinyl chloride, vinyl bromide, and vinyl iodide.[20] Bersohn[21] has made a complete study of the problem of estimating quantitatively the extent of carbon-halogen π bonding from η.

The values of η obtained from the NQR spectra of SiI_4, GeI_4, and SnI_4 were interpreted to indicate a very small degree (about 1 per cent) of double bond character[22] in the halogen bond to the central atom. This could be due to a solid state effect.

The asymmetry of a molecule and the direction of q_{zz} relative to the crystal axes can be investigated by studying the NQR spectrum of a single crystal in a magnetic field. The splitting is a function of orientation, and detailed analysis of the spectra for different orientations enables one to determine the direction of the z axis of the field gradient, q_{zz}. This axis can be compared to the crystal axes.

The above examples are a few of the many applications of NQR and were selected to demonstrate the shortcomings and possible applications of NQR in inorganic systems. When problems of instrument design are overcome to enable commercial construction of a single instrument which can be used for many nuclei, NQR spectroscopy will be utilized considerably by inorganic chemists.

EXERCISES

1. a. Calculate the energies of all the quadrupolar energy states for a nucleus with $I = 2$. Express the energies as a function of eQq.
   b. How many transitions are expected and what is the relationship between the energy of the transitions and eQq?
2. a. Using the equations presented in this chapter for the energies of the 0 and ± 1 levels of a nucleus with $I = 0$ in an asymmetric field, calculate the frequency in terms of eQq and η for the $0 \to +1, 0 \to -1$ transitions.
   b. Express the energy difference of the two above transitions in terms of η and eQq.
   c. Show how η and q can be determined from this data.
3. Describe an NQR experiment that would give information regarding the extent of π bonding in the phosphorus-sulfur bonds in $PSCl_3$ and ϕ_3PS. Can you determine whether the sulfur is hybridized sp^2 and utilizes a p orbital in bonding or whether p_x and p_y orbitals of sulfur participate equally in bonding with NQR experiments? ($I = \frac{3}{2}$ for S^{33})
4. Suppose the compound $X—\langle\bigcirc\rangle Cl$ gave a chlorine spectrum with eQq_{mol} $= 66.50$ mc sec^{-1}. What is the σ constant for the substituent X?
5. It has been reported that the I^{127} quadrupole resonance in AsI_3 is a singlet but has a very large asymmetry parameter.[23] A single crystal x-ray study indicates the As is nearly octahedral. Explain the large asymmetry parameter.
6. Indicate the number of resonance lines expected for the following nuclei under the conditions given:

$$
\begin{array}{llll}
\text{a. I} & (I = \tfrac{5}{2}); & \eta = 0; & H_0 = 0. \\
\text{b. N}^{14} & (I = 1); & \eta = 0; & H_0 = 0. \\
\text{c. As}^{75} & (I = \tfrac{3}{2}); & \eta = 0; & H_0 = 0. \\
\text{d. Sb}^{121} & (I = \tfrac{5}{2}); & \eta = 1; & H_0 = 0. \\
\text{e. N}^{14} & (I = 1); & \eta = 1; & H_0 = 0. \\
\text{f. N}^{14} & (I = 1); & \eta = 1; & H_0 \neq 0.
\end{array}
$$

GENERAL REFERENCES

M. H. Cohen and F. Reif, "Solid State Physics," vol. 5, eds. F. Seitz and D. Turnbull, Academic, New York, 1957.

T. P. Das and E. L. Hahn, "Nuclear Quadrupole Resonance Spectroscopy," Academic, New York, 1958.

R. Livingston, *Record Chem. Progr.*, **20**, 173 (1954).

C. T. O'Konski, "Determination of Organic Structures by Physical Methods," vol. 2, eds. F. C. Nachod and W. D. Phillips, Academic, New York, 1962.

W. J. Orville-Thomas, *Quart Revs.*, **11**, 162 (1957).

REFERENCES CITED

1. T. P. Das and E. L. Hahn, "Nuclear Quadrupole Resonance Spectroscopy," Academic, New York, 1958.
2. C. T. O'Konski, "Determination of Organic Structures by Physical Methods,"

vol. 2, eds. F. C. Nachod and W. D. Phillips, Academic, New York, 1962.
3. J. A. Pople, W. G. Schneider, and H. J. Bernstein, "High Resolution Nuclear Magnetic Resonance," McGraw-Hill, New York, 1959.
4. R. Bersohn, *J. Chem. Phys.*, **20**, 1505 (1952).
5. R. Livingston and H. Zeldes, "Tables of Eigenvalues for Pure Quadrupole Spectra," Oak Ridge Natl. Lab. Rept. ORNL-1913 (1955).
6. C. Dean, *Phys. Rev.,* **86**, 607A (1952).
7. C. H. Townes and B. P. Dailey, *J. Chem. Phys.* **17**, 782 (1949).
8. B. P. Dailey, *J. Chem. Phys.,* **33**, 1641 (1960).
9. M. H. Cohen and F. Reif, "Solid State Physics," vol. 5, eds. F. Seitz and D. Turnbull, Academic, New York, 1957.
10. W. J. Orville–Thomas, *Quart. Revs.,* **11**, 162 (1957).
11. C. H. Townes and B. P. Dailey, *J. Chem. Phys.,* **23**, 118 (1955): W. Gordy, *Disc. Faraday Soc.,* **19**, 14 (1955); M. A. Whitehead and H. H. Jaffe, *Trans. Faraday Soc.,* **57**, 1854 (1961).
12. H. C. Meal, *J. Am. Chem. Soc.,* **74**, 6121 (1952); P. J. Bray and R. G. Barnes, *J. Chem. Phys.,* **27**, 551 (1957). And references cited therein.
13. D. Nakumura, K. Ito, and M. Kubo, *Inorg. Chem.,* **1**, 592 (1962); **2**, 61 (1963); *J. Am. Chem. Soc.,* **82**, 5783 (1960); **83**, 4526 (1961); **84**, 163 (1962).
14. R. Livingston and H. Zeles, *J. Chem. Phys.,* **26**, 351 (1957).
15. A. H. Reddock, *J. Chem. Phys.* **35**, 1085 (1961).
16. A. L. Schawlow, *J. Chem. Phys.,* **22**, 1211 (1954).
17. A. H. Reddock, *J. Chem. Phys.* **35**, 1085 (1961).
18. S. Geller and A. L. Schawlow, *J. Chem. Phys.,* **23**, 779 (1955).
19. H. G. Dehmelt, *Naturwiss,* **37**, 398 (1950).
20. J. A. Howe and J. H. Goldstein, *J. Chem. Phys.* **26**, 7 (1957); **27**, 831 (1957). And references contained therein.
21. R. Bersohn, *J. Chem. Phys.,* **22**, 2078 (1954).
22. H. Robinson, H. G. Dehmelt, and W. Gordy, *J. Chem. Phys.,* **22**, 511 (1954).
23. S. Kojima, et. al., *J. Phys. Soc. Japan,* **9**, 805 (1954).

10 Electron Paramagnetic Resonance Spectroscopy

INTRODUCTION

Electron resonance is a branch of absorption spectroscopy in which radiation of microwave frequency is absorbed by *molecules possessing electrons with unpaired spins*. This phenomenon has been designated by different names: "electron paramagnetic resonance" (EPR), "electron spin resonance" (ESR), and "electron magnetic resonance." These are equivalent and merely emphasize different aspects of the same phenomenon.*

For an electron of spin $s = \frac{1}{2}$, the spin angular momentum quantum number can have values of $m_s = \pm\frac{1}{2}$, which in the absence of a magnetic field leads to a doubly degenerate *spin energy state*. When a magnetic field is applied, this degeneracy is resolved. The low energy state has the spin magnetic moment aligned with the field and corresponds to the quantum number, $m_s = -\frac{1}{2}$, while the high energy state, $m_s = +\frac{1}{2}$, has its moment opposed to the field. There are some similarities in NMR and EPR spectroscopy which are of help in understanding EPR. In NMR spectroscopy the two different energy states arise from the alignment of the nuclear magnetic moments relative to the applied field, and a transition between them occurs upon the application of a radio-frequency field of the appropriate frequency. In EPR, a transition between the two different electron spin energy states occurs upon absorption of a quantum of radiation in the radio frequency or microwave region. The energy, E, of the transition is given by:

$$E = \mathbf{h}\nu = g\beta H_0 \qquad (10\text{-}1)$$

where $\mathbf{h}$ is Planck's constant, ν the frequency of radiation, β the Bohr

* The General References provide general reviews of EPR. The references by Carrington and by Carrington and Longuet-Higgins are especially recommended.

magneton, H_0 the field strength, and g the spectroscopic splitting factor. The quantity g is not a constant but a tensor quantity. For a free electron g has the value of 2.0023 (this quantity is discussed in Appendix A). In many free radicals, the g value of the odd electron is close to that of a free electron, but in metal ions g values are often greatly different from the free electron value.

In general the magnitude of g depends upon the orientation of the molecule containing the unpaired electron with respect to the magnetic field. In a solution or in the gas phase, g is averaged over all orientations because of the free motion of the molecules, but in a crystal, movement is restricted. If the paramagnetic radical or ion is located in a perfectly cubic crystal site (e.g., an octahedral or tetrahedral site), the g value is independent of the orientation of the crystal and is said to be isotropic. In a crystal site of lower symmetry the g value depends upon the orientation of the crystal and is said to be anisotropic. The z direction is defined coincident with the highest-fold rotation axis, which can be determined by x-ray methods. The g_z value is equivalent to $g_\parallel$, the g value obtained when the z axis is parallel with the external magnetic field. The g values along the x and y axes are g_x and g_y, which in a tetragonal site are equal and referred to as $g_\perp$, the g value obtained with the external magnetic field perpendicular to the z axis. If θ is the angle between the magnetic field and the z axis, the experimental g value is given by the following equation:

$$g^2 = g_\parallel{}^2 \cos^2 \theta + g_\perp{}^2 \sin^2 \theta \qquad (10\text{-}2)$$

Small distortions, which go undetected by x-ray methods, can sometimes be determined by EPR from the inequality of the g values. We will return to the topic of g values in a later section.

Although, as in NMR, the ESR spectrum can be obtained by varying either the frequency or the field strength, in practice it is simpler to vary the latter. The relation between field strength and frequency for $g = 2.0$ is: 1 gauss = 2.80 mc sec^{-1}. The energies required to effect a transition are very much different in NMR and EPR. The magnetic moment of an electron is about -9270×10^{24} compared to $+14.1 \times 10^{24}$ ergs gauss^{-1} for a proton. For a magnetic field of 10,000 gauss, the required frequency for an EPR transition, when $g = 2.0$, is about 28,000 mc sec^{-1} compared to about 40 mc sec^{-1} for proton magnetic resonance transitions. At field strengths commonly employed (3200 gauss) to give signals of adequate intensity, EPR transitions occur at frequencies in the microwave region (9000 mc sec^{-1}) compared to frequencies in the radio frequency region for NMR. Hence, the instrumentation for the two methods must be different.

PRESENTATION OF THE SPECTRUM

As in NMR, the EPR spectrum can be represented by plotting intensity against the strength of the applied field, but EPR spectra are commonly presented as derivative curves, i.e., the first derivative (the slope) of the absorption curves is plotted against the strength of the magnetic field. Much greater sensitivity can be achieved by this detection method if the line shape is broad. The two modes of presentation are easily interconverted, and the relationship between the two kinds of spectra is illustrated in Fig. 10-1. In (a), a single absorption peak with no fine structure

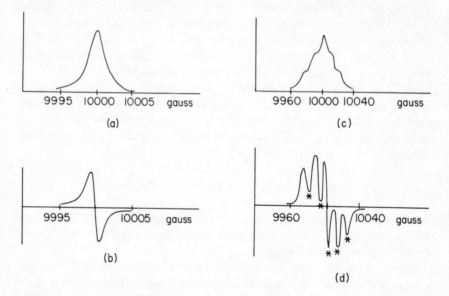

Fig. 10–1. Comparison of Spectral Presentation as Absorption (a and c) and Derivative (b and d) Curves.

is represented; (b) is the derivative curve that corresponds to (a). The derivative curve crosses the abscissa at a maximum in the absorption curve, for the slope changes sign at a maximum. Curve (c) is the absorption counterpart of curve (d). Note that the shoulders in (c) never pass through a maximum and as a result the absorption peaks in (d) corresponding to these shoulders do not cross the abscissa. The number of peaks and shoulders in the absorption curve can be determined from the number of minima (marked with an asterisk in (d)) or maxima in the derivative curve.

HYPERFINE SPLITTING IN SOME SIMPLE SYSTEMS

When an unpaired electron comes in the vicinity of a nucleus with a spin I, an interaction takes place which causes the absorption signal to be split into $2I+1$ components. The cause of this splitting is the nuclear spin-electron spin coupling arising mainly from the Fermi contact term.

This effect is simply illustrated by considering as an example a hydrogen atom ($I = \frac{1}{2}$ for the proton). The EPR spectrum of a hydrogen atom in a solid matrix consists of two peaks of equal intensity centered at $g = 2.0023$. The two energy levels of a free electron in a magnetic field are shown in Fig. 10-2a with $m_s = -\frac{1}{2}$ aligned with the field and $m_s = +\frac{1}{2}$ aligned opposed to the field. The spectrum of a free electron would consist of a single peak corresponding to a transition between these levels. For each value of the electron spin angular momentum quantum number m_s, the nuclear spin angular momentum quantum number m_I, can have values of $\pm\frac{1}{2}$, giving rise to four different energy levels (Fig. 10-2b).

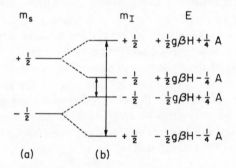

Fig. 10–2. (a) Energy States for an Electron in a Magnetic Field and (b) Effect of a Nuclear Spin ot $\frac{1}{2}$ on These States.

From magnetic considerations, one expects that the interaction of a proton nuclear moment corresponding to quantum number $m_I = +\frac{1}{2}$ with the electron spin moment corresponding to the quantum number $m_s = -\frac{1}{2}$ will lead to a lower energy than the interaction of moments of $m_I = -\frac{1}{2}$ and $m_s = -\frac{1}{2}$. Similarly the interaction of the moment from $m_s = +\frac{1}{2}$ and $m_I = -\frac{1}{2}$ will lead to a lower energy than interaction with $m_I = +\frac{1}{2}$. The energies of the levels are given by

$$E = g\beta H m_s + A m_s m_I$$

where A is referred to as the *hyperfine coupling constant*. Upon substitution of the proper values of m_s and m_I one obtains the energies indicated in Fig. 10-2. The selection rules in EPR are: $\Delta m_I = 0$ and $\Delta m_S = \pm 1$. The two peaks in the spectrum correspond to the transitions shown in Fig. 10-2b where Δm_I does not change and $\Delta m_S = \pm 1$. The energies for the two transitions observed are then $g\beta H \pm \frac{1}{2}A$, and the separation between the two peaks (expressed in gauss or mc sec^{-1}) is just A, the hyperfine coupling constant. The splitting indicated in Fig. 10-2 implies a positive value for A. If A were negative, $m_s = -\frac{1}{2}$, $m_I = -\frac{1}{2}$ would be the low energy state. In general the sign of A cannot be determined from a simple spectrum.

The same argument can easily be extended to a single electron located on a nucleus with spin I other than $\frac{1}{2}$. For such a nucleus, the nuclear magnetic moment can take any of the $2I + 1$ values corresponding to the quantum numbers $-I, -I+1, \ldots, I-1, I$. As in the example in Fig. 10-2, where $I = \frac{1}{2}$, these orientations give rise to $2I + 1$ different nuclear energy states (one for every value of m_I), and when each of these couple with the electron moments ($m_s = \pm\frac{1}{2}$), $2I + 1$ lines result. Since these energy differences are very small, all levels are equally populated and the components will usually be of equal intensity and equal spacing.

The magnitude of the splitting, expressed in terms of a coupling constant, A, depends on the following factors: (1) the magnitude of the nuclear magnetic moment, (2) the electron spin density in the immediate vicinity of the nucleus (this is the Fermi contact interaction, which has been discussed in connection with coupling constants in NMR), and (3) an anisotropic effect which will be discussed later.

HYPERFINE SPLITTINGS IN VARIOUS STRUCTURES

An unpaired electron interacting with a nuclear spin I will give rise to $2I + 1$ lines, all of equal intensity and equal spacing, e.g., three lines are expected for an unpaired electron on nitrogen, where $I = 1$. We shall next consider the effect on the spectrum when the electron interacts with, i.e., is delocalized onto, several nuclei. For simplicity, the species shall be assumed to be rotating very rapidly in all directions, and orbital contributions shall be assumed absent. As an example, the methyl radical will be discussed. As illustrated in Fig. 10-3, addition of the nuclear spin

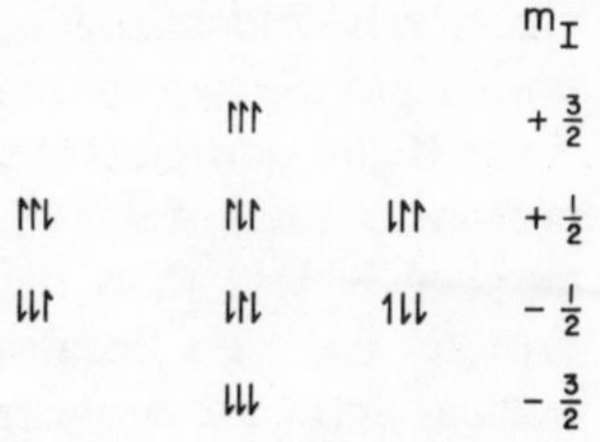

m_I

↑↑↑ $+\frac{3}{2}$

Fig. 10–3. Possible Nuclear Spin Arrangements   ↑↑↓   ↑↓↑   ↓↑↑ $+\frac{1}{2}$
of the Protons in a Methyl Radical.

↓↓↑   ↓↑↓   ↑↓↓ $-\frac{1}{2}$

↓↓↓ $-\frac{3}{2}$

angular momentum quantum numbers of the individual protons results in four different values for the total nuclear spin moment. As indicated in Fig. 10-4, this gives rise to four transitions ($\Delta m_I = 0$, $\Delta m_S = \pm 1$). Since there are three different ways to obtain a total of $m_I = +\frac{1}{2}$ or $-\frac{1}{2}$ (see Fig. 10-3), but only one way to obtain $m_I = +\frac{3}{2}$ or $-\frac{3}{2}$, the former system is three times more probable than the latter and the observed relative intensities for the corresponding transitions (Fig. 10-4) are in the ratio $1:3:3:1$.

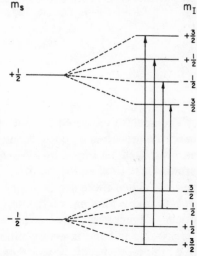

m_s m_I

$+\frac{1}{2}$

$+\frac{3}{2}$
$+\frac{1}{2}$
$-\frac{1}{2}$
$-\frac{3}{2}$

Fig. 10–4. The Four Transitions that Occur in the EPR Spectrum of the Methyl Radical (See Fig. 10–5 for the Spectrum).

$-\frac{1}{2}$

$-\frac{3}{2}$
$-\frac{1}{2}$
$+\frac{1}{2}$
$+\frac{3}{2}$

In general, when the absorption spectrum is split by n *equivalent* nuclei of equal spin I_i, the number of lines is given by $2nI_i + 1$. When the splitting is caused by both a set of n equivalent nuclei of spin I_i and a set of m equivalent nuclei of spin I_j the number of lines is given by $(2nI_i + 1)$

$(2mI_j + 1)$. The following specific cases illustrate the use of these general rules.

(1) If a radical contains n nonequivalent protons onto which the electron is delocalized, a spectrum consisting of 2^n lines will arise corresponding to the two spin states $(m_I = \pm\frac{1}{2})$ for n protons.

(2) If the odd electron is delocalized over a number, n, of equivalent protons, a total of $n + 1$ lines, $(2nI + 1)$, will appear in the spectrum. This number is less than the number of lines expected for nonequivalent protons (i.e., 2^n) because several of the possible arrangements of the nuclear spins are degenerate (see Fig. 10-3). The spectrum of the methyl radical illustrated in Fig. 10-5 contains the four peaks expected from these considerations.

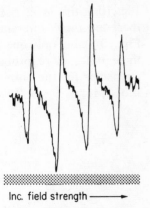

Inc. field strength ———►

Fig. 10–5. The Derivative Spectrum of the Methyl Radical in a CH_4 Matrix at 4.2°K. Asterisk indicates Calibration peak from Diphenylpicrylhydrazyl (DPPH). From F. J. Adrian, et. al., *Advan. Chem. Ser.,* **36**, 50 (1962).

The spectra expected for differing numbers of equivalent protons can easily be predicted by considering the splitting due to each proton in turn, as illustrated in Fig. 10-6. When the signal is split by two equivalent protons, the total m_I for the three levels can have the values $\Sigma m_I = +1, 0,$ and -1. Since there are two ways in which we can arrange the separate m_I's to give a total $m_I = 0$ (namely $+\frac{1}{2}, -\frac{1}{2},$ and $-\frac{1}{2}, +\frac{1}{2}$), the center level is doubly degenerate. Three peaks are observed in the spectrum ($\Delta m_I = 0,$ $\Delta m_S = 1$), and the intensity ratio is $1:2:1$. The case of three protons (e.g., the methyl radical) was dicusssed above and similar considerations are employed for the systems represented in Fig. 10-6 with more than three protons.

In general, the total number of peaks expected for an electron delocalized over n equivalent protons is given by $n + 1$ (i.e., $2nI + 1$), and the relative intensities of the peaks are given by the coefficients of the binomial expansion. It should be remembered in applying this formula that it is restricted to equivalent protons.

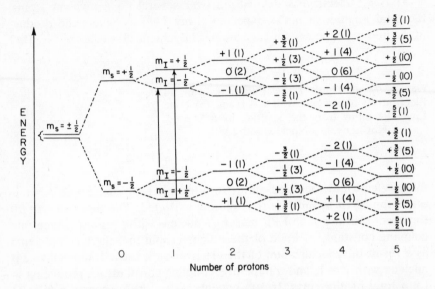

Fig. 10–6. Hyperfine Energy Levels Resulting from Interaction of an Unpaired Electron with Varying Numbers of Equivalent Protons [See A. Carrington, *Quart. Revs.*, **17**, 1963).] Each number in parentheses gives the degeneracy of the level to which it refers, and hence the relative peak intensities for the corresponding transitions.

(3) If the odd electron is delocalized over two sets of nonequivalent protons, the number of lines expected is the product of the number expected for each set $[(2nI_i + 1)(2mI_j + 1)]$. The naphthalene negative ion, which can be prepared by adding sodium to naphthalene, contains an odd electron which is delocalized over the entire naphthalene ring. Naphthalene contains two different sets of four equivalent protons. A total of $n + 1$, or five peaks, is expected for an electron delocalized on either set of four equivalent protons. In the naphthalene negative ion, the two sets of four equivalent protons should give a total of twenty-five lines in the ESR spectrum. This is found experimentally.

(4) If the electron is delocalized on nuclei with spin greater than $\frac{1}{2}$, a procedure similar to that for protons can be applied to calculate the number of peaks expected. If the electron is delocalized over several equivalent nuclei which have spins greater than $\frac{1}{2}$, the number of peaks expected in the spectrum is predicted from the formula: $2nI + 1$. For example, five peaks are expected for an electron delocalized on two

equivalent nitrogen atoms. A procedure similar to that in Fig. 10-3 shows that the intensities of the five peaks will be in the ratio $1 : 2 : 3 : 2 : 1$.

(5) If the electron is delocalized over several nonequivalent atoms, the total number of peaks expected is obtained by taking the product of the number expected for each atom. The scheme illustrated in Fig. 10-7

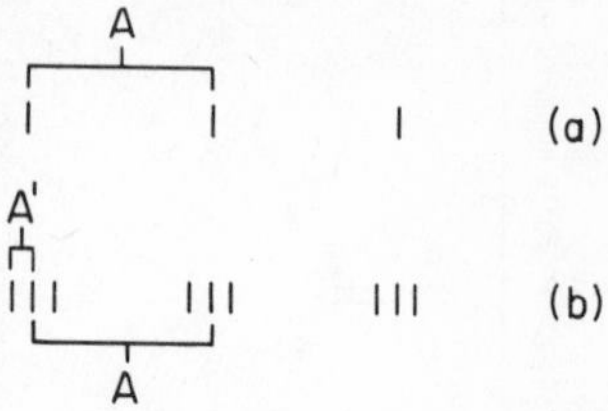

Fig. 10-7. (a) Three Lines Expected from an Electron on a Nucleus with $I = 1$ and (b) Nine Lines Resulting from the Splitting by a Second Nonequivalent Nucleus with $I = 1$.

for an electron delocalized onto two nonequivalent nuclei with $I = 1$ is often employed to indicate the splitting expected. The three lines in (a) represent splitting of an EPR peak by a nucleus with $I = 1$ and a hyperfine coupling constant, A. Each of these lines is split into three components as a result of delocalization of the electron on a second, nonequivalent nucleus with $I = 1$, and a hyperfine coupling constant, A', producing in (b) a total of nine lines. In subsequent discussions a scheme similar to that in Fig. 10-7 will be employed for the interpretation of spectra. The shape of the spectrum and the separations of the peaks will depend upon H, g, and the coupling constants A and A'. Frequently the measured spectrum will not contain all the lines expected, because the g and A values can be such that two lines come very close to one another and are not resolved. For example, the spectrum in Fig. 10-8 could result for the hypothetical radical $H—\overset{\cdot}{X}{}^+ \leftrightarrow \overset{\cdot}{H}—X^+$ where $I = 1$ for X. The two lines in (a) result from the proton splitting. In (b) each line in turn is split into three components due to interaction with nucleus X; thus we would expect six lines, all of equal intensity. Theoretically, it is possible however, to detect only five lines, because the two innermost components are not resolved. They would give rise to a single peak with twice the area of the other peaks (see Fig. 10-8).

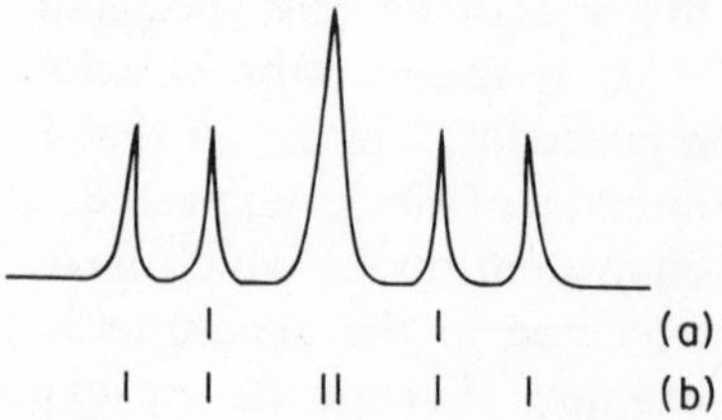

Fig. 10-8. Hypothetical Absorption Spectrum for the Radical $H \cdot X^+$ ($I = 1$ for X).

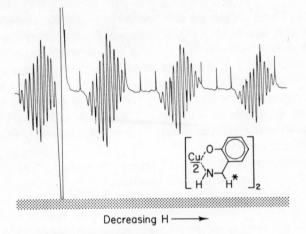

Decreasing H ⟶

Fig. 10–9. EPR Derivative Spectrum of Bis-salicylaldimine copper(II) with Isotopically Pure Cu^{63}. Asterisk indicates calibration peak from DPPH. From A. H. Maki and B. R. McGarvey, *J. Chem. Phys.*, **29**, 35 (1958).

The EPR spectrum of bis-salicylaldimine-copper-(II)[1] (Fig. 10-9) is an interesting example summarizing this discussion. Four main groups of lines result from coupling of the Cu^{63} nucleus ($I = \frac{3}{2}$) with the electron. The hyperfine structure in each of the four groups consists of eleven peaks of intensity ratio $1:2:3:4:5:6:5:4:3:2:1$. These peaks result from splitting by the two equivalent nitrogens and two hydrogens, H′ in Fig. 10-9. The total number of peaks expected is fifteen; $(2n_N I_N + 1)$ $(2n_H I_H + 1) = 5 \times 3 = 15$. The eleven peaks found for each subgroup in the actual spectrum result from overlap of some of the fifteen peaks as indicated in Fig. 10-10.

The splittings by the two equivalent nitrogens are indicated in (b) and the subsequent splitting by two equivalent protons is indicated in (c). The two nitrogens split the resonance into five peaks of relative intensity

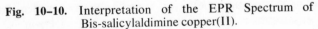

Fig. 10–10. Interpretation of the EPR Spectrum of Bis-salicylaldimine copper(II).

$1:2:3:2:1$. These values are denoted in (b) by $4d$, $4e$, and $4f$ where the intensities correspond to $d=1$, $e=2$, and $f=3$. The splitting by two equivalent protons will give rise to three lines for each line in (b), with an intensity ratio of $1:2:1$. The intensities indicated by letters underneath the lines in (c) result from the summation of the expected intensities. Since the relative intensities are $d=1$, $e=2$, and $f=3$, the ratio of the intensity of the bands in (c) is $1:2:3:4:5:6:5:4:3:2:1$. The experimental spectra agree with this interpretation which is further substantiated by the following results:

(1) Deuteration of the N—H″ groups (see Fig. 10-9) produced a compound which gave an identical spectrum.

(2) When the H′ hydrogens were replaced by methyl groups, the EPR spectrum for this compound consisted of four main, groups, each of which consisted of five lines resulting from nitrogen splitting only. The hyperfine splitting by the N—H″ proton and that by the protons on the methyl group are either too small to be detected or nonexistent.

This spectrum furnishes conclusive proof of the delocalization of the odd electron in this complex onto the ligand. This can be interpreted only as covalence in the metal-ligand interaction.

FACTORS AFFECTING THE MAGNITUDE OF THE g VALUES

The value of g for an unpaired electron in a gaseous atom or ion, for which Russell-Saunders coupling is applicable, is given by the expression

$$g = 1 + \frac{J(J+1)+S(S+1)-L(L+1)}{2J(J+1)} \tag{10-3}$$

where S, L, and J are the same quantities as those defined in Appendix A. For a free electron ($S=\frac{1}{2}$, $L=0$, $J=\frac{1}{2}$), the value of $g=2.0$ is easily calculated from equation (10-3). The actual value for a free electron is 2.0023 where the contribution 0.0023 is due to a relativistic correction. For the halogen atoms in the gas phase, g values predicted by equation 10-3 have been found to agree exactly with experimental values.[2] All halogen atoms have the same ground state term[2] ($P_{3/2}$, $L=1$, $S=\frac{1}{2}$, $J=\frac{3}{2}$); substitution of these values into equation (10-3) yields $g=\frac{4}{3}$, identical with the experimental value. No such agreement is found, however, when the unpaired electron is placed in a chemical environment, either in a free radical, or in a transition metal ion complex crystal lattice. In such a chemical environment the orbital motion of the electron is strongly perturbed and the orbital degeneracy, if it existed before application of the chemical environment, is partly removed or "quenched." Jahn-Teller distortions also serve to remove orbital degeneracy. On the other hand, a certain amount of orbital degeneracy tends to be sustained as the result of spin-orbit coupling, i.e., complete removal of the orbital degeneracy is prevented by spin-orbit coupling but higher fold degeneracies are often decreased by this effect. Qualitatively, this "sustaining effect" implies that if an electron has orbital angular momentum, this is maintained by coupling to the spin angular momentum, and if it has a spin angular momentum this tends to generate orbital angular momentum. Consequently, because of the quenching and sustaining competition, the orbital degeneracy is partly but not completely removed and a net orbital magnetic moment results, giving rise to a g value different from the value 2.0023 expected if the orbital degeneracy were completely removed.

In most free radicals the orbital contributions to the magnetic moment are very small because either the molecule has low symmetry or else if the gross symmetry of the molecule allows degenerate energy levels, the degeneracy is destroyed by Jahn-Teller distortion. Moreover, spin-orbit coupling in free radicals is very small. As a result, the g values are nearly equal to the free electron value of 2.0023. The small deviations (± 0.05, or smaller) often observed for most radicals are accounted for by a mixing of low-lying excited states with the ground state[3]. Thus, g values for free radicals are of limited use. Only when there are significant deviations from the free-electron value, can some information be gained about the nature of the excited states. With transition metal ions, however, the situation is much more complicated and interesting.

The properties of the transition metals are determined to a large extent by the relative magnitudes of the crystal field and spin-orbit coupling. As we saw in the preceding section, these two interactions have opposite effects on the orbital degeneracy. We can distinguish three cases:

(1) The effect of spin-orbit coupling is much larger than that of the crystal field. The rare-earth ions fall in this class because the f-electrons are well shielded from the crystal field effects so that LS coupling is not disturbed and J is a good quantum number. Thus the rare-earth ions are very much like free ions, and as can be seen in Appendix A magnetic moments calculated by equation (10-3) give very good agreement with experimental values.

(2) The effect of the crystal field is strong enough to break the coupling between L and S; hence J is no longer a good quantum number. The splitting of the m_L levels is large (i.e., the orbital degeneracy is quenched) and the EPR transitions are described by the selection rule $\Delta m_s = \pm 1$.

The first row transition metals fall into this category. As noted in Appendix A, the magnetic moments cannot be calculated by equation (10-3), but correspond more nearly to the "spin-only" value (equation A-1 (Appendix A) where $g = 2$). As noted above the orbital degeneracy is not removed completely because of the effect of spin-orbit coupling. Consequently a net orbital magnetic moment results, giving rise to a g value different from the free electron value expected if the orbital degeneracy were completely removed, but closer to 2.0023 than predicted by equation (10-3). Ions which have an orbitally nondegenerate ground state such as $Fe^{3+}(^6S)$ and $Mn^{2+}(^6S)$ give g values nearly equal to the free-electron value, since there is practically no orbital angular momentum. The small deviation from the free electron value is due to slight spin-orbit coupling.

(3) In the strong field case, the effect of the crystal field is very large so that LS coupling is broken down completely. This corresponds to covalent bonding and is applicable to the complexes of the $4d$ and $5d$ transition metals and to the strong-field complexes of the $3d$ transition metals, such as the cyanides. In many of these cases a molecular orbital description gives better results than the crystal field approximation.

We shall now consider briefly two specific examples to illustrate what factors determine the magnitude of the g values. For octahedral nickel (II) complexes, calculations,[4] which include mixing of the $^3A_{2g}$ ground state with the $^3T_{2g}$ excited state, give the following equation for the g value:

$$g = 2 - 8\lambda/10Dq \qquad (10\text{-}4)$$

where λ is the spin orbit coupling constant. In hexaquonickel(II), it is found experimentally that $g = 2.25$ hence $8\lambda/10Dq$ must equal 0.25. From the electronic spectrum one can calculate $10Dq = 8500$ cm^{-1} producing $\lambda = -270$ cm^{-1}. In the complex, λ is reduced considerably from the free ion value of -324 cm^{-1}. In a molecular orbital description[5] the extent to which λ is lowered from the free-ion value is a measure of the extent of mixing of metal and ligand orbitals. This example illustrates how both spin orbit coupling and Dq can affect the magnitude of the g value.

Our second example, Cu^{2+} in a tetragonal field, is illustrated in Fig. 10-11. The expressions derived for the g values are:[5,6,7]

$$g_{||} = 2 - 8\lambda/(E_2 - E_0) \qquad g_{\perp} = 2 - 2\lambda/(E_3 - E_0)$$

where E_0, E_2, and E_3 are the energies illustrated in Fig. 10-11. If the energy differences $E_2 - E_0$ and $E_3 - E_0$ are obtained or estimated from absorption spectra, and $g_{||}$ and $g_{\perp}$ are measured from the EPR spectrum, the spin-orbit coupling constant can be evaluated. It can also be seen from

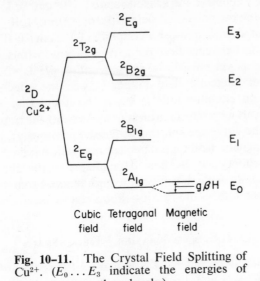

Cubic   Tetragonal   Magnetic
field   field   field

Fig. 10–11. The Crystal Field Splitting of Cu^{2+}. $(E_0 \ldots E_3$ indicate the energies of these levels.)

these equations that the g value approaches 2.0 as the splitting of the energy levels increases. This illustrates the importance of excited state mixing in distorted complexes.

Calculations of this sort can also be employed to indicate the nature of the orbital of the unpaired electron. For example, it has been demonstrated[8] that the unpaired electron in copper(II) acetylacetonate is not in a 4p-like orbital as had been predicted earlier by a simple application of valence bond theory.

The magnitude of the g tensor gives considerable information about ground and excited states in complexes. This application is involved, and the reader is referred to discussions by Carrington and Longuet-Higgins,[9] Roberston,[10] and Ballhausen,[4] for other examples.

INTERACTIONS AFFECTING THE ENERGIES OF UNPAIRED ELECTRONS IN TRANSITION METAL ION COMPLEXES

It may be of interest to consider briefly all the interactions to which unpaired electrons in a transition metal ion are subjected as well as their approximate magnitudes for first row transition metal complexes:

$$W = W_F + V + W_{LS} + W_{SS} + \beta H(L + 2S) + W_N - \gamma \cdot \beta_N \cdot \mathbf{H} \cdot \mathbf{I} \quad (10\text{-}5)$$

W is the energy of the ion in a complex, and the values in parentheses which follow give orders of magnitude for the energies: W_F includes the energies in the free ion in the gaseous state ($\sim 10^5$ cm^{-1}); V is the electrostatic energy due to the crystal field (10^3 to 10^4 cm^{-1}); W_{LS} refers to the energy associated with spin-orbit coupling ($\sim 10^2$ cm^{-1}); W_{SS} is the magnetic interaction between electron spins (~ 1 cm^{-1}) (this effect has not been discussed as yet but will be subsequently); $\beta H(L + 2S)$ is the effect of the external magnetic field (1 cm^{-1}), i.e., the effect discussed in conjunction with equation (10-1); W_N is the interaction of the nuclear moment (if $I \neq 0$) with the electron spin undergoing the transition ($\sim 10^{-2}$ cm^{-1}) (this is the hyperfine splitting discussed previously); $\gamma \cdot \beta_N \cdot \mathbf{H} \cdot \mathbf{I}$ is the effect of the magnetic field on the nuclear magnetic moment ($\sim 10^{-3}$ cm^{-1}) (this effect accounts for the field dependence of the chemical shift in NMR but is usually negligible in ESR experiments). From this discussion, the order of magnitude of the various effects can be ascertained.

Zero-field Splitting and Kramers' Degeneracy

Before treating the problem of how many EPR peaks are expected for transition metal ion complexes, the topics zero-field splitting and Kramers' degeneracy must be discussed. As mentioned previously, when a metal ion is placed in a crystalline field, the degeneracy of the d orbitals will be resolved by the electrostatic interactions (V in equation 10-5). The spin degeneracy will remain until a magnetic field is applied. When the species contains more than one unpaired electron, the spin degeneracy can also be resolved by the crystal field. Thus the *spin levels* may be split even in the absence of a magnetic field; this phenomenon is called *zero-field splitting*. However, when the species contains an odd number of unpaired electrons, the spin degeneracy of every level remains doubly degenerate; this is known as *Kramers' degeneracy*.[11] For an even number of unpaired electrons, the spin degeneracy may be removed entirely by the crystal field. These concepts and the consequences of zero-field splitting will be illustrated with a few examples.

Consider the case of a molecule or ion with two unpaired electrons, i.e., $S = 1$ and $m_S = -1, 0, +1$. (The total spin quantum number S is the sum of the spin quantum numbers of each of the unpaired electrons.) In the absence of zero-field splitting, the two possible transitions, $0 \rightarrow +1$, $-1 \rightarrow 0$ ($\Delta m_S = \pm 1$), are degenerate and only one signal is observed in the EPR spectrum (Fig. 10-12a). Zero-field splitting removes the degeneracy in m_S as indicated in Fig. 10-12b. When subsequent splitting by the applied field occurs, the two resulting transitions are not degenerate. As a result, in this example, two peaks are observed in the spectrum when zero-field splitting exists but only one when it is absent. Fig. 10-12b is the energy level diagram for the splitting of the ground state, $^3A_{2g}$, of Ni ^{II} in an octahedral field.

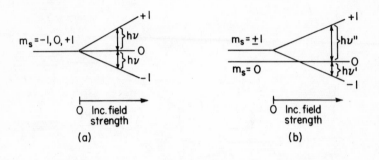

Fig. 10-12. The Energy Level Diagram and Spectrum for a Molecule or Ion with $S = 1$, (a) in the Absence of and (b) in the Presence of Zero-field Splitting.

The splitting of other metal ions can be described by procedures similar to those employed in Fig. 10-12. The energy level diagram for $Mn^{II}(d^5)$ is represented in Fig. 10-13. This is an interesting example, because there are an odd number of electrons and Kramers' degeneracy must exist. The term symbol for the free ion ground state is ^6S. As indicated in Fig. 10-13, the zero-field splitting produces three doubly degenerate spin states ($m_S = \pm\frac{5}{2}, \pm\frac{3}{2}, \pm\frac{1}{2}$) (Kramers' degeneracy). Each of these is split into two singlets by the applied field, producing six levels. As a result of this splitting, five transitions ($-\frac{5}{2} \rightarrow -\frac{3}{2}, -\frac{3}{2} \rightarrow -\frac{1}{2}, -\frac{1}{2} \rightarrow \frac{1}{2}, \frac{1}{2} \rightarrow \frac{3}{2}, \frac{3}{2} \rightarrow \frac{5}{2}$) are expected. The spectrum is further complicated by the hyperfine splitting due to the manganese nucleus ($I = \frac{5}{2}$). Thus, five peaks each split into six hyperfine components are expected.

In contrast to hyperfine splitting, the term *fine splitting* is used when an absorption band is split because of nondegeneracy arising from zero-field splitting. Components of fine splitting have varying intensities: the intensity is greatest for the central lines and smallest for the outermost lines. The separation between lines varies as $3 \cos^2 \theta - 1$, where θ is again the angle between the direction of the field and the z axis.

In certain cases, the magnitude of the zero-field splitting exceeds the energies of ususl EPR transitions e.g., in V^{3+}. When this happens it is not possible to observe EPR transitions with $\Delta m_S = \pm 1$, but it has been possible to observe a weak transition corresponding to $\Delta m_S = 2$, i.e., between the $m_S = \pm 1$ levels. The line was further split into eight components,[12] since $I = \frac{7}{2}$ for V^{51}.

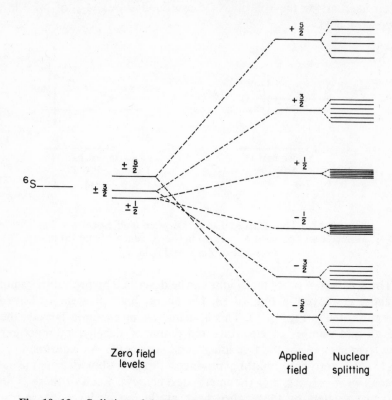

Fig. 10–13.   Splitting of the Levels in the Octahedral Mn^{II} Complex. Reproduced in part from D. J. E. Ingram, "Spectroscopy at Radio and Microwave Frequencies," Butterworths, London, 1955.

We shall now discuss the topic of effective spin, S'. When a metal ion is subjected to a cubic crystal field and the lowest state is an orbital singlet, (e.g., an A state) then the splitting of the spin degeneracy is generally small and the effective spin S' is equivalent to the electronic spin. Assuming that zero-field splitting is operative, we would then expect $2S$ transitions. An example is Ni^{2+} (d^8) which has a $^3A_{2g}$ ground state in an octahedral field and shows two transitions in the EPR spectrum. However, when the cubic field leaves an orbitally degenerate ground state (e.g., a T state), the effect of lower symmetry fields and spin-orbit coupling will resolve this degeneracy as well as the spin degeneracy. In the case of an odd number of unpaired electrons, Kramers' degeneracy leaves the lowest spin state doubly degenerate. If the splitting is large, this doublet will be well isolated from higher lying doublets. Transitions will then be observed only in the low lying doublet, and the effective spin will appear to have a value of only $\frac{1}{2}$ ($S' = \frac{1}{2}$). An example is Co^{2+}. The cubic field leaves a ^4F ground state which, as a result of lower symmetry fields and spin orbit coupling, gives rise to six doublets. The lowest doublet is separated from the next by about 200 cm^{-1}. Thus, the effective spin has a value of $\frac{1}{2}$ ($S' = \frac{1}{2}$) instead of $\frac{3}{2}$ ($S = \frac{3}{2}$).[13] The application of these concepts to various transition metal ions in different crystalline fields has been treated in detail[13] and the predicted splittings correlated with experimental results.

The magnitude of the zero-field splitting in transition metal ions can generally be described as arising from the crystal field. However, we have seen above that Mn^{2+} (d^5) which has a spherically symmetric electron distribution, so that the ^6S ground state is not split by the crystal field, also shows a zero-field splitting. Spin-orbit coupling mixes excited states which are split by the crystal field, and this mixing gives rise to a small zero field splitting in Mn^{2+}. The spin-spin interaction (W_{SS} in equation (11-5)) has a negligible effect. However, for biradicals ($S = 1$) the spin-spin term is often solely responsible for the zero-field splitting. The triplet state of naphthalene will be discussed as an example.[14]

It has been known for some time that complex organic molecules, such as naphthalene, phosphoresce after being optically excited. After the molecule which has a singlet ground state is excited to the first singlet excited state, it loses energy and drops back to a lower lying triplet excited state. Radiative decay (phosphorescence) from the latter to the ground state is relatively slow, because the transition is multiplicity forbidden. Since the triplet state contains two unpaired electrons, it should in theory be possible to obtain an EPR spectrum. In the past, attempts to observe a spectrum on randomly oriented molecules have failed.

More recently the EPR spectrum has been obtained for a dilute single crystal of naphthalene in durene. This spectrum consists of two transitions, as expected if zero-field splitting is present. In the absence of a crystal field effect or spin-orbit coupling the magnitude of the zero-field splitting can only be explained in terms of spin-spin interaction between the two π electrons in the triplet state. Spin-orbit coupling would mix the singlet and triplet states, and limit the lifetime of the triplet state. This is inconsistent with the long lifetimes observed for the triplet state. Moreover, the g value obtained, $g = 2.0030$, indicates that there is very little spin-orbit coupling. However, spin-spin interaction, W_{SS}, can also split the spin degeneracy. This effect does not mix singlets and triplets and is not inconsistent with the observed lifetime of the triplet. It has been pointed out by van der Waals and de Groot[15] that spin-spin interaction in molecules of certain symmetry (e.g., naphthalene) makes the $\Delta m_S = 2$ transition allowed; this has indeed been observed.

ANISOTROPY IN THE HYPERFINE COUPLING CONSTANT

EPR spectra can be obtained for neutral radicals in the gas phase and for radicals or ions in the liquid or solid phase. Spectra in the gas phase are complicated, however, because excited rotational states are populated. Relatively simple spectra were obtained for the halogen atoms in the gas phase.[2] As mentioned earlier, these species exist in a $^2P_{3/2}$ state and give g values of 4/3. The degeneracy $(2J + 1)$ is four, leading to $2J$ transitions which are each split into $2I + 1$ components. This leads to a total number of $2J(2I + 1)$ lines, as was observed experimentally for F, Cl^{35}, and $Br,^{79}$ i.e., six lines for F and twelve for Cl and Br. In general, however, gas phase spectra are not so simple. Since rotational states in condensed media are nonquantized and orbital contributions are largely quenched, these effects are not encountered in EPR spectra which are obtained on samples in solution or in the solid state.

In an earlier discussion we have seen that anisotropy of the g value can occur. Only when the absorbing species is rotating rapidly in all directions or when it has spherical symmetry is the g value found to be isotropic. These same considerations are true for the hyperfine splitting constant. When the species is either rotating or spherically symmetric, the coupling constant is isotropic, and the energy of the transition, E (excluding fine splitting) is given by:

$$E = \mathbf{h}\nu = g\beta H_0 + Am_I \qquad (10\text{-}6)$$

When a radical is rigidly held in position, as in a solid matrix or in a crystal, the electron may be subjected to magnetic anisotropies, this effect can lead to an anisotropy in the hyperfine coupling constant. To account for this, the coupling constant is factored into an isotropic and an anisotropic part. The anisotropy in the coupling constant has the same angular dependence as the g value. Equation (10-6) can be rewritten to take account of anisotropy in both g and A:

$$E = \mathbf{h}\nu = (\tfrac{1}{3}g_{\parallel} + \tfrac{2}{3}g_{\perp})\beta H_0 + Am_I +$$

$$[\tfrac{1}{3}(g_{\parallel} - g_{\perp})\beta H_0 + Bm_1](3\cos^2\theta - 1) \quad (10\text{-}7)$$

where θ is the angle between the direction of the magnetic field and the z axis, A is called the isotropic coupling constant, and B is called the anisotropic coupling constant. It is seen readily that for a freely rotating radical, equation (10-7) reduces to equation (10-6). In a powdered sample the crystals are randomly oriented, and a wide range of angles are present. Consequently, it is found that the spectra of such samples consist only of broad lines. In a later section we shall see how A, the isotropic coupling constant, has been correlated with spin density in a variety of organic free radicals.

Since the nucleus is not affected by the external magnetic field directly but only indirectly according to the manner in which the neighboring electrons move, the magnitude of the coupling constant does not usually depend on the strength of the external field but, in those cases where the anisotropic contribution is important, only upon its direction.

The effect of anisotropy on the spectrum of a radical in a solid matrix is illustrated by the derivative spectrum of NO_2 in an argon matrix (Fig. 10-14). The three lines from the nitrogen hyperfine interaction

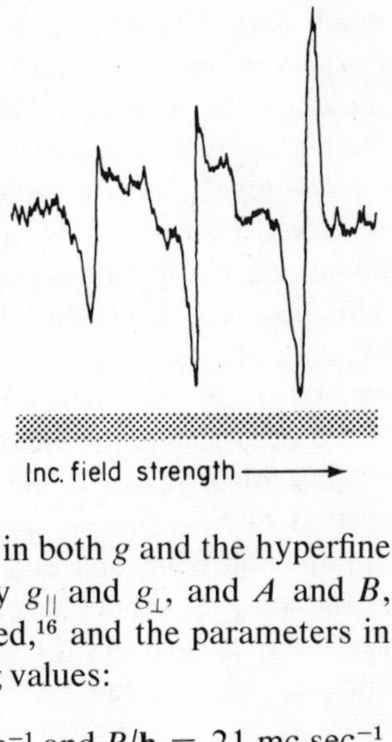

Fig. 10–14. EPR Spectrum of NO_2 in Solid Argon at 4.2°K. From F. J. Adrian, et al., *Advan. Chem. Ser.*, **36**, 50 (1962).

Inc. field strength ⟶

have variable widths indicating an anisotropy in both g and the hyperfine splitting, accounted for in equation (10-7) by $g_{\parallel}$ and $g_{\perp}$, and A and B, respectively. This spectrum has been analyzed,[16] and the parameters in equation (10-7) are found to have the following values:

$g_{\parallel} = 1.9920, g_{\perp} = 2.0033, A/\mathbf{h} = 146$ mc sec^{-1} and $B/\mathbf{h} = 21$ mc sec^{-1}.

The procedure for calculating the hyperfine coupling constants and g tensors from the spectrum has been described.[17] It was concluded from the NO_2 spectrum and from other data that the NO_2 molecule has axial symmetry in the argon matrix, because of very rapid rotation in the matrix about an axis which is perpendicular to the molecular symmetry axis.

The isotropic and anisotropic coupling constants derived above are usually applied only to free radicals. Although the same treatment could be used for metal ions, generally the coupling constant is expressed as A and B (or $A_{\parallel}$ and $A_{\perp}$) where, in a manner analogous to the anisotropic g values, $A(A_{\parallel})$ is the coupling constant parallel to the external field and $B(A_{\perp})$, the coupling constant perpendicular to the field.

NUCLEAR QUADRUPOLE INTERACTION

A nucleus which has a nuclear spin $I \geqq 1$ also has a quadrupole moment, and the unpaired electron interacts with both the nuclear magnetic moment and the electric quadrupole moment. The electric field gradient at the nucleus can interact with the quadrupole moment as in NQR and this interaction affects the spin energy states via the nuclear magnetic coupling as a second order perturbation. The effect of quadrupole interaction is usually complicated because it is accompanied by a much larger magnetic hyperfine interaction. The orientation of the nucleus is quantized with respect to both the electric field gradient and the magnetic field axis. When the magnetic field and the crystal axes are parallel, the only quadrupole effect is a small displacement of all the energy levels by a constant amount which produces no change in the observed transitions. However, when the two axes are not parallel, the effect is a competition between the electric field and the magnetic field. This has two effects on the spacing of the hyperfine lines: (1) a displacement of all energy levels by a constant amount and (2) a change in the separation of the energy levels which causes the spacing to be greater at the ends than in the middle.

This quadrupole effect can easily be distinguished from another second order effect which produces a gradual increase or decrease in the spacing from one end of the spectrum to the other. This variation in the spacing occurs when the magnetic field produced by the nucleus becomes comparable in magnitude to the external field. This kind of unequal spacing can be eliminated by increasing the applied magnetic field.

A further effect of this competition between the electric field and the magnetic field is the appearance of additional lines which are normally forbidden by the selection rule $\Delta m_I = 0$. Both $\Delta m_I = \pm 1$ and $\Delta m_I = \pm 2$ transitions are sometimes observed. The EPR spectrum[18] for K_2Cu $(SO_4)_2 \cdot 6H_2O$ is illustrated in Fig. 10-15. The four main peaks are due to the hyperfine splitting by Cu^{63} ($I = \frac{3}{2}$). Cu^{65} ($I = \frac{3}{2}$) has a slightly larger nuclear magnetic moment and should give rise to four peaks of which only two peaks, at the extremes of the spectrum, are resolved. The four small intensity transitions are the $\Delta m_I = \pm 1$ transitions which are also split into two components as a result of the different magnetic moments of

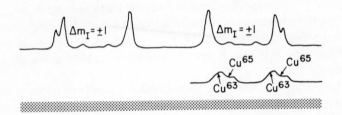

$\Delta m_I = \pm 1$ $\Delta m_I = \pm 1$ Cu^{65} Cu^{65} Cu^{63} Cu^{63}

Fig. 10–15.   EPR Spectrum for $CuK_2(SO_4)_2 \cdot 6H_2O$.

Cu^{63} and Cu^{65} nuclei. Two of these peaks are reproduced, on an expanded scale, in the lower right hand corner of the figure.

For most complexes the quadrupole interaction is small or not observed at all, but many of the Cu^{2+} complexes show a pronounced quadrupole interaction.

THE SPIN HAMILTONIAN

The *spin Hamiltonian* is a mathematical expression of the different interactions that exist in transition metal ions or radicals. It can be thought of as a shorthand way of representing the interactions described above. The EPR spin Hamiltonian for an ion in an axially symmetric field, i.e., tetragonal or trigonal (which includes most ions) is :

$$H = D[S_z^2 - \tfrac{1}{3}S(S+1)] + g_{||}H_zS_z + g_\perp(H_xS_x + H_yS_y) +$$
$$A_{||}S_zI_z + A_\perp(S_xI_x + S_yI_y) + Q'[I_z^2 - \tfrac{1}{3}I(I+1)] - \gamma\beta_N H_0 I \qquad (10\text{-}8)$$

The first term describes the zero-field splitting, the next two terms describe the effect of the magnetic field on the spin multiplicity remaining after zero-field splitting, the terms in $A_{||}$ and $A_\perp$ measure the hyperfine splitting parallel and perpendicular to the main axis, Q' measures the small changes in the spectrum produced by the quadrupole interaction. All of these effects have been discussed previously. The final term takes into account the fact that the nuclear magnetic moment μ_N can interact directly with the external field $\mu_N H_0 = \gamma\beta_N H_0 \cdot \mathbf{I}$, where γ is the nuclear magnetogyric ratio and β_N the nuclear Bohr magneton. This interaction can only affect the paramagnetic resonance when the unpaired electrons are coupled to the nucleus by nuclear hyperfine or quadrupole interactions. Even when such coupling occurs, the effect is usually negligible in comparison with the other terms.

In the case of a distortion of lower symmetry, the g values become g_x, g_y, and g_z; the hyperfine interaction constants become A_x, A_y and A_z, and two additional terms need to be included, i.e., $E(S_x^2 - S_y^2)$ as an additional zero-field splitting and $Q'' (I_x^2 - I_y^2)$ as a further quadrupole interaction. The symbols P and P' are often employed for Q' and Q'', respectively.

The importance of the spin Hamiltonian is that it provides a standard phenomenological way in which the EPR spectrum can be described in terms of a small number of constants. Once values for the constants have been determined from experiment, calculations relating these parameters back to the electronic configurations and the energy states of the ion are possible, but this process is often quite complicated. It should be remembered that if the effective spin S' is different from the spin S, S' should be substituted into the spin Hamiltonian. It should also be pointed out that not all terms in equation (10-8) are of importance for any metal ion. For a nucleus with no nuclear spin, all terms containing I are zero. In the absence of zero-field splitting, as in the case with Cu^{2+} or Ti^{3+}, the first term is equal to zero.

LINE WIDTHS IN SOLID STATE EPR

In this section we shall discuss briefly a number of factors, other than those which are instrumental, which affect line width. As in NMR, spin-lattice, spin-spin, and exchange interactions are important.

Broadening due to spin-lattice relaxation results from the interaction of the paramagnetic ions with the thermal vibrations of the lattice. The variation in spin-lattice relaxation times in different systems is quite large. For some compounds it is sufficiently long to allow the observation of spectra at room temperature, while in others this is not possible. Since relaxation times increase as the temperature decreases, many salts of the transition metals need to be cooled to liquid N_2, H_2, or He temperatures before good spectra are observed.

Spin-spin interaction results from the small magnetic fields that exist on neighboring paramagnetic ions. As a result of these fields, the total field at the ions is slightly altered and the energy levels are shifted. A distribution of energies results which produces broadening of the signal. Since this effect varies as $(1/r^3) \cdot (1 - 3 \cos^2 \theta)$, where r is the distance between ions and θ the angle between the field and the symmetry axis, this kind of broadening will show a marked dependence upon the direction of the field. The effect can be reduced by increasing the distance between paramagnetic ions by diluting the salt with an isomorphous diamagnetic material, for example: small amounts of $CuSO_4$ in a $ZnSO_4$ crystal.

Line widths are altered considerably by exchange processes. This effect can also be reduced by dilution. If the exchange occurs between equivalent ions, the lines broaden at the base and become narrower at the center. When exchange involves dissimilar ions, the resonances of the separate lines merge to produce a single broad line. Such an effect is observed for $CuSO_4 \cdot 5H_2O$ which has two distinct copper sites per unit cell.[19]

ELECTRON DELOCALIZATION

We have mentioned that evidence concerning electron delocalization could be obtained from the EPR spectrum. In some cases, the magnitude of the hyperfine interaction constant can be employed to measure the unpaired electron density on an atom in a delocalized system. For example, an odd electron in a $1s$ orbital of hydrogen gives rise to a hyperfine splitting constant, A, of 508 gauss. The magnitude of the splitting is mainly dependent upon nuclear spin-electron spin *contact interaction* (i.e., the isotropic hyperfine interaction constant A in equation (10-7)) which is a function of the probability of the electron being at the nucleus. For a free atom this dependence is expressed by the equation:

$$A_N = P_N \rho \qquad (10\text{-}9)$$

where A_N is the hyperfine constant in an atom N, ρ is the fraction of unpaired electrons in the valence state, and P_N is the hyperfine constant for a *single* electron in the valence state. (In the above example of a hydrogen atom $P_H = 508$.) As an example, if A_H were 20 in a certain molecule the spin density at the proton in that molecule is approximately $20/508 = 0.04$ from equation (10-9). The relative importance of structures which leave the unpaired electron localized on a hydrogen is negligible. Hence, spin densities at protons are quite small, usually falling in the range 0.04 to 0.96.

The π electron density *at the atom to which the hydrogen is bonded* can be obtained from the equation:

$$A_H = Q \rho^\pi \qquad (10\text{-}10)$$

where for the specific example of the odd electron in the π orbital of an sp^2 carbon containing a C—H bond, A_H would be the proton hyperfine constant, Q is the proton hyperfine constant for unit *spin density on the carbon,* and ρ^π is the spin density on the carbon. It should be emphasized that equation (10-10) refers to net spin density, i.e., ρ^π is the probability of an electron with spin up occupying the orbital minus the probability for an electron with spin down occupying the same orbital. The value for Q has been estimated from the spectrum of benzene negative ion which consists of seven peaks with A values of 3.75 gauss. The probability of the electron being at any one carbon is $\frac{1}{6}$ so substitution of $|A| = 3.75$ and $\rho = \frac{1}{6}$ into equation (10-10) yields $|Q| = 22.5$ gauss per unpaired electron. In the methyl radical, $\rho = 1$ and A is found to be 23 in excellent agreement with the Q value found for the benzene negative ion. The evidence for electron delocalization in the naphthalene negative ion was discussed previously. From the measured A values for the two nonequivalent α and β sets of protons the spin density at each of the α and β carbon atoms can be calculated using equation (10-10) with $|Q| = 22.5$. The values obtained in this way agree well with those calculated from simple molecular orbital theory. Similar studies have been carried out on the negative ions formed by nitrobenzene, toluene, xylene, and many other polyaromatic species. The positive ions formed when these species are oxidized by dissolving them in H_2SO_4 have also been investigated.

Extension of the above considerations to other atoms depends upon evaluation of P_N of equation (10-9) for electrons directly located on an atom. For systems in which the electron density on an adjacent atom is to be evaluated from proton hyperfine splitting, Q of equation (10-10) must be determined. The first problem has been treated theoretically[20] and is more complex than for an electron on a proton because more effects contribute to the magnitude of A. For an electron in a p orbital of C^{13}, contributions from carbon $1s$ electrons and from $2s$ electrons, the effect of a neighboring atom on the distribution of s character in the carbon bonds, and the effect whereby an unpaired π electron on a neighboring atom can induce through electron correlation net spin density in the σ bond, which involves the carbon atom, all must be considered in interpreting A.

APPLICATIONS

There have been several EPR investigations similar to that of the bis-salicylaldimine copper complex described above, in which evidence for electron delocalization into ligands is provided. The EPR spectrum of $IrCl_6^{2-}$ consists of a quartet of peaks due to splitting by the iridium nucleus. Each of these peaks contains hyperfine structure resulting from electron delocalization onto the chlorine atoms.[21] In molecular orbital terminology, the orbital containing the unpaired electron is composed of an appreciable fraction of chlorine orbitals. A valence bond formulation would give appreciable weight to a resonance form in which the metal orbitals contain paired electrons and chlorine has seven electrons.

From the extensive hyperfine splitting by the ligand in the bis-salicylaldimine copper complex (Fig. 10–9), it must be concluded that the metal-ligand bonds have a large amount of covalent character, and an accurate description of the bonding in this complex requires the use of a model which emphasizes covalence. The theory for the bis-salicylaldimine copper[1] complex and a number of similar complexes has been discussed extensively.[22]

In the molecular orbital model, the metal $3d$, $4s$, and $4p$ atomic orbitals are combined with the oxygen and nitrogen σ and π orbitals. Although strictly speaking the complexes considered only have D_{2h} symmetry, it is assumed that there is little difference between the oxygens and nitrogens and that the effective symmetry is D_{4h}. The combination of metal and ligand orbitals to produce molecular orbitals is indicated in Fig. 10-16. Since the odd electron involved in the EPR transition is in an antibonding orbital, and since any mixing with this orbital will also involve antibonding orbitals, our concern will be with these orbitals. The B_{1g}^{**} orbital is a σ antibonding orbital, B_{2g}^{**} is an in-plane (x–y) π antibonding orbital, and E_g^{**} are out-of-plane π antibonding orbitals (Fig. 10-16). The antibonding orbitals, important to the interpretation of the EPR spectrum,[1] can be represented by the following equations:[1]

$$B_{1g}^{**} = \alpha d_{x^2-y^2} - \alpha'(-\sigma_x^a + \sigma_y^b + \sigma_x^c - \sigma_y^d)/2$$

$$B_{2g}^{**} = \beta_1 d_{xy} - \beta_1'(p_y^a + p_x^b - p_y^c - p_x^d)/2$$

$$E_g^{**} \begin{cases} = \beta d_{xz} - \beta'(p_z^a - p_z^c)/\sqrt{2} \\ = \beta d_{yz} - \beta'(p_z^b - p_z^d)/\sqrt{2} \end{cases}$$

where α, β_1, and β are the coefficients related to the metal atomic orbital character of the molecular orbital. The primed coefficients are obtained by normalization of the molecular orbital. For example, normalization of the B_{1g}^{**} orbital gives: $\alpha^2 + \alpha'^2 - 2\alpha\alpha'S = 1$ where S is the overlap integral. The σ's and p's refer to the ligand σ and π orbitals.

The important terms in the spin Hamiltonian for Cu^{2+} (neglecting quadrupole effects) are:

$$H = \beta[g_{\parallel}H_zS_z + g_{\perp}(H_xS_x + H_yS_y)] + AI_zS_z + B(I_xS_x + I_yS_y)$$

Expressions can be derived to calculate $g_\parallel$, $g_\perp$, A, and B from the EPR spectra. Estimation of the energy differences $\Delta E_{xy} = E_{xy} - E_{x^2-y^2}$ and

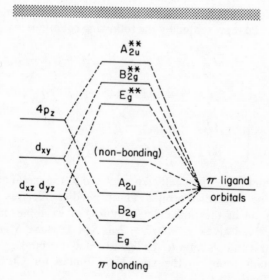

Fig. 10–16. Molecular Orbital Diagram for Planar Complexes of D_{4h} Symmetry.

$\Delta E_{xz} = E_{xz} - E_{x^2-y^2}$ from absorption spectra then allows values for α, β, and β_1 to be calculated.[1] For the bis-salicylaldimine copper complex, the following values were determined:[1] $\alpha^2 = 0.83$, $\beta^2 \geqslant 0.91$, $\beta_1{}^2 = 0.72$. The coefficient α describes the σ antibonding, and β_1 and β the in-plane and out-of-plane π antibonding, respectively. These values will range from 0.5 for a completely covalent bond to 1.0 for a completely ionic bond. The values given above for the bis-salicylaldimine copper complex indicate that the σ bonding is appreciably covalent and that the degree of π bonding is considerably greater in the plane than out of the plane. (A smaller value for β indicates more π bonding.)

Data for a number of Cu^{2+} complexes have been compiled by Kivelson and Neiman,[22] some of which are presented in Table 10-1.

TABLE 10-1. AN ANALYSIS OF THE EPR SPECTRA OF A NUMBER OF Cu^{2+} COMPLEXES

LIGAND	$g\|\| - 2.0023$	$g_\perp - 2.0023$	$\Delta E_{xy}(cm^{-1})$	$A(cm^{-1})$	α^2	$\beta_1{}^2$
Salicylaldimine	0.1981	0.0427	16,300	−0.0185	0.76	0.72
Histidine	0.2277	0.0607	15,600	−0.018	0.78	0.78
2,2′-Dipyridyl	0.2677	0.0797	14,900	−0.017	0.80	0.84
1,10-Phenanthroline	0.2777	0.0857	15,200	−0.015	0.76	0.95
Oxalate	0.3137	0.0757	15,400	−0.017	0.84	0.92
EDTA	0.3347	0.0877	13,900	−0.016	0.84	0.89
Citrate	0.3467	0.0717	13,700	−0.015	0.82	0.93

RATE OF ELECTRON EXCHANGE REACTIONS BY EPR

A strict analytical application of EPR involves rate studies of reactions which are not extremely fast, by simply following the signal intensity of a paramagnetic reactant or product as a function of time. In addition, very rapid electron exchange reactions can also be studied. For example, as naphthalene is added to a solution of naphthalene negative ion, an electron exchange reaction occurs which results in a broadening of the hyperfine components of the EPR resonance line. The broadening occurs because with rapid exchange the electron is subjected to a distribution of different internal fields by virtue of being on several different molecules. As with proton exchange in NMR, electron exchange results in an uncertainty in the field or frequency required to produce the transition. The additional width of the resonance line, $\Delta \nu$, is given by the equation:

$$\Delta\nu = (1/2\pi)(1/\tau) \qquad (11\text{-}11)$$

where τ is the mean jump time for an electron. For a process first order in naphthalene concentration, the following equation results:

$$k[\mathrm{N}] = 1/\tau = 2\pi\Delta\nu \tag{11-12}$$

where $[\mathrm{N}]$ is the naphthalene molarity. The calculated[23] rate constant for the exchange between naphthalene and potassium naphthalene negative ion in tetrahydrofuran is $(6 \pm 1) \times 10^7$ liters mole^{-1}. Very rapid electron rapid electron transfer reactions can be evaluated by this technique.

MISCELLANEOUS APPLICATIONS

When the EPR spectrum for $CuSiF_6 \cdot 6H_2O$, diluted with the corresponding diamagnetic Zn salt, was obtained at 90° K, the spectrum was found to consist of one band with partly resolved hyperfine structure and a nearly isotropic g value.[24] In a cubic field, the ground state of Cu^{2+} is orbitally doubly degenerate. Although $Cu(H_2O)_6SiF_6$ has trigonal rather than cubic symmetry, this orbital degeneracy is not destroyed. Thus Jahn-Teller distortion will occur. However, there are three distortions with the same energy that will resolve the orbital degeneracy. These are three tetragonal distortions with mutually perpendicular axes (elongation along the three axes connecting *trans* ligands). As a result three EPR transitions are expected, one for each species. Since only one transition was found, it was proposed that the crystal field resonates among the three distortions.[25] When the temperature is lowered, the spectrum becomes anisotropic and consists of three sets of lines corresponding to three different copper ions distorted by three different tetragonal distortions.[26] The transition takes place between 50° and 12° k; the three perpendicular tetragonal axes form the edges of a unit cube and the trigonal axis is the body diagonal. Other mixed copper salts have been found to undergo similar transitions: $(Cu,Mg)_3La_2(NO_3)_{12} \cdot 24D_2O$ between 33° and 45° K, and $(Zn,Cu)(BrO_3)_2 \cdot 6H_2O$, incomplete below 7°K. The following parameters were reported for $CuSiF_6 \cdot 6H_2O$:[27]

90° K	20° K
$g_{\parallel}$ 2.221 ± 0.005	$g_z = 2.46 \pm 0.01$
$g_{\perp}$ 2.230 ± 0.005	$g_x = 2.10 \pm 0.01$
A 0.0021 ± 0.0005 cm^{-1}	$g_y = 2.10 \pm 0.01$
B 0.0028 ± 0.0005 cm^{-1}	$A_z = 0.0110 \pm 0.0003$ cm^{-1}
	$\left.\begin{array}{c} A_x \\ A_y \end{array}\right\} < 0.0030$ cm^{-1}

No quadrupole interaction was resolved. A similar behavior (i.e., a resonating crystal field at elevated temperatures) was detected in the spectrum of some tris complexes of copper(II) with 2,2'-dipyridine and 1,10-phenanthroline.[28]

The EPR spectrum of the complex: $[(NH_3)_5Co—O—O—Co(NH_3)_5]^{5+}$ is an interesting example to demonstrate how structural information can be derived from spin density information and from hyperfine splitting. This complex can be formulated as: (1) two cobalt(III) atoms connected by an O_2^- bridge; (2) cobalt(III) and cobalt(IV) atoms connected by a peroxy, O_2^{2-} bridge; (3) two equivalent cobalt atoms due to equal interaction of one unpaired electron with both cobalt atoms; (4) interaction of the electron with both cobalt atoms but more with one than the other.

If (1) were the structure, a single line would result, while (2) would give rise to eight lines ($I = \frac{7}{2}$ for Co). Structure (3) would result in fifteen lines and (4) in sixty-four. It was found[29] that the spectrum consists of fifteen lines, eliminating the unlikely structures (2) and (4) and supporting appreciable contribution from (3). This result does not eliminate (1); and indeed when the cobalt hyperfine interaction constant is compared with that for other cobalt complexes, it is found to be low in this complex. This indicates appreciable contribution of (1) to the actual structure, because this removes electron density from the cobalt and, as indicated by equation (11-9), this will decrease A.

One of the advantages of EPR is its extreme sensitivity to very small amounts of paramagnetic materials. For example, under favorable conditions a signal for diphenylpicrylhydrazyl (DPPH) radical can be detected if there are 10^{-12} gram of material in the spectrometer. This great sensitivity has been exploited in a study of the radicals formed by heating sulfur. When sulfur is heated, the diamagnetic S_8 ring is cleaved to produce high molecular weight S_x chains which have one unpaired electron at each end. The chains are so long that the concentration of radicals is low, and paramagnetism cannot be detected with a Gouy balance. An EPR signal was detected,[30] and the number of unpaired electrons (which is proportional to the area under the absorption curve) was determined by comparing the area of this peak with the area of a peak resulting from a known concentration of added radicals from DPPH. The total number of radicals in the system is thus determined, and since the total amount of sulfur used is also known, the average molecular weight of the species $\cdot SS_xS\cdot$ can be calculated. The radical concentration at 300° C was $1.1 \times 10^{-3}M$, and the average chain length at 171° C was 1.5×10^6 atoms. By studying the radical concentration as a function of temperature, a heat of dissociation of the S—S bond of 33.4 kcal mole^{-1} per bond was obtained.

There have been several studies reported in which EPR has been employed to identify and provide structural information about radicals generated with high energy radiation.[31] The materials O_2^-, ClO, ClO_2, PO_3^{2-}, SO_3^-, and ClO_3 are among the many interesting radicals produced by this technique.

EXERCISES

1. Convert the derivative curves in Fig. 10-17 to absorption curves:

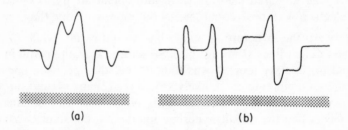

(a)   (b)

Fig. 10–17.   A Derivative Spectrum.

2. a. How many hyperfine peaks would be expected from delocalization of the odd electron in dibenzene chromium onto the rings?

    b. Using a procedure similar to that in Fig. 10-3, explain how the number of peaks arises and what the relative intensities would be.

3. a. Copper(II) acetate is a dimer, and the two copper atoms are shown by x-ray to be close enough to form a "copper-copper bond". The EPR spectrum consists of seven lines with intensity ratios $1:2:3:4:3:2:1$. Copper nuclei have an I value of $\frac{3}{2}$, and copper acetate consists of a ground state which is a singlet and an excited state which is a triplet. Explain the number and relative intensity of the lines in the spectrum. [For answer, see B. Bleaney and K. D. Bowers, *Proc. Roy. Soc. (London),* **A214**, 451 (1952).

    b. What would you expect to happen to the signal intensity as a sample of copper acetate is cooled? Why?

4. Predict the EPR spectrum for $(SO_3)_2NO^{2-}$

5. The mono negative ion 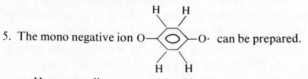 can be prepared.

    a. How many lines are expected in the spectrum, and what would be the relative intensities of these?

b. What evidence would you employ to indicate electron delocalization onto the oxygen?

c. The magnitude of A in this material is 2.37 gauss. Compare the spin density on hydrogen in this molecule with that on a hydrogen atom.

d. Using equation (10–10) calculate the spin density on the carbon atom. (For answer, see B. Venkataraman and G. K. Fraenkel, *J. Chem., Phys.,* **24**, 737 (1956)).

6. The C^{13} hyperfine coupling in methyl radical is 41 gauss and the proton hyperfine coupling is 23 gauss. Sketch the spectrum expected for $\cdot C^{13}H_3$ radical. (For answer, see T. Cole, et. al., *Mol. Phys.,* **1**, 406 (1958)).

7. Assume that all hyperfine lines can be resolved and sketch the spectrum for chlorobenzene ion radical.

8. Assuming all other factors constant, would line broadening be greater for a bimolecular process with a rate constant of 10^7 or 10^{10}?

9. How many lines would you expect in the EPR spectrum of:
   $(CN)_5CoO_2Co(NH_3)_5$. Explain.

10. The spectrum in Fig. 10-18 is obtained for the NH_2 radical:

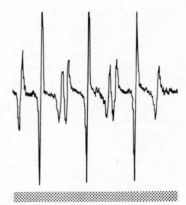

Fig. 10–18. Spectrum of the NH_2 Radical.

a. Convert it to a derivative spectrum.

b. How could you determine whether the larger or smaller splitting is due to hydrogen?

c. Assume the larger splitting is due to hydrogen. Construct a diagram similar to Fig. 10-7 to explain the spectrum.

11. a. How many lines would you expect in the spectrum of the hypothetical molecule SCl_3 (I for $S = O$ and $Cl = \frac{3}{2}$).

    b. Using a procedure similar to that in Fig. 10-4 and Fig. 10-5. explain how this number arises and indicate the transitions with arrows. State what the expected relative intensities would be.

12. Predict the number of spectral lines for:
    a. $Co(H_2O)_6^{2+}$.
    b. $Cr(H_2O)_6^{2+}$.
    Indicate how zero-field splitting and Kramers' degeneracy applies in these examples.

REFERENCES CITED

1. A. H. Maki and B. R. McGarvey, *J. Chem. Phys.*, **29**, 35 (1958).
2. N. Vanderkooi, Jr., and J. S. Mackenzie, *Advan. Chem. Ser.*, **36**, 98 (1962).
3. M. C. R. Symons, *Advan. Chem. Ser.*, **36**, 76 (1962).
4. C. J. Ballhausen, "Introduction to Ligand Field Theory," McGraw-Hill, New York, 1962.
5. D. Polder, *Physica*, **9**, 709 (1942).
6. A. Abragam and M. H. L. Pryce, *Proc. Roy. Soc. (London)*, **A205**, 135 (1951).
7. A. Abragam and M. H. L. Pryce, *Proc. Roy. Soc. (London)*, **A206**, 164 (1951).
8. T. Okamura and M. Date, *Phys. Rev.*, **94**, 314 (1954); A. H. Maki and B. R. McGarvey, *J. Chem. Phys.*, **29**, 31 (1958).
9. A. Carrington and H. C. Longuet-Higgins, *Quart. Revs.*, **14**, 427 (1960).
10. R. E. Robertson, "Determination of Organic Structures by Physical Methods," vol. 2, eds. F. C. Nachod and W. D. Phillips, Academic, New York, 1962.
11. H. A. Kramers, *Proc. Amsterdam Acad. Sci.*, **33**, 959 (1930); H. A. Kramers, "Quantum Mechanics," p. 384, North-Holland, Amsterdam, 1957.
12. G. M. Zverev and A. M. Prokhorov, *J. Exp. Theoret. Phys. (USSR)*, **34**, 1023 (1958); *Soviet Phys. JEPT*, (English Transl.), **7**, 707 (1958).
13. D. J. E. Ingram, "Spectroscopy at Radio and Microwave Frequencies," Butterworths, London, 1955.
14. C. A. Hutchinson, Jr., and B. W. Mangum, *J. Chem. Phys.*, **34**, 908 (1961). And references cited therein.
15. J. H. van der Waals and M. S. de Groot, *Mol. Phys.*, **2**, 333 (1959).
16. F. J. Adrian, *J. Chem. Phys.*, **36**, 1692 (1962).
17. D. S. Schonland, *Proc. Phys. Soc. (London)*, **73**, 788 (1959).
18. B. Bleaney, K. D. Bowers, and D. J. E. Ingram, *Proc. Phys. Soc. (London)*, **A64**, 758 (1951).
19. D. M. S. Bagguley and J. H. E. Griffiths, *Nature*, **162**, 538 (1948).
20. M. Karplus and G. K. Fraenkel, *J. Chem. Phys.*, **35**, 1312 (1961).
21. J. H. E. Griffiths, J. Owen, and I. M. Ward, *Proc. Roy. Soc.*, **A219**, 526 (1953).
22. D. Kivelson and R. Neiman, *J. Chem. Phys.*, **35**, 149 (1961).
23. R. L. Ward and S. I. Weissman, *J. Am. Chem. Soc.*, **79**, 2086 (1957).
24. B. Leaney and D. J. E. Ingram, *Proc. Phys, Soc.*, **63**, 408 (1950).
25. A. Abragam and M. H. L. Pryce, *Proc. Phys. Soc.*, **63**, 409 (1950).
26. B. Bleaney and K. D. Bowers, *Proc. Phys. Soc.*, **65**, 667 (1952).
27. B. Bleaney, K. D. Bowers, and R. S. Trenam, *Proc. Roy. Soc. (London)*, **A228**, 157 (1955).
28. H. C. Allen, Jr., G. E. Kokoszka, and R. G. Inskeep. *J. Am. Chem. Soc.*, **86**, 1023 (1964).
29. E. A. V. Ebeworth and J. A. Weil, *J. Phys. Chem.*, **63**, 1890 (1959).
30. D. M. Gardner and G. K. Fraenkel, *J. Am. Chem. Soc.*, **78**, 3279 (1956).
31. M. C. R. Symons, *Advan. Chem. Ser.*, **36**, 76 (1962). Gives more details of studies on the systems and cited literature.

GENERAL REFERENCES

R. Bersohn, "Determination of Organic Structures by Physical Methods," vol. 2, eds. F. C. Nachod and W. D. Phillips, Academic, New York, 1962.

A. Carrington, *Quart. Revs.,* **17**, 67 (1963). Highly recommended.

A. Carrington and H. C. Longuet-Higgins, *Quart. Revs.,* **14**, 427 (1960). Highly recommended.

D. J. E. Ingram, "Free Radicals Studied by ESR," Butterworths, London, 1955.

M. St. C. Flett, "Physical Aids to the Organic Chemist", Elsevier, Amsterdam, 1962.

D. J. E. Ingram, "Spectroscopy at Radio and Microwave Frequencies," Butterworths, London, 1955.

J. A. McMillan, *J. Chem. Educ.,* **38**, 438 (1961).

G. E. Pake, "Paramagnetic Resonance," W. A. Benjamin, New York, 1962. Highly recommended for EPR of transition metal ions.

R. E. Robertson, "Determination of Organic Structures by Physical Methods," vol. 2, eds. F. C. Nachod and W. D. Phillips, Academic, New York, 1962.

J. E. Wertz, *Chem. Revs.,* **55**, 829 (1955).

11 *Mössbauer Spectroscopy*

INTRODUCTION

Mössbauer spectroscopy, which will be abbreviated as MB spectroscopy in this text, involves nuclear transitions which result from the absorption of γ-rays by the sample. The conditions for absorption depend upon the electron density about the nucleus, and the number of peaks obtained is related to the symmetry of the compound. As a result considerable structural information can be obtained from MB spectra.

To understand the principles of this method, first consider a gaseous system consisting of a radioactive source of γ-rays and the sample which can absorb γ-rays. When a gamma ray is emitted by the source nucleus, it decays to the ground state. The energies of the emitted γ-rays, E_γ, have a range of 10 to 100 kev and are given by equation (11-1):

$$E_\gamma = E_r + D - R \tag{11-1}$$

where E_r is the difference in energy between the excited state and ground state of the source nucleus; D, the Doppler shift, is due to the translational motion of the nucleus, and R is the recoil energy of the nucleus. The recoil energy is generally 10^{-2} to 10^{-3} ev and is given by the equation:

$$R = E_\gamma^2/2mc^2 \tag{11-2}$$

where m is the mass of the nucleus and c is the velocity of light. The energy of a γ-ray emitted from a nucleus moving in the same direction as the emitted ray is different from the energy of a γ-ray emitted from a nucleus moving in the opposite direction. The distribution of energies resulting from the translational motion of the source nuclei in many directions is referred to as Doppler broadening. The left hand curve of Fig. 11-1 represents the distribution of energies of emitted γ-rays, E_γ, resulting from Doppler broadening. If the dotted line in Fig. 11-1 is taken as E_r, the energy difference between the nuclear ground and excited states of the source, then the breadth of the curve results from

Doppler broadening and the energy difference, R, between the dotted line and the average energy of the left hand curve is the recoil energy transmitted to the source nucleus when a γ-ray is emitted.

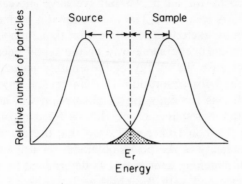

Fig. 11–1. Distribution of Energies of
Emitted and Absorbed γ-rays.

In MB spectroscopy the sample and source nuclei are the same, and the energy of the γ-ray absorbed for a transition in the sample is given by:

$$E_\gamma = E_r + D + R \qquad (11\text{-}3)$$

In this case, R is positive because the exciting γ-ray must have energy necessary to bring about the transition and effect recoil of the absorbing nucleus. The quantity D has the same significance as before. The curve in the right half of Fig. 11-1 shows the distribution of γ-ray energies necessary for absorption. The relationship of the sample and source energies can be seen from the entire figure. As indicated by the shaded region, there is only a very slight probability that the γ-ray energy from the source will match that required for absorption by the sample. Since the nuclear energy levels are quantized, there is accordingly a very low probability that the γ-ray from the source will be absorbed to give a nuclear transition in the sample. The main cause for nonmatching of γ-ray energies is the recoil energy. If this quantity, R, could be reduced, or if conditions for a recoilless transition could be found, the sample would have a higher probability of absorbing γ-rays from the source. As indicated by equation (11-2), R can be decreased by increasing, m, the mass. This can be effected by placing the nucleus of the sample and source in a crystal so that the mass is effectively that of the crystal. Because of the large mass of the crystal, the recoil energy will be small as indicated by equation (11-2). For this reason, MB spectra are almost always obtained on solids employing solid sources.

By placing our source and sample in solid lattices, we have not effected recoilless transitions for all nuclei but we have increased the probability of a recoilless transition. The reason for this is that the energy of the γ-ray may cause excitation of lattice vibrational modes. This energy term would function in the same way as the recoil energy in the gas, i.e., it would decrease the energy of the emitted particle and increase the energy required for absorption. Certain crystal properties and experimental conditions for emission or absorption will leave the lattice in its initial vibrational state, i.e., conditions for a recoilless transition will be satisfied. It should be emphasized that these conditions simply determine the intensity of the peaks obtained, for it is only the number of particles with matching energy that is determined by this effect. We shall not be concerned with the absolute intensity of a band so this aspect of MB spectroscopy will not be discussed. It should be mentioned however that for some materials (usually molecular and not ionic solids) lattice and molecular vibrational modes are excited to such an extent that very few recoilless transitions occur at room temperature and no spectrum is obtained. Frequently, the spectrum can be obtained by lowering the temperature of the sample appreciably. This subject is treated in references 1–4 which contain a more detailed discussion of the entire subject of MB spectroscopy.

Our main concern will be with the factors affecting the energy required for γ-ray absorption by the sample. There are three main types of interaction of the nuclei with the chemical environment that result in small changes in the energy required for absorption: (1) resonance line shifts from change in electron environment, (2) quadrupole interactions, and (3) magnetic interactions. These effects give us information of chemical significance and will be our prime concern.

Before discussing these factors, it is best to describe the procedure for obtaining spectra and to illustrate a typical MB spectrum. The electron environment about the nucleus in the sample affects the energy of the γ particle necessary to effect the *nuclear* transition in the sample from the ground to excited state. The energy of γ-rays from the source can be varied over the range of the energy differences arising from the electron environment by moving the source relative to the sample. The higher the velocity at which the source is moved toward the sample, the higher the average energy of the emitted γ-ray (by the Doppler effect) and vice versa. Obtaining a MB spectrum consists of moving the source relative to the sample until the source velocity at which maximum absorption of γ-rays occurs is determined. Consider, as a simple example, the MB spectrum of $Fe^{3+} Fe^{III}(CN)_6$ (Fe^{III} and Fe^{3+} designate strong and weak field iron (III)). This substance contains iron in two different chemical environments and two different energy γ-rays are required to effect transitions in the different iron nuclei. To obtain the MB spectrum, the source is moved toward the fixed sample at a certain velocity and the number of γ-rays passing through the sample are counted. The procedure is repeated for a whole series of source velocities, and the corresponding count is plotted (as in Fig. 11-2) to produce the MB spectrum. The peaks corres-

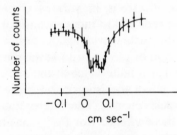

Fig. 11-2. MB Spectrum of FeFe(CN)$_6$.

pond to source velocities at which maximum γ-ray absorption by the sample occurs. Negative relative velocities correspond to moving the source away from the sample.

The relative velocity at which the source is being moved is plotted along the abscissa of Fig. 11-2, and this quantity is related to the energy of the γ-ray. For an Fe^{57} source emitting a 14.4 kev γ-ray, the energy is changed 4.8×10^{-7} ev or 0.011 cal mole^{-1} for every cm sec^{-1} velocity imposed upon the source. Referring back to the abscissa of Fig. 11-2, one sees that the energy difference in the nuclear transitions for Fe^{3+} and Fe^{III} in FeFe(CN)$_6$ is very small, corresponding to about 2×10^{-8} ev. It can thus be seen that the MB spectrum in Fig. 11-2 resembles IR, UV, and NMR spectra in that intensity is plotted against frequency or energy of the radiation.

The peak in the spectrum in Fig. 11-2 at 0.003 cm sec^{-1} is assigned[5] to Fe^{III} and that at 0.053 to the cation Fe^{3+} by comparison of this spectrum with those for a large number of cyanide complexes of iron. Different line positions which result from different chemical environments are indicated by the values for the source velocity in units of cm sec^{-1} or mm sec^{-1} and are referred to as *isomer shifts* or chemical shifts. The symbol δ is used to indicate an isomer shift. We shall now proceed with a brief, qualitative discussion of the various factors affecting line position and shape of MB spectra.

RESONANCE LINE SHIFTS FROM CHANGE IN ELECTRON ENVIRONMENT

The two different peaks in Fig. 11-2 arise from the isomer shift. The isomer shift arises because the electron density *at the nucleus* interacts with the positive nuclear charge, and the relative energies of the ground and excited nuclear states are affected in much the same way that positive nuclear charge affects the energy of the electrons. Depending on the relative change in energy between the ground and excited nuclear states by interaction with the electrons in various chemical environments, different energies will be required to induce transitions in various materials. The interaction of the nucleus with an electron will depend upon the value for the wave function of the electron at the nucleus. Only electron density in the *s* orbitals has a finite value at the nucleus, so electrons in *p, d,* and *f* orbitals can affect the isomer shift only by screening the *s* electrons from the nuclear charge. The interpretation of isomer shift data is complicated by these effects. For Fe^{57} it has been shown that increasing *s* electron density at the nucleus produces a negative shift in the value for δ; i.e., a smaller positive number or a larger negative number corresponds to greater *s* electron density at the nucleus. The shielding by the *3d* electrons has been computed[6] for iron(III) and the results applied[7] to the interpretation of isomer shift data in some spin-free iron complexes. A quantitative correlation between δ and *s* electron density is proposed in these complexes. The sign of the shift depends upon the difference between the effective nuclear charge radius, *r*, of the excited and ground states $(r_{ex}^2 - r_g^2)$. For the Fe^{57} nucleus the excited state is smaller than the ground state, and an increase in density produces a negative shift. This is not necessarily true for other isotopes.

It should be mentioned that the isomer shift measured is actually the difference in *s* electron density of the sample and the source. For Fe^{57} a value of zero indicates the same *s* electron density about the sample and source while a negative δ indicates the sample has more *s* electron density at the nucleus, and *vice versa*. Thus the composition and properties of the source are very important. These factors and other effects which contribute to the magnitude of the resonance line shifts have been reviewed.[1]

QUADRUPOLE INTERACTIONS

If the ground or excited nuclear configuration possesses a quadrupole moment, the energy levels in that state will be split to an extent, ΔE_Q, depending upon the magnitude of the quadrupole moment and the field gradient at the nucleus. This is the same type of splitting discussed in NQR spectroscopy. For a single asymmetric chemical environment about the nucleus, multiple peaks are obtained in the MB spectrum corres-

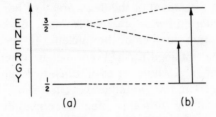

(a)   (b)

Fig. 11–3. Nuclear Energy Levels for the Ground and First Excited State of an Fe^{57} Nucleus. (a) Zero field gradient (b). An appreciable field gradient.

ponding to transitions involving different orientations of the quadrupole moment of the ground and/or excited states.

For Fe^{57}, the ground state has an I value of $\frac{1}{2}$, but the first excited state has a value of $\frac{3}{2}$. When there is no field gradient at the nucleus, the excited levels are degenerate; but in the presence of a field gradient, this level is split. In axially symmetric fields (linear, square planar, etc.) there

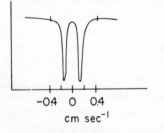

-04   0   04
cm sec^{-1}

Fig. 11–4. MB Spectrum for $Fe(CO)_5$ at Liquid Nitrogen Temperature. From L. M. Epstein, *J. Chem. Phys.*, **36**, 2731 (1962).

are $I + \frac{1}{2}$ different levels for half-integral spins ($\frac{3}{2}$, $\frac{5}{2}$, $\frac{7}{2}$, etc.) and $I + 1$ different levels for integral spins ($I = 1, 2, 3$, etc.). The splitting of the excited state will not occur in a spherically symmetric field but will only occur when there is a field gradient at the nucleus caused by asymmetric s electron distribution in a compound. A field gradient exists in the trigonal bipyramidal molecule iron pentacarbonyl, so a splitting of the nuclear excited state is expected. The two expected transitions (designated by arrows in Fig. 11-3) give rise to a doublet in the spectrum,[8] as indicated in Fig. 11-4.

MAGNETIC INTERACTIONS

This nuclear effect is analogous to the Zeeman splitting of atomic orbitals by a magnetic field. The magnetic field at the nucleus produced by the surroundings can interact with the nuclear magnetic moment. This interaction causes a removal of the degeneracy of nuclear energy levels. The number of different levels obtained from this effect is determined by the magnetic quantum number of the nucleus. In general $2I + 1$ values $(+I, \ldots, -I)$ can be obtained for a given nucleus where I is the nuclear spin quantum number. A whole series of transitions can occur to and from these different levels in the ground and excited state. The selection rule is: $\Delta I = 0, \pm 1$. Splitting from this effect is commonly observed only in ferromagnetic or antiferromagnetic crystals.

APPLICATIONS

Many applications of this technique which are mainly of interest to physicists have been summarized[1,2] but will not be discussed here. A few chemical applications have been selected for discussion which are illustrative of the kind of information that can be obtained from MB spectroscopy. Mössbauer resonances have been observed in the following nuclei: Au^{197}, Dy^{161}, Er^{166}, Fe^{57}, Gd^{155}, Ge^{73}, Hf^{177}, I^{127}, I^{129}, Ir^{191}, Ir^{193}, Ni^{61}, Pt^{195}, Re^{187}, Sb^{123}, Sn^{119}, Ta^{181}, Tm^{169}, W^{182}, Yb^{170}, Zn^{67}.

Facsimilies of spectra obtained on some iron complexes are given in Fig. 11-5. For spin-free iron complexes in which all six ligands are equivalent, a virtually spherical electric field at the nucleus is expected for $Fe^{3+}(d^5)$ but not for $Fe^{2+}(d^6)$. In the d^5 case each d orbital has one electron, producing a spherical charge distribution; but there is asymmetry for the spin-free d^6 case. As a result of the field gradients at the nucleus, quadrupole splitting should be detected in the spectrum of spin-free iron(II) complexes but not for spin-free iron(III) complexes. This is borne out in spectra A and B of the complexes illustrated in Fig. 11-5. For spin-paired complexes, iron(II) has a configuration t_{2g}^6 and iron(III) t_{2g}^5. As a result quadrupole splitting is now expected for iron(III) but not iron(II) in the strong field complexes. This conclusion is confirmed experimentally by the spectra of ferrocyanide and ferricyanide ions. When the ligand arrangement in a strong field iron(II) complex does not consist of six equivalent ligands $[Fe(CN)_5NH_3]^{3-}$, quadrupole splitting of the strong field iron(II) will result.

Values measured at room temperature for ΔE_Q and the isomer shift, δ, for a number of iron complexes have been collected[1] and are listed

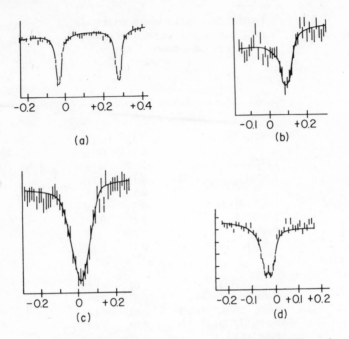

Fig. 11-5. Mössbauer Spectra of Some Iron(II) and Iron(III) Complexes. (a) Spin-free iron(II) — $FeSO_4 \cdot 7H_2O$. (b) Spin-free iron(III) — $FeCl_3$. (c) Spin-paired iron(II) — $K_4Fe(CN)_6 \cdot 3H_2O$. (d) Spin-paired iron(III) — $K_3Fe(CN)_6$. From P. R. Brady, P. P. F. Wigley, and J. F. Duncan, *Rev. Pure Appl. Chem.*, **12**, 181 (1962).

in Table 11-1. For iron complexes, isomer shifts in a positive direction correspond to a decrease in electron density in the region of the nucleus. For spin-free complexes a correlation exists between isomer shift and s electron density. An increase in δ of 0.02 cm sec^{-1} is equivalent to a decrease in charge density of 8 per cent at the nucleus.[7] The negative values obtained for the spin-paired ferricyanides compared to spin-free iron(III) complexes indicate more electron density at the nucleus in the ferricyanide ions. This has been explained as being due to extensive π bonding in the ferricyanides which removes d electron density from the metal ion which in turn decreases the shielding of the s electrons. This effect increases s electron density at the nucleus and decreases δ. In general more positive shifts are obtained for σ bonded complexes and negative shifts for those in which there is extensive π bonding.[5]

The MB spectrum of the material prepared from iron(III) sulfate and $K_4Fe(CN)_6$ is identical to the spectra for the compounds prepared from

TABLE 11-1. QUADRUPOLE SPLITTING,
ΔE_Q, AND ISOMER SHIFT, δ, FOR SOME
IRON COMPOUNDS (δ AND
ΔE_Q IN CM SEC^{-1})

Compound	ΔE_Q	δ
Spin-free Fe^{2+}		
$FeSO_4 \cdot 7H_2O$	0.32	0.119
	0.315	0.13
$FeSO_4$ (anhydrous)	0.27	0.12
$Fe(NH_4)_2(SO_4)_2 \cdot 6H_2O$	0.175	0.119
	0.175	0.13
$FeCl_2 \cdot 4H_2O$	0.300	0.135
$FeC_4H_4O_6$	0.26	0.125
FeF_2	0.268	–
$FeC_2O_4 \cdot 2H_2O$	0.17	0.125
Spin-free Fe^{3+}		
$FeCl_3 \cdot 6H_2O$	0.02	0.085
$FeCl_3$ (anhydrous)	0.02	0.05
$FeCl_3 \cdot 2NH_4Cl \cdot H_2O$	0.03	0.045
$Fe(NO_3)_3 \cdot 9H_2O$	0.04	0.04
$Fe_2(C_2O_4)_3$	0.05	0.045
$Fe_2(C_4H_4O_6)_3$	0.077	0.043
Fe_2O_3	0.012	0.047
Spin-paired Fe^{II}		
$K_4[Fe(CN)_6] \cdot 3H_2O$	–	−0.013
	–	−0.016
	<0.01	+0.005
$Na_4[Fe(CN)_6] \cdot 10H_2O$	<0.02	−1.01
$Na_4[Fe(CN)_5NH_3]$	0.06	−0.005
$K_2[Fe(CN)_5NO]$	0.185	−0.027
	0.176	−0.028
$Zn[Fe(CN)_5NO]$	0.190	−0.027
Spin-paired Fe^{III}		
$K_3[Fe(CN)_6]$	–	−0.012
	–	−0.017
	0.026	−0.015
$Na_3[Fe(CN)_6]$	0.060	−0.017

either iron(II) sulfate and $K_3Fe(CN)_6$ or by atmospheric oxidation of the compound from iron(II) sulfate and $K_4Fe(CN)_6$. The spectra of these materials indicate that the cation is spin-free iron(III), while the anion is spin-paired iron(II).

The MB spectrum of sodium nitroprusside, $Na_2Fe(CN)_5NO$, has been investigated.[8] This material has been formulated earlier as iron(II) and NO^+ because the complex is diamagnetic. The MB spectrum consists of a doublet with a ΔE_Q value of 1.76 mm/sec^{-1} and a δ value of -0.165 mm/sec^{-1}. The δ value is far too negative for an Fe^{II} complex. Comparison of this value with reported results[7] on a series of iron complexes suggests that the iron δ value is close to that of iron(IV). The magnetism and MB spectrum are consistent with a structure in which there is extensive π bonding between the odd electron in the t_{2g} set of the orbitals of iron and the odd electron on nitrogen, as illustrated in Fig. 11-6. The filled π bonding orbital has a large contribution from the

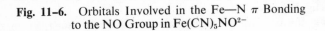

Fig. 11–6. Orbitals Involved in the Fe—N π Bonding to the NO Group in $Fe(CN)_5NO^{2-}$

nitrogen atomic orbital and the empty π antibonding orbital has a larger contribution from the iron atomic orbital. As a result, more of the π electron density is localized on nitrogen and the δ value for iron approaches that of iron(IV) because of decreased shielding of the s electrons by the d electrons. Since electron density is being placed in what was previously a π antibonding orbital of nitric oxide, a decrease in the N—O infrared stretching frequency is observed. The very large quadrupole splitting is consistent with very extensive π bonding in the Fe—N—O link.

The MB spectra of the iron pentacarbonyls: $Fe(CO)_5$, $Fe_2(CO)_9$, and $Fe_3(CO)_{12}$ have been reported.[9] The results are as expected from the known structures for both $Fe(CO)_5$ and $Fe_2(CO)_9$. The structure of $Fe_3(CO)_{12}$ deduced from its MB spectrum is not in agreement with the structure reported from a single crystal x-ray study.

Mössbauer spectra of several tin compounds have been observed.[10] In compounds of the general formula SnX_4 (where X is a halogen), a correlation is obtained between the electronegativity of X and δ. As the electronegativity of X is increased, δ increases. The ΔE_Q values for the compounds $(C_6H_5)_3SnX$ also increase with increasing electronegativity of X, because the more electronegative X causes a larger field gradient at the nucleus. The quadrupole splitting found in SnF_4 is consistent with a polymeric structure containing six-coordinate tin with both bridging and nonbridging fluorines.

EXERCISES

1. What effect does increasing electron density at the nucleus have on the relative energies of the ground and excited states of Fe^{57} and Sn^{119}? (Deduce this from the fact that increasing electron density produces a negative shift in the δ value.) Explain in terms of effective nuclear charge radii of these states.
2. Suppose you read an article in which the author claimed the two peaks in a MB spectrum of a spin-paired iron(III) complex was the result of Jahn Teller distortion. Criticize this conclusion.
3. Draw the structure for SnF_4 and explain why quadrupole splitting is observed in this compound but not in $SnCl_4$.
4. Suppose you were interested in determining whether Sn—O or Sn—S π bonding were present and which was greater in the compounds $(C_6H_5)_3SnOCH_3$ and $(C_6H_5)_3SnSCH_3$. Describe experiments involving MB spectroscopy which might shed light on this problem.
5. Would you expect the ΔE_Q value to be greatest in $SnCl_2Br_2$, $SnCl_3Br$, or SnF_3I?
6. The product obtained from the reaction of ferrous sulfate and potassium ferricyanide gives rise to the spectrum in Fig. 11-7. Interpret this spectrum.

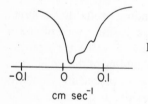

Fig. 11–7. M.B. Spectrum of the Reaction Product of $FeSO_4$ and $K_3Fe(CN)_6$.

-0.1   0   0.1

cm sec^{-1}

GENERAL REFERENCES

H. Frauenfelder, "The Mössbauer Effect" W. A. Benjamin, New York, 1962.
G. K. Wertheim, "Mössbauer Effect: Principles and Applications," Academic, New York, 1964.

REFERENCES CITED

1. P. R. Brady, P. P. F. Wigley, and J. F. Duncan, *Rev. Pure Appl. Chem.,* **12**, 165 (1962).
2. H. Frauenfelder, "The Mössbauer Effect," W. A. Benjamin, New York, 1962.
3. R. L. Mössbauer, *Science,* **137**, 731 (1962).
4. V. I. Goldanskii, "The Mössbauer Effect and its Application to Chemistry," English translation, Consultants Bureau, New York, 1964.

5. J. F. Duncan and P. W. R. Wigley, *J. Chem. Soc.*, **1963**, 1120.

6. R. E. Watson and A. J. Freeman, *Phys. Rev.*, **120**, 1125 (1960).

7. L. R. Walker, G. K. Wertheim, and V. Jaccarino, *Phys. Rev. Letters,* **6**, 98 (1961).

8. L. M. Epstein, *J. Chem. Phys.*, **36**, 2731 (1962).

9. R. H. Herber, W. R. Kingston, and G. K. Wertheim, *Inorg. Chem.*, **2**, 153 (1963).

10. V. I. Goldanskii, Seminar at University of Illinois, May 2, 1963.

12 *Mass Spectrometry*

INTRODUCTION

OPERATION AND REPRESENTATION OF SPECTRA

There are many different types of mass spectrometers available, and there are references[1-4] that detail the construction and relative merits of the various types of instruments. These references are also recommended for a more advanced treatment of this subject. Many of the basic principles of mass spectrometry can be simply illustrated by describing the mass spectrometer first employed by Dempster.[5] A schematic diagram is contained in Fig. 12-1. The sample contained in a reservoir is

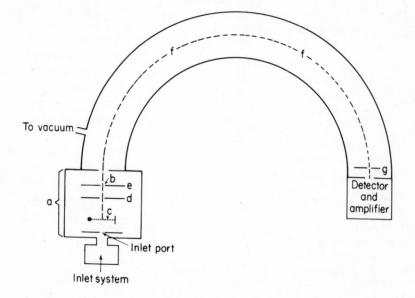

Fig. 12–1. A Schematic Diagram of a 180° Deflection Mass Spectrometer.

added through the port, enters the ion source (a) and passes through the electron beam at (c). (The beam is indicated by a dotted line.) Impact of the sample with an energetic electron produces a positive ion which moves toward the accelerating plates (d) and (e), because of a small potential difference between the back wall (inlet) and the front wall of this compartment. Negative ions are attracted to the back wall which is positively charged relative to the front and are discharged. The positive ions pass through (d) and (e) and by virtue of a large potential difference (a few thousand volts) between these plates, the velocity of the ions is increased considerably, and they leave the ion source through (b). Charged ions move in a circular path under the influence of a magnetic field. The semicircle indicated by (f) is the path traced by an accelerated ion moving in a magnetic field of strength H. The radius of the semicircle, r, depends upon the following: (1) the accelerating potential, V, i.e., the potential difference between plates (d) and (e); (2) the mass, m, of the ion; (3) the charge, e, of the ion; and (4) the magnetic field strength, H. The relationship between these quantities is given* by equation (12-1);

$$m/e = H^2r^2/2V \qquad\qquad (12\text{-}1)$$

When the ions pass through slit (g) into the detector, a signal is recorded. The source and path through which the ions pass must be kept under a vacuum of about 10^{-7} mm of mercury to provide a long mean free path for the ion. The sample vapor pressure in the inlet should be at least 10^{-2} mm Hg at the temperature of the inlet system, although special techniques[3] permit use of lower pressures. In general only one or two micromoles of sample are required.

Since it is possible to determine H, V, and r experimentally, only the ratio m/e can be determined. As a result, a dipositive ion of mass 54 gives rise to the same line as a monopositive ion of mass 27. Under usual conditions for running a mass spectrometer, most of the ions are produced as singly charged species. Doubly charged ions are much less frequently encountered, whereas more highly charged ions are not present in significant concentrations.

Obtaining the mass spectrum consists of determining the m/e ratio for

---

*This equation is simply derived: The potential energy of the ion, eV, is converted to kinetic energy $\frac{1}{2}mv^2$ (where m is the mass and v the velocity). At full acceleration, $eV = \frac{1}{2}mv^2$. (12-2) In the magnetic field the centrifugal force mv^2/r is balanced by centripetal force Hev. Solving $Hev = mv^2/r$ for r yields $r = mv/eH$. Using this equation to eliminate v from (12-2) produces (12-1).

all fragments produced when a molecule is bombarded by a high intensity electron beam. To do this, the detector slit could be moved and the value r measured for all the particles continuously produced by electron bombardment in the ion source. This is not feasible experimentally. It is much simpler to vary H or V continuously (see equation 12-1) so all particles eventually travel in a semicircle of fixed radius. The signal intensity, which is directly related to the number of ions striking the detector, can be plotted as a function of H or V, whichever is being varied. In practice it is easiest to measure a varying potential, so the field is often held constant. If H and r are constant, V is inversely related to m/e (by equation 12-1) and m/e can be plotted versus the signal intensity to produce a conventional mass spectrum. A narrow region of a typical spectrum is illustrated in Fig. 12-2. The attenuation of each peak (i.e., the reduction in intensity) is indicated by the number of horizontal lines above each

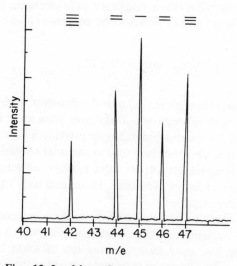

Fig. 12–2. Mass Spectrum of Fragments with m/e in the Range 40 to 48. The peaks have been automatically attenuated and the number of horizontal lines above each peak indicates the attenuation factor.

peak. Attenuation is necessary to keep all peaks on the chart. On instruments in which the potential is varied, a pen device can be employed which marks m/e values on the chart paper at certain values for the potential. For accurate work in the high m/e region (~ 400) this device is not adequate because small differences in potential correspond to appreciable differences in m/e (the difference in potential corresponding to m/e of 400 and 401 can be compared to the difference between 100 and 101 by using equation 11-1). In the high m/e region, calibration can be effected by running the spectrum of the sample twice; once alone and once with a reference material of known pattern added. The m/e values for the unknown can be obtained by interpolation between known mass peaks of the reference. In the low m/e region, peaks at 28 and 32 resulting from the small amount of air present can be employed to standardize the instrument.

Two variations on the principle of operation of the mass spectrometer described above are available in different instruments and will be briefly mentioned here. One type of instrument is similar to the above except the spectrum of negatively charged species is obtained. In the other, a time of flight instrument, the semicircular path and magnet are replaced by a straight path (no magnetic field). The ions are not produced continuously but in spurts and are allowed to diffuse toward the detector. Heavy ions will move more slowly than light ions. The spectrum is a plot of intensity versus the time of flight of the particle.

The mass spectrum obtained from the instrument may be a very long and cumbersome record. As a result, the data are often replotted and summarized by a bar graph which plots intensity (relative abundance of the fragments) on the ordinate and the m/e ratio on the abscissa. The relative abundance is given as the per cent intensity of a given peak relative to the most intense peak in the spectrum. Often it is informative to express the intensity in terms of *total ionization units, S*. This is an expression of the per cent each peak contributes to the total ionization and is obtained by dividing the intensity of a given peak by the sum of the intensities of all the peaks. When the spectrum has not been obtained over the range from 1 to the molecular weight of the material, the lower limit is indicated on the ordinate as a subscript to Σ (e.g., Σ_{12} means the spectrum was recorded from 12 to the molecular weight). A typical graph is illustrated in Fig. 12-3. For the comparison of the intensity of various peaks in the same spectrum, the relative abundance is adequate. For comparison of the intensity of peaks in different spectra, total ionization units should be employed. In general, a peak with an intensity equal to 1 per cent of Σ is easily detected.

Our next concern is with the method of indicating the resolving power of the instrument. For many inorganic and organic applications, it is necessary to know the m/e ratio to one unit (i.e., whether it is 249 or 250). The resolution of the instrument is sometimes expressed as $m/\Delta m$ where two peaks m and $m + \Delta m$ are separately resolved and the minimum intensity between the two peaks is only 2 per cent of the total of m. For example, a resolution of 250 means that two peaks with m/e of 251 and 250 are separated and at the minimum between them the pen returns to

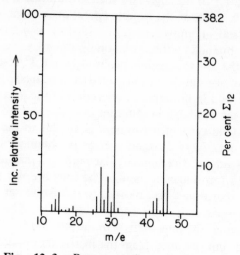

Fig. 12–3. Representation of the Mass Spectrum of Ethanol.

within 2 per cent of the total ion current (plotted as intensity in Fig. 12-2) to the base line. Instruments with poor resolution will not do this with high mass peaks, and the magnitude of the m/e peaks resolved is the criterion for resolution.

PROCESS THAT CAN OCCUR WHEN A MOLECULE AND A HIGH ENERGY ELECTRON COMBINE

It is important to emphasize the rather obvious point that a detector analyzes only those species impinging on it. We must, therefore, be concerned not only with the species produced in the ionization process but also with the reactions these species may undergo in the 10^{-5} seconds required to travel from the accelerating plates to the detector. When a molecule, A, is bombarded with electrons of moderate energy, the initial processes which can occur are summarized by equations (12-3) to 12-5):

$$A + e^- \rightarrow A^+ + 2e^- \tag{12-3}$$

$$A + e^- \rightarrow A^{n+} + (n + 1)e^- \tag{12-4}$$

$$A + e^- \rightarrow A^- \tag{12-5}$$

The process represented by reaction (12-3) is the most common and the most important in mass spectrometry. It will occur if the energy of the bombarding electron is equal to or higher than the ionization energy of the molecule (7 to 15 ev). When the energy of the bombarding electron beam is just equal to the ionization potential, all of the electron's energy must be transferred to the molecule to remove an electron. The probability of this happening is low. As the energy of the bombarding electron increases, the probability that a collision will induce ionization increases, and a higher intensity peak results. As the energy of the bombarding electron is increased further, much of this excess energy can be given to the molecular ion that is formed. This excess energy can be high enough to break bonds in the ion, and fragmentation of the particle results. The acceleration potential of the bombarding electron which is just great enough to initiate fragmentation is referred to as the *appearance potential* of the fragment ion. When the electron energy is large enough, more than one bond in the molecule can be broken. The following sequence summarizes the processes that can occur when a hypothetical molecule B—C—D—E is bombarded with an electron:

(a) Ionization process

$$BCDE + e^- \rightarrow B\text{—}C\text{—}D\text{—}E^+ + 2e^- \qquad (12\text{-}6)$$

(b) Fragmentation of the positive ion

$$B\text{—}C\text{—}D\text{—}E^+ \rightarrow B^+ + CDE\cdot \qquad (12\text{-}7)$$

$$BCDE^+ \rightarrow BC^+ + DE\cdot \qquad (12\text{-}8)$$

$$BC^+ \rightarrow B^+ + C\cdot \qquad (12\text{-}9)$$

$$\text{or} \quad BC^+ \rightarrow B\cdot + C^+ \qquad (12\text{-}10)$$

$$BCDE^+ \rightarrow DE^+ + BC\cdot \qquad (12\text{-}11)$$

$$DE^+ \quad \rightarrow D^+ + E\cdot \qquad (12\text{-}12)$$

$$\text{or } DE^+ \rightarrow D\cdot + E^+ \qquad (12\text{-}13)$$

$$BCDE^+ \rightarrow BE^+ + CD\cdot \text{ etc.} \qquad (12\text{-}14)$$

$$BCDE^+ \rightarrow CD^+ + BE\cdot \text{ etc.} \qquad (12\text{-}15)$$

(c) Pair production

$$BCDE + e^- \rightarrow BC^+ + DE^- + e^- \qquad (12\text{-}16)$$

(d) Resonance capture

$$BCDE + e^- \rightarrow BCDE^- \qquad (12\text{-}17)$$

Other modes of cleavage are possible, but only positively charged species will travel to the detector and give rise to peaks in the mass spectrum. For the scheme above, peaks corresponding to B^+, BC^+, C^+, DE^+, D^+, E^+, BE^+, and CD^+ will occur in the spectrum if B, C, D, and E have different masses. More energy will have to be imparted to the $BCDE^+$ ion to get cleavage into B^+, $C\cdot$, and DE (equation 12-9) than for cleavage into $BC^+ + DE\cdot$ (equation 12-8).

In equation (12-14), the ion has rearranged in the dissociation process, leading to fragments which contain bonds that are not originally present in the molecule B—C—D—E. These rearrangement processes complicate the interpretation of a mass spectrum, and familiarity with many examples is necessary to be able to predict when rearrangements will occur. In general this concept is invoked to explain the occurrence of peaks of unexpected mass or unexpected intensity.

A final process, ion-molecule reactions, can give rise to mass peaks in the spectrum which are greater than the molecular weight of the sample. This process is represented by equation (12-18).

$$BCDE^+ + CDE\cdot \rightarrow BCDEC^+ + DE\cdot \qquad (12\text{-}18)$$

The reaction involves the molecular ion colliding with a neutral molecule and as such is a second order rate process, the rate of which is proportional to the product of the concentration of the reactants. The intensity of peaks resulting from this process will depend upon the product of the partial pressures of $BCDE^+$ and CDE. Examination of the spectrum at different pressures causes variation in the relative intensity of these peaks, and as a result the occurrence of this process can be easily detected.

APPLICATIONS

FINGERPRINT APPLICATION AND THE INTERPRETATION OF MASS SPECTRA

The fingerprint application is immediately obvious. For this purpose an electron beam of 40 to 80 ev is usually employed to yield reproducible spectra, for this accelerating potential is above the appearance potential of most fragments. As indicated by equations (12-6) to (12-16), a large number of different fragmentation processes can occur, resulting in a large number of peaks in the spectra of simple molecules. Fig. 12-3 contains the peaks with appreciable intensity that are found in the mass spectrum of ethanol. Counting the very weak peaks, which are not illustrated, a total of about 30 peaks are found. These weak peaks are valuable for a fingerprint application but generally are not accounted for in the interpretation of the spectrum (i.e. assigning the fragmentation processes leading to the peaks). Useful compilations of references to the mass spectra of many compounds (mainly organic) are contained in references 2, 3, and 13. An interesting fingerprint application is illustrated in Fig. 12-4 where the mass spectra of the three isomers of ethylpyridine are indicated. Pronounced differences occur in the spectra of these similar compounds. Optical antipodes and racemates give rise to identical spectra. Impurities create a problem in fingerprint applications because the major fragments of these impurities give rise to several low intensity peaks in the spectrum. If the same material is prepared in two different solvents, the spectra may appear to be quite different if all solvent has not been removed. Contamination from hydrocarbon grease also gives rise to many lines.

The interpretation of a mass spectrum involves assigning each of the major peaks in a spectrum to particular fragments. An intense peak corresponds to a high probability for the formation of this ion in the fragmentation process. In the absence of rearrangement (equation 12-14), the arrangement of atoms in the molecule can often be deduced from the mass of the fragments that are produced. For example, a strong peak at m/e of 30 for the compound methyl hydroxylamine would favor the structure CH_3NHOH over H_2NOCH_3 because an m/e 30 peak could result from cleavage of the O—N bond in the former case but cannot result by any simple cleavage mechanism for the latter compound.

It is often helpful in assigning the peaks in a spectrum to be able to predict probable fragmentation products for various molecular structures. The energy required to produce a fragment from the molecular ion depends upon the activation energy for bond cleavage which is often related to the strength of the bond to be broken. The distribution of ions detected depends not only on this but also on the stability of the resulting positive ion. In most cases it is found that the stability of the positive ion is of greatest importance. This stability is related to the effectiveness with which the resulting fragment can delocalize the positive charge. Fragmentation of $HOCH_2—CH_2NH_2^+$ can occur to produce $\cdot CH_2OH$ and $CH_2NH_2^+$ ($m/e = 30$) or $\cdot CH_2NH_2$ and CH_2OH^+ ($m/e = 31$). Since nitrogen is not as electronegative as oxygen, the resonance form

$CH_2{=}NH_2{}^+$ contributes more to the stability of this ion than a similar form, $CH_2{=}OH^+$ does to its ion. As a result, charge is more effectively delocalized in the species $CH_2NH_2{}^+$ than in CH_2OH^+, and the $m/e = 30$ peak is about ten times more intense than the $m/e = 31$ peak. Charge is not stabilized as effectively by sulfur as it is by oxygen because carbon-sulfur π bonding is not as effective as carbon-oxygen π bonding. As a result, the $m/e = 31$ peak for CH_2OH^+ from $HSCH_2CH_2OH$ is about half the intensity of the $m/e = 47$ peak which arises from CH_2SH^+.

Rearrangements of the positive ion will occur when a more stable species results. For example, the ion ⌊⌊O⌋⌋–$CH_2{}^+$ rearranges to ⌊⌊O⌋⌋$^+$. The intensity of the peak for this fragment is much greater than would have been expected if rearrangement were not considered.

Many more examples and a thorough discussion of factors leading to stable ions produced from organic compounds are contained in Biemann's text.[3] Generalizations for predicting when rearrangements are expected are also discussed. If, starting with a given structure, one can account for the principal fragments and assign the peaks in the mass spectrum by a reasonable fragmentation pattern, this assignment amounts to considerable support for that structure.

EFFECT OF ISOTOPES ON THE APPEARANCE OF A MASS SPECTRUM

When the spectrum of a compound containing an element which has more than one stable, abundant isotope is examined, more than one peak will be obtained for each fragment containing this element. In the spectrum of CH_3Br, two peaks of nearly equal intensity will occur at m/e of 94 and 96 corresponding mainly to $(CH_3Br^{79})^+$ and $(CH_3Br^{81})^+$. The abundance of Br^{79} and Br^{81} is almost the same (50.54 vs. 49.46 per cent). In addition to these peaks there will be small peaks resulting from the small natural abundance of D and C.[13] Various combinations of masses, C^{12}, C^{13}, D, H, Br^{79}, and Br^{81} can occur, giving rise to small peaks for the C^{13} and D species. Two peaks of nearly equal intensity and separated by two mass units are obtained for all fragments containing bromine. In a molecule containing two equivalent bromine atoms, a triplet with ratios $1:2:1$ would result from different combinations of isotopes in fragments containing two bromine atoms. This criterion is useful in assigning peaks to fragments. The various combinations of C, H, N, and O isotopes that can give rise to peaks of different mass have been compiled[2] along with the expected relative intensities of these peaks.

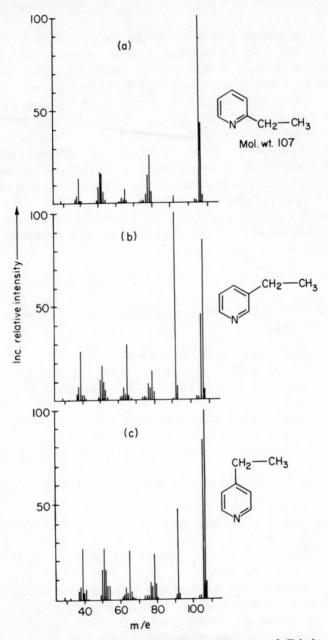

Fig. 12-4. Mass Spectra of Three Isomers of Ethylpyridine. From *Mass Spectrometry* by K. Biemann.
Copyright 1960. McGraw-Hill Book Company. Used by
permission.

Another important application of the mass spectrometer involving isotopes is the study of exchange reactions involving nonradioactive isotopes. The product of the exchange or labeled starting material is examined for isotope content as a function of time to obtain the rate of exchange. The product or starting material can be degraded to a gaseous material containing the label, and the isotopic ratio obtained from the mass spectrum. These materials may also be examined directly, and the location and amount of label incorporated, deduced from an analysis of the change in spectrum of various fragments. By determining which peaks in the spectrum change on incorporation of the isotope, one can determine which parts of a molecule have undergone exchange. In the reaction of methanol with benzoic acid, it has been shown by a tracer study involving mass spectral analysis that the ester oxygen in the product comes from methanol:

$$C_6H_5\overset{O}{\overset{\|}{C}}{-}OH + CH_3O^{18}H \rightarrow C_6H_5\overset{O}{\overset{\|}{C}}{-}O^{18}CH_3 + H_2O$$

In another interesting application it was shown that the following exchange reactions occurred:

$$BF_3 + BX_3 \rightarrow BX_2F + BF_2X$$
$$3RBX_2 + 2BF_3 \rightarrow 3RBF_2 + 2BX_3 \text{ (also } BF_nX_m)$$
$$3R_2BX + BF_3 \rightarrow 3R_2BF + BX_3 \text{ (also } BF_nX_m)$$

where R is alkyl or vinyl and X is Cl or Br. Fragments corresponding to the products were obtained, although only starting materials were recovered on attempted separation.[6] A four-center intermediate of the type:

was proposed for the exchange. In order to determine whether or not alkyl groups were exchanged in the reaction:

$$RBX_2 + 2BF_3 \rightarrow 3RBF_2 + BX_3 \text{ (and } BX_mF_n)$$

the boron trifluoride was enriched in B^{10}. The absence of enrichment of B^{10} in fragments in the mass spectrum containing alkyl or vinyl groups enabled the authors to conclude that neither alkyl nor vinyl groups were exchanged under conditions where RBX_2 species were stable.

It should be pointed out that in all of the above applications it is not necessary to label all molecules of the compound. A slight enrichment will suffice.

Molecular Weight Determinations

If the molecular ion (formed by a process similar to equation 12-6) is stable, the determination of the molecular weight of a substance can be made directly from the highest mass peak whose relative intensity is independent of pressure. In about 80 per cent of the compounds studied, the molecular ion is stable enough for this application, and for the other 20 per cent, the molecular weight can often be deduced from the fragments produced. The main problem becomes one of ascertaining that the peak selected is the molecular ion peak[3]. The molecule $Fe(CO)_4(CF_2-CF_2-CF_2-CF_2)$ was shown to be a monomer, with a molecular weight of 368, from the molecular ion peak in the mass spectrum. Conventional methods for determining the molecular weight gave unreliable results.[7] Similarly, the compound $C_6F_8Fe(CO)_3$ was shown to be a monomer.[7]

Evaluation of Heats of Sublimation and Species in the Vapor over High Melting Solids

Evaluation of the heat of sublimation is based upon the fact that the intensity of the peaks in a spectrum is directly proportional to the pressure of the sample in the ion source. The sample is placed in a reservoir containing a very small pin hole (a Knudsen cell) which is connected to the ion source so that the only way sample can enter the source is by diffusion through the hole. If the cell is thermostated and enough sample placed in the cell so that the solid phase is always present, the heat of sublimation of the solid can be obtained by studying the change in peak intensity (which is related to vapor pressure) as a function of sample temperature. The small amount of sample diffusing into the ion beam does not radically affect the equilibrium. Some interesting results concerning the nature of the species present in the vapor over some high melting solids have been obtained from this type of study. Monomers, dimers, and trimers were found over lithium chloride, while monomers and dimers were found in the vapor over sodium, potassium, and cesium chloride.[8]

The species Cr, CrO, CrO_2, O, and O_2 were found over solid Cr_2O_3. Appearance potentials and bond dissociation energies of these species are reported.[9] The vapors over MoO_3 were found to consist of trimer, tetramer, and pentamer. Vapor pressures, free energy changes, and enthalpies of sublimation were evaluated.[10]

Appearance Potentials and Ionization Potentials

As mentioned earlier, the molecular ion is produced whenever collision occurs with an electron with energy equal to or greater than the ionization energy of the molecule. A typical curve relating electron energy to the number of ion fragments of a particular type produced (i.e., relative intensity of a given peak) is illustrated in Fig. 12-5. This is referred to as an ionization efficiency curve. At electron energies well below the ionization energy, no ions are produced. When the energy of the electron beam equals the ionization energy, a very low intensity peak results, for in the collision all of the energy of the electron will have to be imparted to the molecule, and this is not too probable. As the electron energy is increased, the probability that the electron will impart enough energy to the molecule to cause ionization is increased, and a more intense peak results until a plateau finally occurs in the curve. The tail of this curve at low energies results because of the variation in the energies of the electrons in the bombarding beam. Therefore, the curve has to be extrapolated (dotted line in Fig. 12-5) to produce the ionization energy.

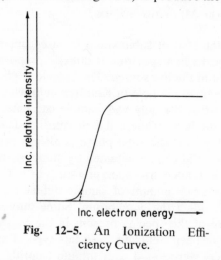

Fig. 12–5. An Ionization Efficiency Curve.

Various procedures for extrapolation and the error introduced by these procedures have been discussed in detail.[11] When the peak observed is that of the molecular ion, $e^- + RX \rightarrow RX^+ + 2e^-$, the ionization energy of the molecule can be obtained by extrapolation of the ionization efficiency curve. When the peak is that of a fragment, extrapolation of the ionization efficiency curve produces the appearance potential of that fragment. For example, if the peak being investigated is that of the fragment R^+ from the molecule R—X, the appearance potential, A_{R+}, is obtained by extrapolation of the ion efficiency curve for this peak. The appearance potential is related to the following quantities:

$$A_R{}^+ = D_{R-X} + I_R + E_k + E_e \qquad (12\text{-}19)$$

where D_{R-X} is the gas phase dissociation energy of the bond R—X; I_R is the ionization potential of R; E_k is the kinetic energy of the particles produced; and E_e is the excitation energy of the fragments (i.e., the electronic, vibration, and rotational energy if the fragments are produced in excited states). Generally E_k and E_e are small and equation (12-19) is adequately approximated by:

$$A_R{}^+ = D_{R-X} + I_R \qquad (12\text{-}20)$$

If D_{R-X} is known, I_R can be calculated from appearance potential data. Often I_R is known, and D_{R-X} can be calculated. The value for I_R must be less than I_X for equation (12-20) to apply; otherwise, X is dissociated or electronically excited. Experiments of this sort provide one of the best methods for evaluating bond dissociation energies but give less exact ionization potential data than can be obtained by other means.

An article on the mass spectrometric study of phosphine and diphosphine contains a nice summary of some of the information that can be obtained from these studies. Ionization energies and appearance potentials of the principal positive ions formed are reported. The energetics of the fragmentation processes are discussed and a mechanism is proposed.[12]

EXERCISES

1. If the accelerating potential in a mass spectrometer is decreased in running a spectrum, will the large or small m/e ratios be recorded first?
2. Sulfur-carbon π bonding is not as effective as nitrogen-carbon π bonding. In the mass spectrum of $HSCH_2CH_2NH_2$ would the $m/e = 30$ or $m/e = 47$ peak be more intense?
3. Refer to Fig. 12-4 and recall the discussion on the relation of charge delocalization and stability of the positive ion. Explain why the mass 92 peak corresponding to $\underset{N}{\bigcirc} CH_2{}^+$ is most intense for the isomer of ethyl pyridene with the ethyl group in the 3 position.
4. a. What m/e peak in the mass spectrum of CH_4 would you examine as a function of accelerating potential in order to determine the ionization potential of the methyl radical?

b. Write an equation for the appearance potential of the fragment in part (a) in terms of ionization potential and dissociation energy.

c. In evaluating the dissociation energy of part (b) from thermochemical data, what is wrong with using one-fourth the value for the heat of formation (from gaseous carbon and hydrogen) of CH_4?

REFERENCES CITED

1. H. E. Duckworth, "Mass Spectroscopy," Cambridge, New York, 1958.

2. J. H. Beynon, "Mass Spectrometry and Its Applications to Organic Chemistry," Elsevier, Amsterdam, 1960.

3. K. Biemann, "Mass Spectrometry," McGraw-Hill, New York, 1962.

4. F. W. Lafferty, "Mass Spectrometry of Organic Ions, "Academic, New York, 1963.

5. A. J. Dempster, *Phys. Rev.,* **11,** 316 (1918).

6. F. E. Brinckman and F. G. A. Stone, *J. Am. Chem. Soc.,* **82,** 6235 (1960).

7. H. A. Hoehn, L. Pratt, K. Watterson, and G. Wilkinson, *J. Chem. Soc.,* **1961,** 2738.

8. T. A. Milne and H. M. Klein, *J. Chem. Phys.,* **33,** 1628 (1960).

9. R. T. Grimley, R. P. Burns, and M. G. Inghram, *J. Chem. Phys.* **34,** 664 (1961).

10. J. Berkowitz, M. G. Inghram, and W. A. Chupka, *J. Chem. Phys.,* **26.** 842 (1957).

11. G. P. Barnard, "Mass Spectrometry," Institute of Physics, London, England, 1953.

12. Y. Wada and R. W. Kiser, *Inorg. Chem.,* **3,** 174 (1964).

13. H. Budzikiewicz, C. Djerassi, and D. H. Williams, "Interpretation of Mass Spectra of Organic Compounds" Holden-Day, San Francisco, 1964.

APPENDIX A. *Magnetism*

The determination of magnetic susceptibility is briefly reviewed here because it may be used in conjunction with electronic spectra to establish the structure of complexes and because an understanding of magnetism is helpful in understanding magnetic resonance spectroscopy. There are several excellent detailed treatments of this subject.[1-5]

CONTRIBUTIONS TO MAGNETIC PROPERTIES

The main contribution to bulk magnetic properties of substances arises from the magnetic moment resulting from motion of the charged electrons. Effects from the nucleons are minor and will not be considered here. When a substance is placed in a magnetic field, there will be field-induced motion of the electrons in this material in such a direction as to generate a magnetic moment which is opposed to the applied field. As a result the material will be repelled by the stronger part of a nonuniform magnetic field and is said to be *diamagnetic*. This diamagnetic effect does not exist in the absence of a magnetic field but is present in all substances placed in a magnetic field. It is usually the principal effect for materials in which all electron spins are paired.

Substances which contain one or more unpaired electrons have a permanent magnetic moment which exists in the absence of a magnetic field and arises from the net spin and orbital angular momenta of the unpaired electrons. Such substances are said to be *paramagnetic*. When a paramagnetic substance is placed in an external magnetic field, the permanent atomic or molecular magnetic moments align themselves in the same direction as the field and consequently are attracted to it. A substance which is paramagnetic is attracted into a magnetic field with a force proportional to the field strength times the field gradient.

The magnitude of the paramagnetic effect is one or two orders of magnitude greater than the diamagnetic effect. Hence, the paramagnetic effect is dominant in all substances containing unpaired electrons.

There are more complex forms of magnetic behavior than the diamagnetic and paramagnetic effects discussed above. The more common of these are *ferromagnetism* and *antiferromagnetism*. These effects will not be discussed here.

Two properties of an unpaired electron, the spin and orbital moments, contribute to the magnitude of the paramagnetic moment. Spin and orbital angular momenta in atoms were described in Chapter 1 where they were designated by the spin and orbital quantum numbers, m_s and m_l. A simple qualitative description of the spin and orbital contributions to the moment will be presented. Moving charge associated with the model of an electron spinning on its axis ($m_s \pm \frac{1}{2}$) produces a magnetic moment. The contribution to the total moment arising from this effect is described as the *spin moment*. The orbital angular momentum associated with an electron in an orbital indicates circulation of the electron about the nucleus. This motion will also give rise to moving charge and a magnetic moment described as the *orbital moment* results. These physical models have no quantum mechanical basis and should be regarded merely as conceptual aids.

The spin-only value, i.e., the contribution to the moment from only the electron spin effect, is given by the equation:

$$\mu_S = g\sqrt{S(S + 1)} \tag{A-1}$$

where μ_S is the spin moment in units of Bohr magnetons (one $BM = eh/4\pi mc$), S is the sum of the spin quantum numbers of the electrons, and g is the Lande' splitting factor which is the ratio of the magnetic moment of the electron to the total angular momentum of the electron. For a free electron g has the value 2.00023. For a many-electron system the spin-only moment is evaluated from equation (A-1) by employing $g = 2$ and the sum of the spin quantum numbers of all the unpaired electrons as the value for S, (e.g., $\frac{3}{2}$ for three unpaired electrons). The sum of the spins of paired electrons equals zero. Using this procedure, it can be easily shown (with equation A-1) that the spin-only moments for 1, 2, 3, 4, and 5 unpaired electrons are 1.73, 2.83, 3.87, 4.90, and 5.92 BM respectively. Another convenient way of calculating this involves use of equation (A-2) which is equivalent to equation (A-1):

$$\mu_S = \sqrt{n(n + 2)} \tag{A-2}$$

where n is the number of unpaired electrons.

When there is appreciable spin-orbit coupling in a molecule or ion which gives splitting of the ground state that is large compared to kT, there will be an appreciable contribution to the moment from this coupling. This situation prevails for atoms in the gas phase and for most of the rare earth ions. The moment expected when spin-orbit coupling is present is given by equation (A-3):

$$\mu_{s.o.} = g\sqrt{J(J + 1)}BM \tag{A-3}$$

Recall that J is the total angular momentum of the ground state given, according to LS coupling, by: $|L + S|$, $|L + S - 1|$, ..., $|L - S|$ (see Chapter 1). If the shell is less than half filled with electrons, the ground state is $|L - S|$; and if it is more than half filled, it is $|L + S|$. For free gaseous atoms, the g factor is given by:

$$g = 1 + \frac{J(J + 1) + S(S + 1) - L(L + 1)}{2J(J + 1)} \tag{A-4}$$

In view of the extensive shielding of the inner $4f$ orbitals in a rare earth complex, these ions behave very much like orbitals in gaseous ions. Equation (A-3) can be employed to calculate the magnetic moments of many of these complexes with a fair degree of accuracy. For example, Pr^{3+} has the configuration $4f^2 6s^2 6p^6$. As a result, $S = 1$, $L = 5$, and since the shell is less than half filled, the minimum value of J is used, i.e., $|L - S| = 4$. Solving equations (A-3), and (A-4) yields $\mu = 3.58$ BM, compared to a measured value of 3.47.

There is an additional factor affecting the magnitude of the magnetic moment, namely temperature independent paramagnetism, TIP. The magnetic field can cause a change in the ground state of the ion. This change can be described by a magnetic-field-induced mixing of the ground and an excited state, lowering the energy of the ground state. The state being mixed in may be a singlet or a multiplet, so the effect of this mixing may result in an increase or decrease in the actual moment compared to the expected one. If the excited state being mixed has an orbital magnetic moment different from the ground state, the measured magnetism is correspondingly increased or decreased. The extent of this interaction is directly dependent upon the field strength and inversely proportional to the energy separation of the higher state and the ground state. If the state being mixed in is separated from the ground state by an amount much greater than kT, then this excited level is not populated and cannot make a direct contribution to the susceptibility. In this case the only excited state contribution to the susceptibility arises from field-induced mixing with the ground state and is temperature independent. This is the effect referred to by the term TIP. The majority of the difference between the experimental and calculated values for Pr^{3+} is due to TIP.

EFFECT OF THE LIGAND FIELD ON SPIN-ORBIT COUPLING

The experimental magnetic moments for first row transition metal ions do not agree very well with those calculated by equations (A-3) and (A-4). The range of moments commonly obtained is listed in Table A-1. The moments are often found to be close to those calculated for the spin-only value.

The discrepancy between the measured results and those calculated from equations A-3 and A-4 arises because the ligands remove the degeneracy of the set of d orbitals. As mentioned in Chapter 6 (the section on spin-orbit coupling), a simple model for spin-orbit coupling involves electron occupation of equivalent, degenerate orbitals which enables the electron to revolve about an axis. For example, when rotation occurs by occupation of d_{xy} and $d_{x^2-y^2}$ orbitals, classically this gives the electron an orbital angular momentum about the z axis. A ligand field splits the degeneracy of the $d_{x^2-y^2}$ and d_{xy} orbitals, and spin-orbit coupling cannot occur via this model for this set of orbitals. In an O_h or T_d complex ion, the e_g set of orbitals $(d_{x^2-y^2}, d_{z^2})$ cannot be employed by the electrons to rotate about an axis, and these orbitals cannot contribute to the orbital angular momentum. Secondly, when the T_{2g} set of orbitals in a complex is half-filled or filled, rotation involving d_{xy}, d_{yz}, and d_{xz} orbitals is not possible, and orbital contributions from this set are quenched. As long as a t_{2g} level is not half-filled or completely filled, degenerate arrangements of the electrons in these three orbitals

TABLE A-1. CALCULATED AND MEASURED MOMENTS FOR
SOME TRANSITION METAL IONS

Ion	Configuration	Ground State L	S	Term Symbol	μ_S	Measured Range, μ_{eff}
Ti^{3+}	$3d^1$	2	$\frac{1}{2}$	^2D	1.73	1.7
V^{4+}	$3d^1$	2	$\frac{1}{2}$	^2D	1.73	1.7–1.8
Cu^{2+}	$3d^9$	2	$\frac{1}{2}$	^2D	1.73	1.7–2.2
V^{3+}	$3d^2$	3	1	^3F	2.83	2.6–2.8
Ni^{2+}	$3d^8$	3	1	^3F	2.83	2.8–4.0
Cr^{3+}	$3d^3$	3	$\frac{3}{2}$	^4F	3.87	3.8
Co^{2+}	$3d^7$	3	$\frac{3}{2}$	^4F	3.87	4.1–5.2
Fe^{2+}	$3d^6$	2	2	^5D	4.90	5.1–5.5
Mn^{2+}	$3d^5$	0	$\frac{5}{2}$	^6S	5.92	5.9

provide a mechanism whereby electrons can circulate about the z axis, by occupying the d_{xz} and d_{yz} orbitals. As a consequence of the principles outlined above, values for the magnetic moment close to the spin-only value are expected for the spin-free six-coordinate complexes: t_{2g}^3, $t_{2g}^3 e_g^1$, $t_{2g}^3 e_g^2$, $t_{2g}^6 e_g^2$, $t_{2g}^6 e_g^3$; and for the spin paired complexes t_{2g}^6, $t_{2g}^6 e_g^1$. Contributions to the moment from spin-orbit coupling are expected for other configurations, but the magnitude of this contribution is less than that calculated by equations (A-3) and (A-4) for a gaseous ion. Similar reasoning can be employed to make predictions about tetrahedral complexes. For example, the moment of a d^8 tetrahedral complex, $e_g^4 t_{2g}^4$ should have contributions from spin-orbit coupling. The model described above is only a very approximate treatment, because in complexes containing more than one d electron, electron-electron repulsions are important. These complexes should be described by considering the splitting of the ground state spectroscopic term by the ligand field. In general, orbital contributions are expected in those complexes in which the ground state is triply degenerate (e.g., T_{2g}) and values approximating the spin-only values are obtained for nondegenerate and doubly-degenerate ground states (e.g., A_{2g} or E_g). Information regarding ground states terms can be obtained from the Tanabe and Sugano diagrams (Appendix C) for O_h and T_d complexes.

For those first row transition metal ions in which quenching of the orbital contribution is expected to be complete, TIP accounts for the deviations of the measured moment, μ, from the spin-only moment, μ_S. For those ions where spin-orbit coupling is appreciable the following equation shows the contribution of this effect to the measured moment, μ:

$$\mu = \mu_S[(1 - \alpha)\lambda/\Delta] \qquad (A-5)$$

where α is a constant for a metal ion, λ is the spin-orbit coupling constant (values for α and λ are tabulated by Figgis and Lewis[1]), and Δ is the separation of the ground and excited states and can be obtained from the electronic spectra.

For those ions in which appreciable contributions to the magnetic moment from spin-orbit coupling are expected, Figgis and Lewis[1] have plotted the variation in the expected moment μ_{eff} as a function of λ and temperature for various configurations. Deviation of the measured moment from that expected (as given by the plots in Figgis and Lewis) can be used as evidence for deviation of a structure from perfect O_h or T_d symmetry.

MEASUREMENT OF MAGNETIC PROPERTIES

The experimental determination of magnetic properties does not usually involve measurement of the magnetic moment, μ, but instead measurement of the magnetic susceptibility from which the moment is calculated. The volume magnetic susceptibility, χ, is defined by equation (A-6) where I is the intensity of magnetization

$$\chi = I/H \qquad (A-6)$$

induced by the field of strength, H, per unit volume of substance. This quantity is related to the force the material experiences when subjected to a magnetic field gradient and procedures are described[1] for measuring this force. A paramagnetic substance can be thought to consist of molecular magnetic dipoles which tend to orient themselves parallel to the direction of the field. The quantity I is a measure of the extent to which this occurs. The lining up of the magnetic dipoles is opposed by the thermal motion of the particles, and in a paramagnetic substance at room temperature only a small fraction of the molecules have their magnetic moments aligned with the field. The quantity χ is a dimensionless quantity which is positive for paramagnetic substances and negative for diamagnetic substances. Often the susceptibility is defined as the weight susceptibility χ_g where

$$\chi_g = \chi/\text{density}$$

or it can be defined as the molar susceptibility, χ_M, where

$$\chi_M = (M/d)\chi \qquad (A-7)$$

The quantity χ_M, which is the induced moment, I, per mole per unit applied field, H, has the units cc/mole^{-1}. For normal paramagnetic and diamagnetic substances χ, χ_g, and χ_M are constants independent of field strength.

When a substance exhibits an unusually large paramagnetism, it is referred to as a ferromagnetic material. Ferromagnetism results when magnetic dipoles in a substance can interact with one another causing extensive alignment of the moments with the field. Very large values of I result. For these materials the susceptibilities are field-strength dependent. In most complexes the paramagnetic centers (metal ions) are separated from one another by ligands and ferromagnetism is not usually encountered. Complexes which do not exhibit ferromagnetism are said to be magnetically dilute.

The susceptibility measured for a given material will consist of contributions from paramagnetic and diamagnetic susceptibilities, the former being much greater. However, for molecules containing a large number of diamagnetic atoms per paramagnetic atom (as in a metal ion complex with large organic ligands), the diamagnetic contribution can be appreciable. The measured susceptibility should be corrected by subtracting the diamagnetic contribution from it. It is found that diamagnetism is an additive quantity and the diamagnetism of a molecule can be obtained by adding up the diamagnetism of each atom in the molecule. Reporting values for the diamagnetism of various atoms are summarized in reference 1. For this correction, the sum of the diamagnetic corrections for each atom in the molecule is added to the measured molar susceptibility, i.e.,

paramagnetic susceptibility = measured susceptibility − diamagnetic
susceptibility   (A-8)

This formula leads to a positive correction to the measured susceptibility because the value of the diamagnetic susceptibility is negative. This takes into account the difference in direction of the diamagnetic and paramagnetic moments. The next problem is the conversion of paramagnetic susceptibility into a magnetic moment. Equation (A-9) can be derived for this purpose:

$$\mu_{\text{eff}} = 2.84(\chi_A' T)^{1/2} \tag{A-9}$$

where T is the absolute temperature, χ_A' is the molar susceptibility corrected for diamagnetic effects and μ_{eff} is the magnetic moment of the compound in units of Bohr magnetons. This equation holds for substances that obey the Curie law $\chi_A' = C/T$ where C is a constant. In practice it is found that for many compounds the temperature variation of the susceptibility is expressed not by the Curie Law but by the Curie-Weiss law: $\chi_A' = C/(T - \theta)$ where θ is also a constant. Often θ is not known (unless the temperature dependence of χ_A' is measured), and equation (A-9) is used to calculate the moment. Since θ is often 30°C or less, use of equation (A-9) introduces an error of a few tenths of a BM at most, which is insignificant in most applications.

SOME APPLICATIONS OF MAGNETIC DATA

As mentioned in the chapter on crystal field theory, the strong and weak field complexes of several transition metal ions differ in the number of unpaired electrons in the complexes. When this number can be ascertained readily from a comparison of the measured magnetic moment and that calculated for the spin-only moment (equation A-1), it is possible to distinguish spin-paired from spin-free complexes. For example, K_3FeF_6 has a magnetic moment of 6.0 BM and is a spin-free complex, while spin-paired $K_3Fe(CN)_6$ has a moment of only 2.3 BM. Determining the number of unpaired electrons can also give information regarding the oxidation state of a metal ion in a complex.

Magnetic measurements[6] have shown that cupric acetate monohydrate (d^9), is diamagnetic at low temperature. This indicates formulation of this material as $[Cu(OAc)_2H_2O]_n$ where n is an even integer and where there are "copper-copper bonds." An x-ray study indicated the molecule is dimeric and the copper atoms are close enough to be interacting. At higher temperatures a paramagnetic excited state is populated, giving rise to an appreciable magnetic moment. Since the population of this state is a function of temperature, the moment will change appreciably with temperature.

Magnetism has been of considerable utility in establishing the structure of many complexes.[16] A few nickel(II) and cobalt(II) complexes will be discussed here to illustrate the application. The literature can be consulted for many other examples;[1,7,8,16] In an octahedral field Ni^{II} has a nondegenerate ground state, $^3A_2(t_{2g}^6e_g^2)$, and no contribution from spin orbit coupling is expected. The measured moments are in the range 2.8 to 3.3 BM, very close to the spin-only value of 2.83. Values for octahedral complexes slightly above the spin-only value arises from slight mixing of a multiplet excited state in which spin-orbit coupling is appreciable. Tetrahedral nickel(II) has a T_1 ground state essentially ($e_g^4t_{2g}^4$), and a large orbital contribution to the moment is expected. As a result, even though both octahedral and tetrahedral nickel(II) complexes contain two unpaired electrons, tetrahedral complexes have magnetic moments around 4 BM compared to 3.3 BM or less for octahedral complexes. Nyholm[6] has suggested that an inverse relationship exists between the magnitude of the moment and the distortion of nickel(II) complexes from tetrahedral symmetry. Experimentally it is found that $NiCl_4^{2-}$,[9] $Ni(HMPA)_4^{2+}$ [10] (HMPA = hexamethylphosphoramide), and $NiX_2 \cdot 2(C_6H_5)_3AsO$[11] (X = halogen) have moments in excess of 4 BM. The complex $NiX_2 \cdot 2(C_6H_5)_3P$,[12] which is known to be seriously distorted, has a moment of about 3 BM. Considerable information regarding the structures of $NiX_2 \cdot 2HMPA$ and $CoX_2 \cdot 2HMPA$ complexes (where X = Cl^-, Br^-, I^-, NO_3^-) was obtained from magnetic and spectroscopic studies considered together.[13]

In octahedral cobalt(II) the ground state is $^4T_{1g}$ and a large orbital contribution to the moment is expected. Mixing of a singlet excited state lowers the moment but a value in excess of 5 BM is expected. The ground state for tetrahedral cobalt(II) is $^4A_2$ and a low moment is usually obtained. An excited triplet state is comparatively low in energy and can be mixed with the ground state. Moments in the range 4 to 5 BM have been predicted[1,9] and are found experimentally. Cotton[14] has found that for tetrahedral cobalt(II) an inverse relationship exists between the magnitude of the moment of a complex and the value of Dq for the ligands (in accordance with equation A-5).

It should be emphasized that magnetism should be employed in conjunction with electronic spectroscopy to deduce the structure of complexes.

TEMPERATURE DEPENDENCE OF MAGNETISM

It is found experimentally, for some compounds, that magnetic susceptibility (corrected for diamagnetism) plotted versus the reciprocal of the absolute temperature produces a straight line with zero intercept:

$$\chi_A' = C/T \tag{A-10}$$

where C, the slope, is the Curie constant. Equation (A-10) is known as the Curie law and can be derived from theoretical considerations. Many more compounds are found to obey the Curie-Weiss law, A-11:

$$\chi_A' = C/(T - \theta) \tag{A-11}$$

where θ, an empirical constant, is the temperature at which the line intercepts the T axis in a plot of $1/\chi_A$ vs T. Equation (A-11) differs from equation (A-10) in that the intercept is not zero. In some systems the deviation from the Curie law is due to interionic or intermolecular interactions. As a result of these interactions the orientations of the magnetic dipoles are influenced by the orientations of the neighbors; i.e., the sample is not magnetically dilute. Under these conditions, the magnetic moment at a given temperature should be calculated from the susceptibility by equation (A-12):

$$\mu_{eff} = 2.84\sqrt{\chi_A(T - \theta)} \tag{A-12}$$

instead of equation (A-9). In many instances, the cause of the deviation from the Curie law is not due to the above effect, and it is incorrect to employ equation (A-12) to calculate the moment.

If the θ value is positive the sample is said to exhibit ferromagnetic behavior, while negative θ values correspond to antiferromagnetic behavior. The susceptibility of cupric acetate as a function of temperature indicates antiferromagnetic behavior, for at low temperatures the paramagnetic excited state is not populated, i.e., the electron spins are paired. In $LiCuCl_3 \cdot 2H_2O$ a positive θ value is obtained[15] and is interpreted to result from interactions of $Cu_2Cl_6{}^{2-}$ ions with each other to form chains. X-ray results support this structure. The ground state in the $Cu_2Cl_6{}^{2-}$ ion is a triplet, and the copper ions are not magnetically dilute. For a more complete discussion of this problem, for examples of compounds that are not magnetically dilute, and for a discussion of the temperature dependence of the susceptibility of ferromagnetic and antiferromagnetic materials, see reference 1.

D_{2h}	E	$C_2{}^z$	$C_2{}^y$	$C_2{}^x$	i	σ_{xy}	σ_{xz}	σ_{yz}		
A_g	1	1	1	1	1	1	1	1		$\alpha_{xx}, \alpha_{yy}, \alpha_{zz}$
A_u	1	1	1	1	-1	-1	-1	-1		
B_{1g}	1	1	-1	-1	1	1	-1	-1	R_z	α_{xy}
B_{1u}	1	1	-1	-1	-1	-1	1	1	T_z	
B_{2g}	1	-1	1	-1	1	-1	1	-1	R_y	α_{xz}
B_{2u}	1	-1	1	-1	-1	1	-1	1	T_y	
B_{3g}	1	-1	-1	1	1	-1	-1	1	R_x	α_{yz}
B_{3u}	1	-1	-1	1	-1	1	1	-1	T_x	

C_s	E	σ_{xy}		
A'	1	1	$T_x, T_y; R_z$	$\alpha_{xx}, \alpha_{yy}, \alpha_{zz}, \alpha_{xy}$
A''	1	-1	$T_z; R_x, R_y$	α_{yz}, α_{xz}

C_2	E	$C_2{}^z$		
A	1	1	$T_z; R_z$	$\alpha_{xx}, \alpha_{yy}, \alpha_{zz}, \alpha_{xy}$
B	1	-1	$T_x, T_y; R_x, R_y$	α_{yz}, α_{xz}

C_{4h}	E	C_4	$C_4{}^3$	$C_2{}^z$	i	S_4	$S_4{}^3$	σ_h		
A_g	1	1	1	1	1	1	1	1	R_z	$\alpha_{xx} + \alpha_{yy}, \alpha_{zz}$
A_u	1	1	1	1	-1	-1	-1	-1	T_z	$\alpha_{xx} - \alpha_{yy}, \alpha_{xy}$
B_g	1	-1	-1	1	1	-1	-1	1		
B_u	1	-1	-1	1	-1	1	1	-1		
E_g	$\begin{cases} 1 \\ 1 \end{cases}$	$\begin{matrix} i \\ -i \end{matrix}$	$\begin{matrix} -i \\ i \end{matrix}$	$\begin{matrix} -1 \\ -1 \end{matrix}$	$\begin{matrix} 1 \\ 1 \end{matrix}$	$\begin{matrix} -i \\ i \end{matrix}$	$\begin{matrix} i \\ -i \end{matrix}$	$\begin{matrix} -1 \\ -1 \end{matrix}$	(R_x, R_y)	$(\alpha_{yz}, \alpha_{xz})$
E_u	$\begin{cases} 1 \\ 1 \end{cases}$	$\begin{matrix} i \\ -i \end{matrix}$	$\begin{matrix} -i \\ i \end{matrix}$	$\begin{matrix} -1 \\ -1 \end{matrix}$	$\begin{matrix} -1 \\ -1 \end{matrix}$	$\begin{matrix} i \\ -i \end{matrix}$	$\begin{matrix} -i \\ i \end{matrix}$	$\begin{matrix} 1 \\ 1 \end{matrix}$	(T_x, T_y)	

$C_{4v}^{\ b}$	E	$2C_4^z$	C_2^z	$2\sigma_v$	$2\sigma_d$		
A_1	1	1	1	1	1	T_z	$\alpha_{xx}+\alpha_{yy}, \alpha_{zz}$
A_2	1	1	1	-1	-1	R_z	
B_1	1	-1	1	1	-1		$\alpha_{xx}-\alpha_{yy}$
B_2	1	-1	1	-1	1		α_{xy}
E	2	0	-2	0	0	$(T_x, T_y); (R_x, R_y)$	$(\alpha_{yz}, \alpha_{xz})$

^{b} If the C_{4v} molecule contains a square array of atoms, the σ_v planes should pass through the larger number of atoms of the square array or should intersect the largest possible number of bonds.

D_{2d}	E	$2S_4^z$	C_2^z	$2C_2$	$2\sigma_d$		
A_1	1	1	1	1	1		$\alpha_{xx}+\alpha_{yy}, \alpha_{zz}$
A_2	1	1	1	-1	-1	R_z	
B_1	1	-1	1	1	-1		$\alpha_{xx}-\alpha_{yy}$
B_2	1	-1	1	-1	1	T_z	α_{xy}
E	2	0	-2	0	0	$(T_x, T_y); (R_x, R_y)$	$(\alpha_{yz}, \alpha_{xz})$

D_{3h}	E	$2C_3$	$3C_2$	σ_h	$2S_3$	$3\sigma_v$		
A_1'	1	1	1	1	1	1		$\alpha_{xx}+\alpha_{yy}, \alpha_{zz}$
A_1''	1	1	1	-1	-1	-1		
A_2'	1	1	-1	1	1	-1	R_z	
A_2''	1	1	-1	-1	-1	1	T_z	
E'	2	-1	0	2	-1	0	(T_x, T_y)	$(\alpha_{xx}-\alpha_{yy}, \alpha_{xy})$
E''	2	-1	0	-2	1	0	(R_x, R_y)	$(\alpha_{yz}, \alpha_{xz})$

D_{4h}	E	$2C_4$	C_2^z	$2C_2$	$2C_2'$	i	$2S_4$	σ_h	$2\sigma_v$	$2\sigma_d$		
A_{1g}	1	1	1	1	1	1	1	1	1	1		$\alpha_{xx}+\alpha_{yy}, \alpha_{zz}$
A_{1u}	1	1	1	1	1	-1	-1	-1	-1	-1		
A_{2g}	1	1	1	-1	-1	1	1	1	-1	-1	R_z	
A_{2u}	1	1	1	-1	-1	-1	-1	-1	1	1	T_z	
B_{1g}	1	-1	1	1	-1	1	-1	1	1	-1		$\alpha_{xx}-\alpha_{yy}$
B_{1u}	1	-1	1	1	-1	-1	1	-1	-1	1		
B_{2g}	1	-1	1	-1	1	1	-1	1	-1	1		α_{xy}
B_{2u}	1	-1	1	-1	1	-1	1	-1	1	-1		
E_g	2	0	-2	0	0	2	0	-2	0	0	(R_x, R_y)	$(\alpha_{yz}, \alpha_{xz})$
E_u	2	0	-2	0	0	-2	0	2	0	0	(T_x, T_y)	

T_d	E	$6S_4$	$3C_2$	$8C_3$	$6\sigma_d$		
A_1	1	1	1	1	1		$\alpha_{xx}+\alpha_{yy}+\alpha_{zz}$
A_2	1	−1	1	1	−1		
E	2	0	2	−1	0		$(\alpha_{xx}+\alpha_{yy}-2\alpha_{zz},$ $\alpha_{xx}-\alpha_{yy})$
T_1	3	1	−1	0	−1	R	
T_2	3	−1	−1	0	1	T	$(\alpha_{xy},\alpha_{yz},\alpha_{xz})$

O_h	E	$6C_4$	$3C_4^{\,2}$	$8C_3$	$6C_2$	i	$6S_4$	$3\sigma_h$	$8S_6$	$6\sigma_d$		
A_{1g}	1	1	1	1	1	1	1	1	1	1		$\alpha_{xx}+\alpha_{yy}+\alpha_{zz}$
A_{1u}	1	1	1	1	1	−1	−1	−1	−1	−1		
A_{2g}	1	−1	1	1	−1	1	−1	1	1	−1		
A_{2u}	1	−1	1	1	−1	−1	1	−1	−1	1		
E_g	2	0	2	−1	0	2	0	2	−1	0		$(\alpha_{xx}+\alpha_{yy}-2\alpha_{zz},$ $\alpha_{xx}-\alpha_{yy})$
E_u	2	0	2	−1	0	−2	0	−2	1	0		
T_{1g}	3	1	−1	0	−1	3	1	−1	0	−1	R	
T_{1u}	3	1	−1	0	−1	−3	−1	1	0	1	T	
T_{2g}	3	−1	−1	0	1	3	−1	−1	0	−1		$(\alpha_{xy},\alpha_{yz},\alpha_{xz})$
T_{2u}	3	−1	−1	0	1	−3	1	1	0	−1		

$C_{\infty v}$	E	$\dots 2C_{2\pi/\phi}^{(z)} \dots$	$C_2^{(z)}$	$\infty\sigma_v$		
Σ^+	1	1	1	1	T_z	$\alpha_{xx}+\alpha_{yy},\alpha_{zz}$
Σ^-	1	1	1	−1	R_z	
Π	2	$2\cos\phi$	−2	0	$\begin{Bmatrix}(T_x,T_y)\\(R_x,R_y)\end{Bmatrix}$	$(\alpha_{xz},\alpha_{yz})$
Δ	2	$2\cos 2\phi$	2	0		$(\alpha_{xx}-\alpha_{yy},\alpha_{xy})$
Φ	2	$2\cos 3\phi$	−2	0		

$D_{\infty h}$	$...2C_{2\pi/\phi}...$	$C_2^{(z)}$	$\infty\sigma_v$	i	$...2S_{2\pi/\phi}...$	σ_h	∞C_2		
Σ_g^+	1	1	1	1	1	1	1	1	T_z	$\alpha_{xx}+\alpha_{yy},\ \alpha_{zz}$
Σ_u^+	1	1	1	1	-1	-1	-1	-1		
Σ_g^-	1	1	1	-1	1	1	1	-1	R_z	
Σ_u^-	1	1	1	-1	-1	-1	-1	1		
Π_g	2	$2\cos\phi$	-2	0	2	$-2\cos\phi$	-2	0	(R_x, R_y)	$(\alpha_{xz}.\ \alpha_{yz})$
Π_u	2	$2\cos\phi$	-2	0	-2	$2\cos\phi$	2	0	(T_x, T_y)	
Δ_g	2	$2\cos 2\phi$	2	0	2	$2\cos 2\phi$	2	0		$(\alpha_{xx}-\alpha_{yy},\ \alpha_{xy})$
Δ_u	2	$2\cos 2\phi$	2	0	-2	$-2\cos 2\phi$	-2	0		
Φ_g	2	$2\cos 3\phi$	-2	0	2	$-2\cos 3\phi$	-2	0		
Φ_u	2	$2\cos 3\phi$	-2	0	-2	$2\cos 3\phi$	2	0		

APPENDIX C. *Tanabe and Sugano Diagrams for O_h Fields**

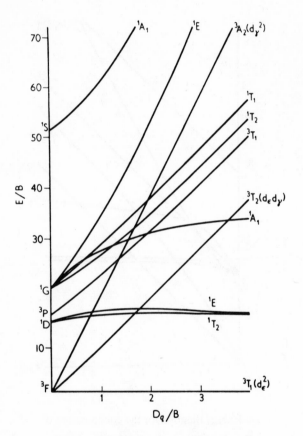

Energy diagram for the configuration d^2.

*These are complete energy diagrams for the configurations indicated reproduced from Y. Tanabe and S. Sugano, *J. Phys. Soc. Japan* **9**, 753, 766 (1964).

γ refers to the ratio of the Racah parameters C/B. Heavy lines perpendicular to the Dq/B axis in d^4, d^5, d^6, and d^7 indicate transitions from weak to strong fields. The calculation of and the assumptions inherent in the calculations are contained in the original paper. The diagrams do not apply to any particular complex but give a qualitative indication of the energies of the various states as a function of Dq/B.

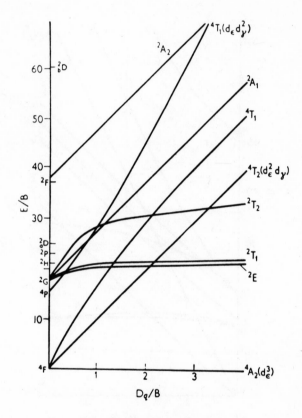

Energy diagram for the configuration d³.

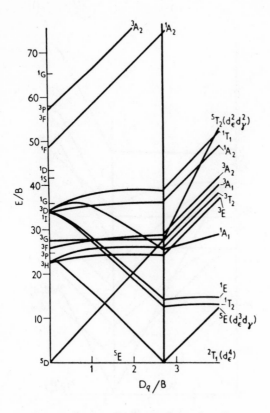

Energy diagram for the configuration d⁴.

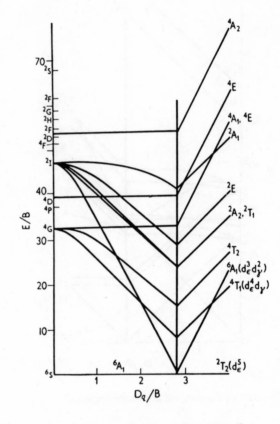

Energy diagram for the configuration d⁵.

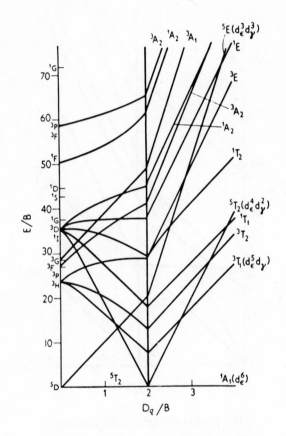

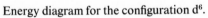

Energy diagram for the configuration d^6.

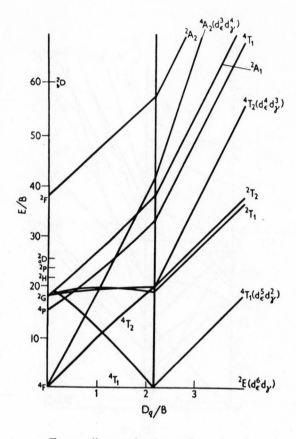

Energy diagram for the configuration d^7.

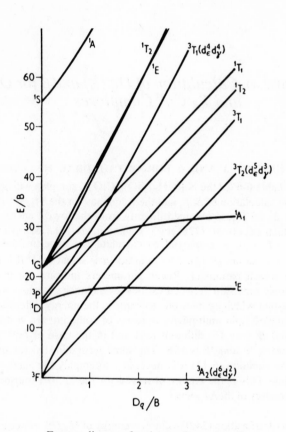

Energy diagram for the configuration d⁸.

APPENDIX D. *Calculation of Dq (Δ) and β for O_h Ni^{II} and T_d Co^{II} Complexes*

CALCULATION OF Δ AND β FOR OCTAHEDRAL Ni^{2+} COMPLEXES

The data in Table 6-6 for the Ni[(CH$_3$)$_2$SO]$_6$(ClO$_4$)$_2$ complex will be employed to illustrate the calculation of Δ, β, and the frequency for the $^3A_{2g} \rightarrow {}^3T_{1g}(F)$ band. The value for Δ, $10\,Dq$, is obtained directly from the lowest energy transition, $^3A_{2g} \rightarrow {}^3T_{2g}$, which occurs at 7728 cm^{-1}. Equation, (6–13) $[(6Dqp - 16(Dq)^2] + [-6Dq - p]E + E^2 = 0$, is employed to calculate the experimental ^3P energy value, i.e., p of equation (6–13). The quantity p is equal to $15B$ for nickel(II) where B is a Racah parameter. Racah parameters indicate the magnitude of the interelectronic repulsion between various levels in the gaseous ion. The quantity B is a constant which enables one to express the energy difference between the levels of highest spin multiplicity in terms of some integer, n, times B, i.e., nB. Both n and B vary for different ions and in the case of Ni^{2+} the energy difference between ^3F and ^3P is $15B$. The same term adjusted for the complex is $15B'$. To use equation (6-13) it is necessary to employ the energy values for the $^3T_{1g}(P)$ state. This is the energy observed for the $^3T_{1g}(P)$ transition (24,038 cm^{-1}) plus the energy of the $^3A_{2g}$ level.

E observed for transition (24,038 cm^{-1}) = energy of $^3T_{1g}(P)$ − energy of $^3A_{2g}$

Energy of $^3T_{1g}(P)$ = E for transition + E of $^3A_{2g}$

∴Combining with equation (6–12) $(E\,{}^3A_{2g} = -12Dq)$

E of $^3T_{1g}$ = 24,038 cm^{-1} − $12Dq$ = 14,762 cm^{-1}

The value of $E = 14,762$ cm^{-1} is employed in equation (6-13) along with $Dq = 773$ to yield a value

$$p = 13,818 \text{ cm}^{-1} = 15B'$$

The gaseous ion $E(^3P)$ value for Ni^{II} is $15B = 15,840$ cm^{-1} and β is (equation 6-15 or 6-14):

$$\beta = \frac{13,818}{15,840} = \frac{15B'}{15B} = 0.873$$

or

$$\beta = \frac{15,840 \text{ cm}^{-1} - 13,818 \text{ cm}^{-1}}{15,840 \text{ cm}^{-1}} \times 100 = 12.7\%$$

To calculate the energies for the $^3T_{1g}(F)$ and $^3T_{1g}(P)$ states, $p = 13,818$ cm^{-1} and $Dq = 773$ cm^{-1} is substituted into equation (6-13) and the equation is solved for E. Two roots $E = 14,762$ cm^{-1} and $3,694$ cm^{-1} are obtained. Since the transition is $^3A_{2g} \rightarrow {}^3T_{1g}(F)$ or $^3T_{1g}(P)$, the absorption bands will correspond to the differences

$$E[^3T_{1g}(F)] - E[^3A_{2g}] \text{ and } E[^3T_{1g}(F)] - E(^3A_{2g})$$

or

$$[^3A_{2g} \rightarrow {}^3T_{1g}(F)] = 3,694 - [-12(773)] = 12,970 \text{ cm}^{-1}$$

and

$$[^3A_{2g} \rightarrow {}^3T_{1g}(P)] = 14,762 - [-12(773)] = 24,038 \text{ cm}^{-1}$$

The agreement of the calculated and experimental values for the 12,970 cm^{-1} band supports the β and Dq values reported above.

CALCULATION OF Δ AND β FOR T_d Co^{2+} COMPLEXES

In a field of tetrahedral symmetry the ^4F ground state of Co^{2+} is split into $^4A_2$, $^4T_2$, and $^4T_1(F)$. The transitions $^4A_2 \rightarrow {}^4T_2$, $^4A_2 \rightarrow {}^4T_1(F)$, and $^4A_2 \rightarrow {}^4T_1(P)$ are designated as ν_1, ν_2, and ν_3, respectively. The following relationships are used to calculate Δ and β:

$$\nu_1 = \Delta \tag{D-1}$$

$$\nu_2 = 1.5\Delta + 7.5B' - Q \tag{D-2}$$

$$\nu_3 = 1.5\Delta + 7.5B' + Q \tag{D-3}$$
$$Q = \tfrac{1}{2}[(0.6\Delta - 15B')^2 + 0.64\Delta^2]^{1/2} \tag{D-4}$$

where B' is the effective value of the Racah interelectronic repulsion term in the complex.

$$\beta = \frac{B'_{complex}}{B_{free\ ion}}$$

or

$$\beta = \frac{B_{free\ ion} - B'_{complex}}{B_{free\ ion}} \times 100 \qquad\qquad (D-5)$$

To demonstrate the calculation, let us consider the spectrum of tetrahedral Co(TMG)$_4^{2+}$ (where TMG is tetramethyl guanidine).[1] The band assigned to ν_3 is a doublet with maxima at 530mμ (18,867 cm^{-1}), $\epsilon = 204$, and 590mμ (16,949 cm^{-1}), $\epsilon = 269$. The near infrared spectrum yields ν_2 a triplet: 1204mμ (8306 cm^{-1}), $\epsilon = 91.5$; 1320mμ (7576 cm^{-1}), $\epsilon = 85.0$; and 1540mμ (6494 cm^{-1}), $\epsilon = 23.5$. The T_1 states are split by spin orbit coupling to the following extent[2] $-\frac{9}{4}\lambda'$, $+\frac{6}{4}\lambda'$, and $+\frac{15}{4}\lambda'$. The energy of $^4A_2 \rightarrow {}^4T_1(F)$ is obtained by averaging the three peaks for the ν_2 band using the above weighting factors.

$$
\begin{aligned}
\tfrac{9}{4}(6494) &= 14,612 \\
\tfrac{6}{4}(7576) &= 11,612 \\
\tfrac{15}{4}(8306) &= 31,148 \\
\hline
\end{aligned}
$$

Total $\tfrac{30}{4}$ 57,124

The average energy of ν_2 is $57,124 \div \frac{30}{4}$. The energy of $^4A_2$ to $^4T_1(P)$ (i.e., ν_3) is obtained by averaging the two peaks to produce 17,908 cm^{-1}. The series of equation (D-1) to (D-4) are now solved to produce Δ and β. Adding equations (D-2) and (D-3) produces:

$$\Delta = \frac{\nu_2 + \nu_3 - 15B'}{3}$$

and substituting ν_2 and ν_3 for Co(TMG)$_4^{2+}$ produces $\Delta = 5(1702\ \text{cm}^{-1} - B')$. Subtracting equation (D-2) from (D-3) produces

$$Q = \tfrac{1}{2}(\nu_3 - \nu_2) = 5146\ \text{cm}^{-1}$$

Squaring both sides of equation (D-4) and rearranging produces

$$4Q^2 = \Delta^2 - 18B'\Delta + 225(B')^2 \qquad\qquad (D-6)$$

Substituting $Q = 5146$ cm^{-1} and $\Delta = 5(1702$ cm$^{-1} - B')$ into equation (D-6) produces an equation which can be solved for B'. One root is 811 cm^{-1} and the other is negative. When the plus root is substituted into $\Delta = 5(1702$ cm$^{-1} - B')$ the value of $\Delta = 4455$ cm^{-1} is obtained. β is evaluated from equation (D-5).

REFERENCES CITED

1. R. S. Drago and R. L. Longhi, *Inorg. Chem.*, **4**, 11 (1965).
2. R. Stahl-Broda and W. Low, *Phys. Rev.*, **113**, 775 (1959).

APPENDIX E. *Normal Vibration Modes for Common Structures*

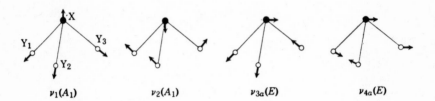

Pyramidal XY_3 Molecules.

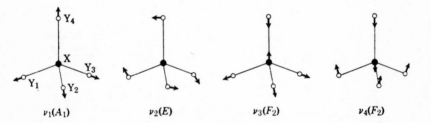

Tetrahedral XY_4 Molecules.

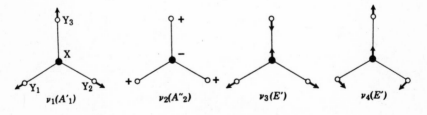

Planar XY_3 Molecules.

414

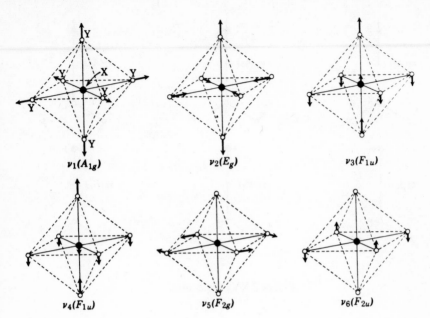

$\nu_1(A_{1g})$ $\nu_2(E_g)$ $\nu_3(F_{1u})$

$\nu_4(F_{1u})$ $\nu_5(F_{2g})$ $\nu_6(F_{2u})$

Octahedral XY_6 Molecules.

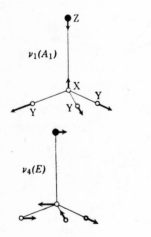
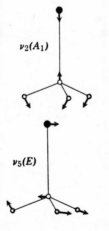
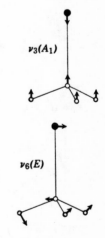

$\nu_1(A_1)$ $\nu_2(A_1)$ $\nu_3(A_1)$

$\nu_4(E)$ $\nu_5(E)$ $\nu_6(E)$

$C_{ev}\ ZXY_3$ Molecules.

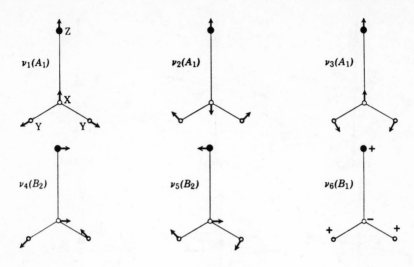

Planar ZXY_2 Molecules.

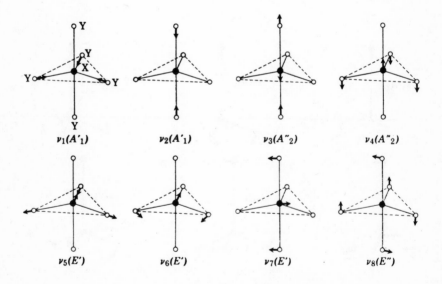

Trigonal Bipyramidal XY_5 Molecules.

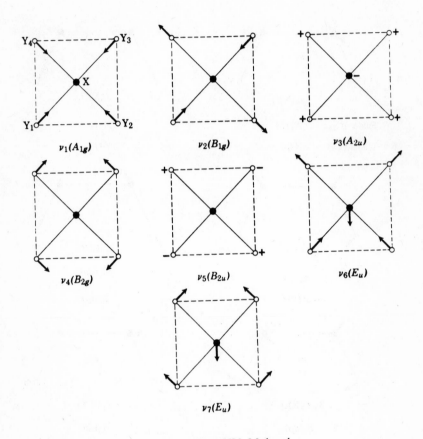

Square-Planar XY_4 Molecules.

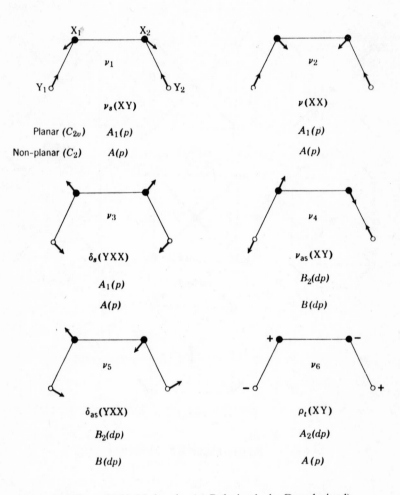

Nonlinear X_2Y_2 Molecules (p; Polarized; dp: Depolarized).

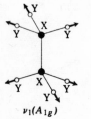

$\nu_1(A_{1g})$

$\nu_2(A_{1g})$

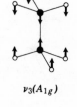

$\nu_3(A_{1g})$

$\nu_4(A_{1u})$

$\nu_5(A_{2u})$

$\nu_6(A_{2u})$

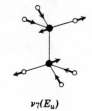

$\nu_7(E_u)$

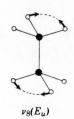

$\nu_8(E_u)$

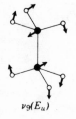

$\nu_9(E_u)$

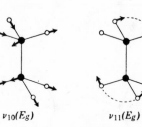

$\nu_{10}(E_g)$

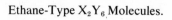

$\nu_{11}(E_g)$

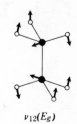

$\nu_{12}(E_g)$

Ethane-Type X_2Y_6 Molecules.

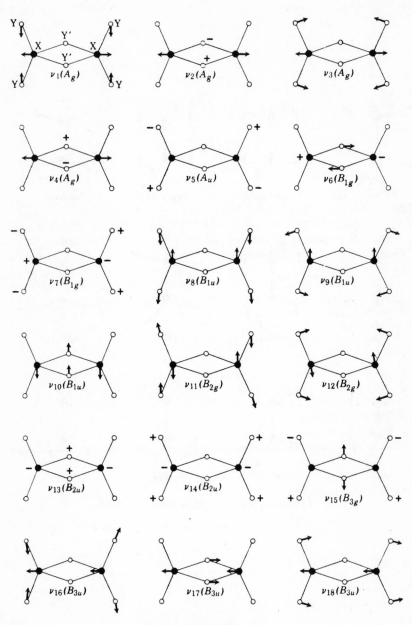

Bridged X_2Y_6 Molecules.

APPENDIX F. *Conversion of Chemical Shift Data*

The chemical shifts, δ (in ppm), relative to $\delta = 0$ for tetramethylsilane for some compounds often employed as external standards are: cyclohexane, -1.6; dioxane, -3.8; H_2O, -5.2; CH_2Cl_2, -5.8; C_6H_5, -6.9; $CHCl_3$, -7.7; and H_2SO_4 (sp. gr. 1.857), -11.6 ppm. (The larger negative value indicates less shielding.) These shifts are obtained on the pure liquids relative to an external standard. As a result, they can be employed to convert data and allow comparison of results between the various materials as external standards. To convert δ obtained toward C_6H_6 as a reference to Si $(CH_3)_4$ (external standard) subtract 5.8 ppm from the C_6H_6 value. One should check to be sure that the sign convention for Δ is that described in this chapter for protons ($\sigma_s - \sigma_R$).

The conversion of results obtained relative to an external standard to an internal standard is not quite as straightforward. If chemical shift values at infinite dilution in CCl_4 are converted to $Si(CH_3)_4$ as a reference by using the above data, τ values do not result. This procedure converts the data to the reference pure $Si(CH_3)_4$. The difference in δ for $Si(CH_3)_4$ in the pure liquid and at infinite dilution in CCl_4 is about 0.4 ppm. The pure liquid is more shielded.

For fluorine shifts, $F_2 = 0$ ppm is often taken as the standard. Shifts, in ppm, for other liquids relative to F_2 are SF_6, 375.6; $CFCl_3$, 414.3; CF_3Cl, 454.2; CF_4, 491.0; CF_3COOH, 507.6; C_6H_5F, 543.2; SiF_4, 598.9; and HF, 625, where the positive value indicates a more highly shielded fluorine.

Many phosphorous chemical shifts have been reported relative to 85 per cent H_3PO_4 as the standard.

421

Index